THE COHERENCE EFFECT

The Coherence Effect

Tapping into the Laws of Nature
that Govern Health, Happiness,
and Higher Brain Functioning

Robert Keith Wallace, Ph.D., Jay B. Marcus,
and Christopher S. Clark, M.D.

Armin Lear Press
Colorado

Library of Congress Cataloging in Publication Data available upon request

Printed in the United States of America

Disclaimer
The advice and information in this book relates to health care. It should be used to supplement rather than replace the advice of your doctor or trained health professional. If you have any serious, acute, or chronic health concerns, please consult a trained health professional who can fully assess your needs and address them effectively. The publisher and authors disclaim liability for any medical outcomes as a result of applying any of the methods discussed in this book.

For further information, contact:

Armin Lear Press
825 Wildlife Lane
Estes Park, CO 80517

ISBN 978-1-7354650-4-3

Contents

Authors' Introduction

Coherence heals. The coherence effect is the healing effect from making the mind and the body function in a more orderly or coherent way. It's the most important factor in whether we're healthy, which is starting to be recognized by modern science and for centuries has been known by the most ancient systems of medicine. This book shows the dramatic effects of naturally generating coherence in the mind and body through meditation, diet, detoxification, exercise, and other programs.

Brain wave coherence, for example, is the new frontier in brain science. When studying brain waves, the term "coherence" means that the cells in different parts of the brain are firing at the same time in the same way (more about this in Chapter 2). This is important because one part of the brain is responsible for memory, one for moral reasoning, and several parts for creativity and other functions. Because success requires many different areas of the brain to work together, the different areas need to be communicating with each other. And they communicate by a synchronous, or coherent, firing. Brain coherence improves mental functioning and is associated with reduced anxiety, depression, PTSD, high blood pressure, high cholesterol, and other disorders. Conversely, the absence of brain wave coherence is associated with autism, schizophrenia, and Alzheimer's disease. These findings are why researchers today are looking so closely at brain wave coherence.

In addition, when the body has normal levels of coherence, its immune and other self-healing systems repair our DNA, keep germs from entering the body, and kill those germs that do gain entry. Several chapters address how we can maintain or enhance the coherent functioning of the immune and other internal repair systems, which will do a thousand times more to keep us healthy than any pharmaceuticals could.

For years, there has been a growing *food is medicine* movement, and many people are devoted to staying healthy and even healing disorders through the foods they eat. Again, more scientifically, this is the coherence effect at work.

Approximately seventy-five years ago, physicist and Nobel Laureate Erwin Schrödinger analyzed what it means to be alive. He said the essential component in our food that keeps us from death is its orderliness or coherence. In other words, *we feed on order-liness*. We feed on the order or coherence in other living systems (plants and animals), and the more orderly our food (we'll see what that means in the coming chapters), the better off we are.

How do programs to create coherence compare to Western medicine? When we look at how Western medicine seeks to remedy our pains and other disorders, it's again based on the coherence principle—trying to prevent and overcome disorder and disease by creating order in the diseased part of the physiology. A pharmaceutical approach may sometimes remedy a disorder, but as often as not medicine just treats the symptoms but not the underlying cause of the disorder. And when several disorders present themselves, the common situation is a patient taking many medications prescribed by many different specialists. But even when the symptoms are addressed, the patient is not healthy if the underlying disorders remain.

This isn't a book full of platitudes advocating the value of all "natural" health strategies, or all forms of meditation, or all diet or exercise programs. They don't all produce coherence in the mind and body, they don't all have significant value, and some are vastly better than others. The book compares the Transcendental Meditation® technique (TM) to other popular meditation or stress reduction practices, including mindfulness, Zen meditation, and meditations learned solely from an app. We look at the published research on whether the meditation techniques produce brain wave coherence, as well as all studies of which we are aware that compare the practical benefits of TM with other stress reduction or meditation techniques on various measures, including relaxation, anxiety, PTSD, blood pressure, and mental flexibility. In every one of these studies, the benefits from TM far outpaced the other techniques.

The book also contains many personal accounts from those who found their meditation programs too difficult, or boring, or who didn't get the benefits they were seeking, but then succeeded with TM. And, as these reports indicate, these individuals succeeded beyond their expectations (as legendary television writer Josh Griffith said, "I thought I was a meditator before starting TM. Boy, was I wrong."). One caveat in these personal reports is that the people we interviewed were TM meditators who were known to be happy with their TM practice (the individuals were not located from a random sample of people who tried various meditation practices). It should be expected that if you interview current TM meditators who at one time tried other techniques, they would report better results with TM. So, while their experiences are genuine, please evaluate these reports with that in mind.

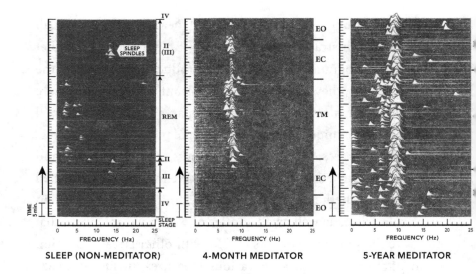

SLEEP (NON-MEDITATOR)   4-MONTH MEDITATOR   5-YEAR MEDITATOR

As discussed in Chapters 3 and 4, the published reports show that the TM technique develops the kind of brain coherence associated with health and high performance. Above are pictures showing brain wave coherence in different individuals during sleep, and after four months practicing TM, and then for a particular individual after five years of TM practice.

The peaks show exceptionally strong coherence. There is not much coherence during sleep. There is significantly more coherence in the meditators. Most importantly, the EC section of the five-year meditation picture shows the brain's coherence with the eyes closed before starting to meditate. This shows that the TM meditator's brain is coherent even when he or she is not meditating. This is an important factor that can bring mental performance and health to the next level. We don't just want coherence when we meditate, we need it all the time for maximum performance and health.

Health professionals apply the coherence principle in the pharmaceuticals they prescribe, but if we want lasting health, we need to apply the principle to those things that really keep us healthy, the everyday things that keep us alive—what we eat, how we eat, our exercise routines, and the quality of our rest and relaxation (meditation). Without a good diet, good digestion, exercise, and adequate rest, no medicines can keep us healthy.

Ancient systems of medicine like Traditional Chinese Medicine, Ayurvedic medicine, and the Greek medicine of Hippocrates were based on creating balance or order inside the human body (for example, the Yin and Yang of Chinese medicine), as well as a balance of the internal and external environments. Maintaining coherence through the daily activities of life has for thousands of years been the cornerstone for health and happiness, and we show how the ancient Ayurvedic system of India works by creating coherence in all of its strategies.

Some of the book's chapters discuss the science of how a deep inner order or coherence can promote healing or happiness and is a predictor of human development. However, this is not a theoretical or philosophical book. It is primarily a guide to specific programs for enhancing inner coherence. Today, inner coherence can be measured scientifically and should be the criterion for determining the best natural health strategies. And what is crucial is that stress, toxins, viruses, fatigue, and other disordering elements confront us *daily*. So, the antidote is a *daily* coherence routine, as we set forth.

One interesting facet of coherence-generating strategies is that they all contribute to the growth of consciousness, giving rise to more settled, clearer thinking, and improved health and happiness. But it's more than that. As Dr. Nader explains in his Foreword, consciousness is primary to life; everything we do, and everything we are is based on consciousness.

Our background is that we've been practicing Transcendental Meditation and studying different meditation techniques for, collectively, almost 150 years, and we've all been involved in teaching or studying Ayurvedic health practices since the mid-1980s. We, therefore, approach this subject from both the perspective of science and long years of personal experience.

Finally, the strategies in this book are not the only ones that create inner coherence, but we don't know of others that work as well. It was suggested that maybe the book promised too much and that our subtitle might be too long. But what we used was actually a truncated version of the subtitle. If we had more space on the cover, we might have called it "Tapping into the Laws of Nature that Govern Health, Strengthen our Immune System, and Promote Happiness, Higher Brain Functioning, Compassion, a Loving Heart, and Higher Values," or something like that. We think you'll see the difference it makes when we increase mind and body coherence.

Robert Keith Wallace, Ph.D., Jay B. Marcus, Chris Clark, M.D.

Foreword

We are at the dawn of a new age of science, one that offers a level of health beyond the shortcomings of modern medicine. The limitations of conventional healthcare approaches are evident from the fact that 40% of the population, 133 million Americans, now have chronic and ongoing diseases that are understood to be incurable. However, in this new age, medicine is beginning to understand that wellness is more than physical. It is also spiritual, mental, and holistic, and it depends on our state of mind, our consciousness. Consciousness is primary to life. Without it, without being conscious, we have no awareness, no happiness, no love, no feelings, no understanding of others, no creativity. Consciousness is the underlying reality that manifests as the human physiology, and it can now be studied scientifically. Our state of consciousness has a fundamental importance to human health and happiness, as the authors demonstrate.

The modern science of consciousness has an ancient source in what is known as the *Veda* (pronounced Vay-duh) and the Vedic (Vay-dik) literature of India, which is perhaps the world's oldest human knowledge. Veda itself means *complete knowledge* in the Sanskrit language, and the Vedic knowledge is the source of yoga, meditation, and the health science known as Ayurveda, which are all covered in this comprehensive book. While the Vedic knowledge is not familiar to most people, many universities and scholars worldwide have translated Vedic literature from its original Sanskrit language, and award advanced degrees for the study of the Veda. Until recently, however, much of what is considered Vedic knowledge has been incomprehensible and misunderstood.

Maharishi Mahesh Yogi, a great scholar of the Vedic knowledge who is best known as the founder of the Transcendental Meditation program, had the insight that the Vedic literature derives its real worth from the value of the sounds or vibrations of the words as they are spoken or listened to in Sanskrit, rather than from the intellectual content or meaning of the words. Vedic sounds resonate in consciousness, and the correct sounds cause the brain and body to become more orderly, resulting in the reduction or elimination of mental and physical disorders. Certain Vedic sounds known as *mantras* are used in the Transcendental Meditation (TM) technique and are part of its effectiveness, while other Vedic sounds can produce successful healing even without a daily meditation routine. Years ago, Maharishi gave me the task of determining which sounds correspond to and heal which part of the body. What I found is intriguing and is explained more fully in my book, *Human Physiology: Expression of Veda and the Vedic Literature.* The correct Vedic sounds have the same impulses as their corresponding part of the physiology, and normal functioning can be restored through the principle of resonance, as when a tuning fork causes another object to vibrate in the same frequency.

The Vedic literature also figures importantly in our desire to understand life, in the age-old quest to *"Know thyself"* of the world's great wisdom traditions. Transcendental Meditation, the classical meditation from the Vedic literature, gets its name because at the deepest point in the practice, we *transcend* or go beyond all thought and experience an expanded state of consciousness, which is both within us and universal. This produces immensely practical benefits, including a perfectly coherent state of mind with maximum healing potential. It also allows us to experience our true self (sometimes capitalized as the "Self"), an experience sought by sages throughout time and called *samadhi* or *satori*, depending on the tradition. By transcending thought, we discover that consciousness is what we are, and in a real sense consciousness is all that there is. Our body changes virtually all of its cells every 7–10 years, so we cannot simply be our body. Yet our sense of Self remains, and we realize, "That is me; I am that." And just as consciousness is primary and materializes into the physical body, there is a universal field of consciousness, which materializes into the physical universe.

When consciousness manifests in the physical realm, its first impulses are vibrations or sounds. These sounds were cognized by the great *rishis* or seers of ancient India, who were able to directly experience the Vedic sounds reverberating in their minds in much the same way that Mozart and Beethoven are said to have had the sounds of their compositions come to them in the mind, fully formed. The sounds that emerge from consciousness in this way are not random; they are coherent and purposeful. And it is their coherence and resonance that attune with and strengthen the body and specific structures, patterns, and networks in our material world. The Veda is like a blueprint, an architectural design. The architect draws the building, which tells us how it will be constructed. Like this, the Veda describes our body in complete detail in terms of its structure and function, which tells us how both the body and the world were constructed and how they can be maintained.

Keith, Jay, and Chris have written an important book to help popularize the new science of consciousness and its practical value in daily life. The authors show what life is from the perspective of both modern and ancient science, and how this knowledge can be used in healing and raising life to its fullest value.

Tony Nader, M.D., Ph.D., M.A.R.R.*

* Tony Nader, M.D., Ph.D., M.A.R.R., is a medical doctor trained at Massachusetts Institute of Technology (Ph.D. in neuroscience) and Harvard University, and a globally recognized Vedic scholar. He is the successor to Maharishi Mahesh Yogi as head of the international Transcendental Meditation organizations in over 100 countries. From the Americas to Asia and Europe to Africa, Dr. Nader guides the Transcendental Meditation program, its advanced practices, and the practical applications of these technologies in all areas of national life, including education, health, business, defense, and agriculture. Dr. Nader's book, *Human Physiology: Expression of Veda and the Vedic Literature*, published by Maharishi Vedic University (1994), explains the foundations of the new science of consciousness and its importance. His lecture explaining consciousness as the underlying reality of everyone and everything can be found at: soundcloud.com/drtonynader/everything-is-consciousness-heres-why-part-1. Dr. Nader's article on this topic, "Consciousness Is All There Is: A Mathematical Approach with Applications," *International J. of Mathematics and Consciousness*, Vol. 1, No. 1 (2015), pp. 1–65, is at: www.ijmac.com/wp-content/uploads/2015/12/IJMACVol1No1.pdf.

Part I

THE IMPORTANCE OF COHERENCE

Chapter 1

The Big Picture:
What is Life and How We Heal

hy is mind and body coherence so important to life? To answer, we need to know what life is from a scientific perspective. And to appreciate the relationship between coherence and life, it will help to first see what science says about death and where something called *entropy* (the opposite of coherence) fits in the picture.

What Science Says About Death

At the beginning of every year, The Edge Foundation, Inc., a formidable group of scientists and thinkers, poses an annual question. For 2017, it was "What scientific term or concept ought to be more widely known?" The answer given by Harvard Professor of Psychology Steven Pinker, a popular science author and member of the National Academy of Sciences, was the Second Law of Thermodynamics. This law of nature is not popularly understood, although, as Dr. Pinker states, it has been described as the scientific equivalent of the works of Shakespeare, and by the eminent physicist Sir Arthur Eddington as occupying the "supreme position among the laws of nature."[1]

The Second Law of Thermodynamics says that any physical system *that is not alive* will go from a state of orderliness or coherence to a state of *entropy*, which means a state of disorderliness or decay. The Second Law of Thermodynamics is the law of nature that results in foods decaying, cars and machines breaking down, and houses falling into disrepair. This famous law says that non-living systems (those that are dead) *always* become more disorderly (entropic) over time. Dead bodies deteriorate as do all non-living organisms; they do not ever become healthier. An automobile left on the street for a number of years begins its inevitable path of decay. The paint fades, the metal rusts, mold forms inside, batteries lose their charge, and so on. Over a long enough period, the Second Law of Thermodynamics results in dead animals and insects decomposing, and automobiles, buildings, and other non-living systems being reduced to ruins.[2]

Moreover, because the environment, and what's in it—what we eat, drink and breathe—gain entropy over time, it affects all of us in our everyday lives. Much time and energy is spent fighting the disordering influence of the Second Law of Thermodynamics. We spend significant resources winterizing our houses and lubricating our cars, and preserving our foods from the inevitable decay caused by this law of nature. Being health conscious, we also try to eat the right foods, and get enough sleep and exercise, all to maintain health and prevent common disorders from ripening into serious disease. Yet, our experience is that decline and disease inevitably occur as we break down, just as what is not alive is decaying all around us. What can we do then, if anything, to postpone this decline and maintain our health and performance at optimum levels as we age? The antidote is in how science looks at what it means to be alive.

What is Life?

In his 1944 classic book, *What is Life?*,[3] Nobel Laureate physicist Erwin Schrödinger analyzed what it means to be alive. He was among the first modern scientists to address this issue. His analysis looked at how living organisms could maintain order (the opposite of the inevitable entropy and decay that occurs in non-living organisms) and even grow and evolve in the midst of a decaying environment brought about by nature's Second Law of Thermodynamics. Schrödinger made the obvious point that living systems avoid entropy and decay by eating, drinking, and breathing, and for plants, assimilating, but he said that this is not the whole story. He said that for a while we were told we feed on energy, but if that was all there was to it, he said any unit of energy, any calorie, should be as good as any other, and that this is not the case when it comes to the calories we need to keep us healthy and alive. We do not eat petroleum, for example, although it is plant life and has lots of calories, and in some contexts is an excellent source of energy. However, petroleum is plant material that has been dead for eons, and thus has been subject to the Second Law of Thermodynamics and has been decaying for centuries. Schrödinger said the precious something contained in our food that keeps us from death is orderliness or coherence. In other words, we feed on orderliness. Schrödinger's actual words were that we feed on "negative entropy," which is just another name for orderliness. Entropy means disorder or decay, so negative entropy is order. We feed on the order or coherence in other living systems (plants and animals), and the more the merrier—not the more food the merrier, the more orderly our food, the better off we are.

Although not commonly appreciated, our need for orderly inputs to overcome the disordering effect of the Second Law of Thermodynamics is why we avoid eating plants or animals that are diseased (disordered), and eat food that is "fresh from the farm," meaning food that is as fresh as possible, not food that is stale (food that has died starts to decay and becomes progressively more disorderly due to the operation of the Second Law of Thermodynamics). Similarly, we drink water that is fresh and not polluted, and we try to breathe clean air to oxygenate the body's cells. With this analysis, we can understand how *eating for orderliness*—we like to use the word "coherence" because of certain principles we'll discuss in the next chapter—plays a crucial role in staying alive and maintaining our health. But it isn't the whole story, and we need to look at what else we can do to generate the coherence that is necessary to overcome entropy, stay alive, and be healthy.

More Recent Understandings of What is Life

While Schrödinger's analysis of what it means to be alive focused on eating or consuming the orderliness around us (how to do this is discussed more fully beginning in Chapter 12), we now understand that *living systems* (plant and animal life), alone, have another means of overcoming the Second Law of Thermodynamics and growing and evolving, and that this also is based on maintaining coherence in the body. At some point, as we and other living organisms grow older and are less able to counteract the disorderly influences of the environment, we become subject to entropy, disease and death. However, the body is programmed with coherence-maintaining systems to fight infections and ward off disease and death. We are born with what is known as homeostatic mechanisms, as well as immune and other self-repair systems that allow us to maintain inner orderliness and, by doing so, we stay healthy (mentally and physically) and stay alive.

The Body's Coherence-Maintaining Systems

We have natural regulators ("homeostats") within the body that act like thermostats to maintain the body's temperature at or near 98.6 degrees Fahrenheit, maintain the pH levels of the fluids outside our cells, and maintain the concentrations of sodium, potassium, and glucose in the blood no matter what we eat and despite changes in the environment. Due to these thermostats when we get too hot, we naturally sweat to cool down; if we get cold, we naturally shiver to get warm and the blood naturally moves from our extremities to where it is needed. Our homeostatic mechanisms help protect us from a changing environment and help us overcome poor lifestyle and dietary choices.

In addition to these regulators or homeostats, when we have at least a normal level of coherence, we have immune systems that also protect us from germs such as bacteria and viruses. The tonsils, thymus gland (located between the lungs), and bone marrow are part of the immune system and make disease fighting cells to destroy the viruses or bacteria that would otherwise do their damage. The spleen filters the blood and also helps destroy foreign substances, and the lymph system filters lymph fluid, nutrients, and waste material and trap bacteria and other foreign substances so they can be readily destroyed by the white blood cells.

What is especially interesting is that these automatic bodily functions (for example, the homeostatic and immune systems) are all proceeding at specific times, motivated either by the immediate need to rid the body of infections, bacteria, and viruses, or according to biological clocks that dictate that certain functions take place and certain chemicals be secreted at specific times each day for optimal health. We can think of the body's processes as being highly regulated in its activities similar to a finely tuned car, just much more complex. If the parts aren't working together as they move, if the pistons are firing at the wrong time, or at the wrong rhythms, the car becomes less efficient, breaks down, or even quits running (entropy takes over).

Like Clockwork We Use Nature's Pharmacopeia

While good running cars are often masterpieces in how they function, it is nothing compared to miracle of the human body. Natural bodily processes are almost unfathomable in their orderliness or coherence and how the body not only wards off disease, but also naturally repairs itself and maintains well-being. Every day we awaken in the morning, excrete the waste from the prior day, eat our meals, and then get tired in the evening and sleep. Although we don't observe it, every day the body is working in an automatic way to manufacture and use hundreds of chemicals to keep the body well-functioning. Our stomach makes pepsin and hydrochloric acid for digestion. Our pineal gland makes the hormone melatonin at night to help us sleep and cortisol in the morning to help us rise. We produce other chemicals, such as ghrelin, a hormone that triggers our hunger when the body needs nutrition. We produce endorphins to reduce pain when we have it, insulin to control sugar levels, and serotonin (aka the happiness hormone) to regulate our moods. The body is in continuous motion as these

7

chemicals and hormones move through the body in an automatic and highly orderly way, meaning the right chemicals are moving in appropriate doses and at appropriate times for healthy biological functioning. The activities taking place in the body on a periodic basis during each 24-hour cycle are referred to as circadian rhythms (around the clock rhythms), and these rhythms and secretion of chemicals are in turn driven by various biological clocks in the body. The classical way of characterizing our biological clocks is that they are like a group of fine Swiss watches, all working together in an integrated and rhythmic way to cause the body to secrete chemicals and hormones and take other action at appropriate times to perform their specific functions.

The understanding that the body has clocks and rhythms doesn't mean that all the body's rhythms are the same. Just as a watch has a second, minute, and hour hand, each moving at their different rhythms or rates, the body's internal orderliness is such that our organs and even our cells all have particular rates and rhythms governing their functioning. We have pulse rates, respiratory rates, rates at which different chemicals must be secreted, rates at which digestive processes occur, rates at which our liver and kidneys must be active to do their jobs, and so on. These rhythms are a part of the body's natural state of coherence. When the rhythms of the body deviate too much from the established norms, the body loses coherence and disease occurs. When the rhythms stop or get seriously out of tune, death results. Modern medicine is good at analyzing what has gone wrong in the body, but it can get lost in the details and fail to appreciate the basics. Simply stated, when there is disease or disorder, the body has not employed the right strategies to overcome entropy and maintain coherence at a deep level of the body's functioning.

The Deep Coherence Effect

To be truly healthy we need coherence at the deepest levels of the physiology. What does this mean? The physiology has different levels ranging from what we can see (what is readily observable or can be easily measured such as the heart rate), to what we can't see, what is not readily observable. At the "deeper" levels of the physiology are the chemical interactions and metabolic processes taking place within the cells. If they become disrupted, this is often the cause of disease.

PHYSIOLOGICAL LEVELS*

Skin (Outer Organ)

Internal Organs (brain, kidneys, liver, and others)

Tissues (groups of related cells)

Cells (skin, stomach, muscle, and others)

DNA

---

* The chart is simplified to eliminate certain levels underlying cell functions, such as proteins and RNA (an acid carrying instructions from the DNA).

The Source of Disease is Typically Deep Within

At the top of our chart, we have the skin, the largest organ of the body. Healthy skin is important since it protects us from bacteria and the ultraviolet rays of the sun, helps regulate the body's temperature and fluids, and contains nerve endings that warn us when something is too hot or sharp. We don't get healthy skin merely by the external activities of washing, moisturizing, and otherwise taking care of it. Beneath the skin are inner workings that are necessary for skin health, such as sufficient red blood cells carrying oxygen to the skin. All the levels of the physiology affect the others, which is why we can cause a disruption of the physiology at the cellular level by outer activities such as getting too much sun on the skin (potentially leading to skin cancers). However, once we have a cancer, we typically have to cut it out surgically or address our healing at the cellular level, such as by using chemotherapy to kill the cancer cells. Our body is composed of systems (for example, nervous system), organs (for example, heart), tissues (for example, muscle tissue), and cells (for example, skin and blood cells). Within the cells numerous activities are occurring, which are essential for health, and healing often requires correcting disorder at this deep level.

Orderly and Rhythmic Functioning Even at the Cellular Level

Science is starting to appreciate that *all* biological functioning is rhythmic and harmonious (that is, aspects of orderly or coherent functioning) when the body is healthy. In an article in *Psychiatry* magazine,[4] Assad Meymandi, M.D., an eminent psychiatrist and neurologist associated with the University of North Carolina School of Medicine at Chapel Hill states:

> Human life is based on rhythm. Day and night, seasonal changes, and all physiological and biological functions are rhythmic. We inhale and exhale, our hearts beat in systole (contraction) and diastole (expansion or relaxation). Sleeping, eating, menstrual cycles, walking, talking, and other, if not all, functions of life are rhythmic.[5]

Even single cells in the body, while their movement appears random, have now been seen to have a coherent style of functioning such that they oscillate at particular rhythms that result in either health or disease. For example, researchers at MIT have developed sophisticated techniques to view images of the interior of red blood cells as they vibrate, and they were able to determine the progress of disease (malaria in this case) just from the rate at which the cells were vibrating.[6] And around 2010, Dr. James Gimzewski, Professor of Chemistry at UCLA, used extremely sensitive measuring devices and found that healthy yeast cells vibrated at a constant, rhythmic rate of about 800 vibrations per second. This produced a pleasant harmonic sound when the vibrations were amplified enough to be heard. However, if the yeast cells were immersed in alcohol, the vibrating slowed and it gave off a screaming or hissing sound as the cells were dying.[7]

Other researchers in England carried this exploration one step further when they looked at both healthy and cancerous human prostate cells. Their sound amplification devices picked up thousands of "notes" being generated by the cells, and they were able to differentiate between normal cells and cancerous ones just by the harmonics of their vibrations. Biologist Peter Gardner said, "The difference between a healthy cell and a cancer cell is like listening to two very large orchestras playing their instruments all at the same time.... But in the cancerous orchestra, the tuba is horribly out of tune."[8]

Even the deepest level of our physiology, the level of the DNA, which contains all the information necessary to create and maintain life, appears to have its own, particular vibrations. The DNA molecule itself is made of a sequence of specific molecules and scientists have identified coherent, low frequency vibrations that appear to be important to the stability and functioning of the DNA.[9]

These and other studies indicate that when we are in a normal state of health, there are rhythmic and harmonious vibrations evidencing an inner coherence at the deepest levels of the physiology. These findings are also in step with modern understandings from physics. Physics is coming to a view that not just the human body, but the entire universe, consists of manifestations of underlying vibrations. According to *string theory* in physics, sometimes called the "theory of everything," all particles in nature are really just manifestations of the vibration of something more elementary, which scientists in this area refer to as "strings." If we think of a guitar string, then different notes will be produced depending on the tension in the string and how it is plucked. According to string theory, the elementary particles of matter that we observe are the "musical notes" resulting from the vibration of these elementary strings. In other words, string theory says that all matter, including the human physiology, simply consists of different underlying vibrations, which determine the characteristics and mass of the molecules and atoms.

If everything is based on elementary, rhythmic or coherent vibrations, it raises the question of whether we can change ourselves at the most fundamental level of the physiology through coherence-generating vibrations or sounds, and what it means for lasting health and high performance. We discuss this fully in the coming chapters.

A Formula for Health and High-Performance Functioning

To summarize, the functioning of the body is highly complex. However, to simplify we can state that the common factor determining health or illness, happiness or unhappiness, life or death, is the presence of at least normal levels of coherence (or the absence of abnormal levels of entropy) at a deep level of the physiology. This may be obvious now that we've stated it, but this general principle of health is overlooked by most as medicine has become so technical and specialized.

This book describes a simple, yet profound formula for enhancing health and even generating happiness and high performance. The goal is to create a high level of coherence throughout the body, including in the brain and at the cellular level. The formula can also be a guide for understanding what works and what doesn't in natural healing. What healthy, happy, and high-performance people have in common is a high level of *coherence* in the functioning of the mind and body at a deep level. And the more we can enhance that coherence, the healthier, happier, and more capable we become. How does an approach aimed at generating coherence compare to conventional understandings?

The Conventional Wisdom about Health, Happiness, and High Performance

Researchers are coming to significant agreement on what is most crucial for health, even if important details are disputed. One of the oldest findings dates back to 1938 when researchers began a long-term study of 238 sophomores at Harvard. They kept track of these students through the years and discovered that their level of happiness was significantly associated with their health. While the influence of happiness on health was a novel idea at the time, it is now widely accepted, and is part of our understanding of the mind's vital role in health. Harvard's Center for Health and Happiness, which is part of Harvard's T.H. Chan School of Public Health, continues to refine the concept, and tells us that positive emotions such as happiness and optimism are very strongly related to good health.[10] Conversely, negative emotions like anger, anxiety, and depression are associated with numerous physical disorders. As a result, it's no longer unconventional for doctors to tell us that the benefits of being happy go beyond the fact that you are not unhappy, and that being happy helps you manage or prevent diseases like heart attacks, strokes, diabetes, and depression.[11]

Does this mean we focus our search for better health on strategies that make us happy? Yes, to some extent, and it may be one of the most important things we can do for our health, but the vexing question is what do we do to become happier? What are the conventional strategies for promoting happiness and do they work? One website claims to understand that happiness is an inner thing (we agree), and it advocates seeing joyfulness as essential to life. Another tells us to feel the pain, but don't mistake it for who you are, and it tells us to be bigger than our sadness. Other conventional wisdom says we need to take time for ourselves each day, to love our lives and see the positive side of things, to spend time each day on things that bring us pleasure, and to get involved in activities that serve others. These approaches may seem simplistic or superficial, but at least some of them will have partial success since seeing the positive and getting involved in helping others will be better for our emotional well-being than dwelling on the negative. But most people recognize that some of this advice just makes a mood of being happy and positive while something more fundamental is necessary.

Other Major Influences on Health

As for other major influences on health, researchers in the West often look at other countries or cultures, and in doing so they typically focus on Japan. Researchers cite the fact that the Japanese on average live the longest lives of any country on the planet with an average lifespan of about eighty-four years. The long lifespan of the Japanese is attributed by many to their healthy diets composed of moderate sized meals (the Japanese favor eating only until 80 percent full); eating fresh vegetables, fruits, and fish; avoiding processed foods, which are linked to obesity and related diseases; and getting lots of exercise (they love the outdoors and many like mountain climbing).[12] The Japanese diet and their exercise patterns would be a vast improvement over the conventions in the Western world, but how do the health guidelines of Japan or any culture compare to the coherence-generating diet and exercise we describe in this book? That is the subject of several chapters.

Another area considered by researchers to be an important influencer of health is getting the right amount of rest and relaxation. According to the National Institutes of Health, sleep deficiency is linked to many chronic health problems, including heart disease, kidney disease, high blood pressure, diabetes, stroke, and depression.[13] And meditation techniques thought to produce rest and relaxation are now mainstream, with even the American Heart Association recommending some meditation techniques as a means of naturally reducing blood pressure. Because of how effectively meditation improves the brain, and since the brain is the control center of the body, we'll analyze different meditation

15

techniques, whether they create brain coherence, and the practical benefits that flow from brain coherence.

To summarize, this is the conventional wisdom: being happy and optimistic, eating right, exercising right, learning to relax (and in the past ten or so years, meditating), and getting a good night's sleep are the major influences on our health. We don't disagree, but as we'll show, the reason these are the principal *health influencers* and the principal factors in a high performing life, is because the best of these health influencers are associated with coherence in the body.

The Role of Modern Medicine in our Health and Performance

While many people do rely just on modern medicine for their health, the statistics suggest that more is needed. The American Medical Association tells us that 40% of the population in the U.S. suffer from chronic diseases. And if we eliminate those under 21, who are not so likely to yet have chronic diseases, we would find that more than 60 percent of adults in the United States have chronic, and generally incurable, diseases. With all we spend on health care, the United States ranks thirty-first among countries in the lifespan of its citizens, tied with Cuba and behind almost every European country.[14]

With all the chronic disease, we have a national health crisis that we accept as normal life. Increasing numbers of Americans have become addicted to pain medications, have mental illnesses, have difficulty shopping or walking a few blocks, and are obese and unable to work. And according to the 2017 Harris Poll, only one-third of Americans say they're happy. Physician Mark Hyman, the Medical Director of the Cleveland Clinic's Center for Functional Medicine and author of a number of popular medical books, tells us why he believes modern medicine fails to keep us healthy. He says that physicians are well-trained to treat the symptoms, but not very capable of addressing the underlying imbalances that cause the illnesses.[15] According to our perspective, this is really another way of saying that modern medicine in not very capable of addressing entropy and the underlying incoherence that cause the illnesses. Hyman describes a common case history of a patient taking medications prescribed by his psychiatrist for anxiety, depression, or sleep disorders; medications prescribed by his gastroenterologist for his heartburn; and still other medications prescribed by other specialists for his high cholesterol or high blood pressure. But even if the symptoms are addressed with medications, the patient is still not healthy if we can't overcome the underlying disorders.[16]

Health's Coherence Principle

As we said in the Introduction, the principle in all of medicine, whether it is allopathic medicine or natural medicine, is to overcome disorders by creating coherence or order in the physiology. Health professionals apply the coherence principle in the pharmaceuticals they prescribe, but poor health results from not applying the principle to the great health influencers. That means applying the principle to the basic things that keep us alive—our food, exercise, and the quality of our rest.

Only Some Natural Health Strategies Promote Coherence

The popular distrust of pharmaceuticals in part has led to a dramatic growth of alternative and natural approaches to health. About a third of the population now uses alternative forms of medicine; but just because a medical approach is alternative or "natural" doesn't mean that it works; it doesn't mean it creates coherence at a fundamental level, which we say is necessary for good health. Conventional medical practitioners see the failure of many natural approaches, and they argue, often rightly, that natural approaches are "alternative" because they are not supported by good enough evidence for them to earn a place in mainstream medicine. On the other side, advocates of alternative and natural healing argue that modern medicine is largely about taking drugs that don't address the underlying disorders and have negative side effects.

The benefits and drawbacks of both conventional and alternative medicine result in many health practitioners today championing themselves as holistic, integrative, or functional medicine health providers. From a theoretical perspective these philosophies make perfect sense. These approaches are said to use conventional or Western medicine when it is needed, as for example, when you have a heart attack or a malignancy and need emergency Western care. But they also use alternative or complementary approaches like changing your diet and adding exercise and relaxation procedures to prevent future heart attacks or deal with the stress of your cancer. Holistic/integrative/functional approaches have various features in common, including claiming to "treat the person" as well as the disease, and claiming to be an evidence-based or biology-based approach that selects the best of all therapeutic approaches in an effort to treat the root cause of the disease. This sounds ideal, but does your integrative or holistic health practitioner really know that he or she is selecting the best of the natural approaches when recommending some particular diet or that you try some form of yoga or meditation? Are all meditation and yoga programs the same? Is wanting to enhance the body's coherence the health practitioner's guide for selecting an approach?

Ancient Coherence-Generating Strategies

Ancient systems of medicine like Traditional Chinese Medicine, Ayurvedic medicine (the Vedic health system), and the Greek medicine of Hippocrates were based on creating balance or order inside the human body (for example, the Yin and Yang of Chinese medicine), as well as a balance of the internal and external environments. And they applied this to what they ate, how much they ate, and finding the foods that were best for a particular disorder, as well as through principles of digestion, herbal remedies, and sound or vibration therapies. The Vedic system adds yoga and meditation. Maintaining coherence through these daily activities of life has for thousands of years been the cornerstone for health and happiness.

This book introduces us to the strategies from the Vedic health system of ancient India. The Vedic strategies have been understood for thousands of years as *creating coherence* in the mind and body and overcoming entropy. The word Veda means complete knowledge in Sanskrit, and the Vedic health system constitutes the world's oldest and most complete natural health-care system. The Indian Vedic health strategies influenced Traditional Chinese Medicine, as well as the medicine of Greece, Egypt, and other ancient civilizations, and for many the healing often goes beyond what modern medicine can accomplish. The Vedic knowledge has been revived in this age by Maharishi Mahesh Yogi, a Vedic scholar principally known for reviving the classical meditation technique of this knowledge, which he named Transcendental Meditation.

Although the Vedic knowledge originates in India, many of the strategies have not been widely available even in India until the latter part of the twentieth century. For example, until Maharishi revived the Transcendental Meditation technique and showed how it is practiced, the generally available meditation techniques in India were much less effective, mostly concentration or focusing techniques that do not reliably produce coherence. And even the vast knowledge of India's Ayurvedic health practices that are part of the Vedic health-care system were subordinated to Western medicine during the period of British rule in India until 1947. Today, there is a revival of the Vedic knowledge taking place, with growing acceptance for this approach, but as with most things, not all Vedic strategies will be authentic and coherence producing, and some will be more effective than others.

We should note that the strategies in this book are not the only ones that can create coherence at a fundamental level of the physiology. However, we don't know of others that more reliably create coherence or are better researched. Those presented in this book affect all the areas that are important to health. They address our happiness, our diet, sleep, our meditation, and exercise, and we prescribe ideal daily routines for health.

Chapter 2

Brain Wave Coherence: The New Frontier of Science's Age of Consciousness

There is an interesting group of studies that should be more widely known. They tell us something important about a mother's touch and about the involvement of brain coherence in healing. Numerous studies show at least temporary benefits from massage and touch in reducing anxiety, stress, pain, and symptoms of arthritis, and in improving circulation and even reducing cancer symptoms.[1] And while benefits are seen with massage and touch therapies, it has been a mystery as to how the effects are produced. Is it the blood circulation from a massage that brings its benefits, and if so, how does touch work when there isn't much of a circulation increase? For example, what is the mechanism that causes the healing when a mother touches a baby, or a husband touches a wife when there isn't any increase in blood circulation? A 2018 study sought to discover the brain science behind how a loved one's touch might reduce pain in a suffering partner.[2]

In this study, Dr. Pavel Goldstein, the lead researcher, decided on the experiment upon noticing that when he held his wife's hand during the birth of their child, her pain significantly decreased. Goldstein was joined in this research with others at a neuroscience laboratory at the University of Colorado in Boulder and with researchers at the University of Haifa in Israel. They measured the brain waves of twenty-two couples as mild pain was induced in the female partner, and they also measured the levels of empathy of the male who was trying to alleviate his partner's pain. The researchers found that holding hands decreased the pain as they expected, but what was unexpected was that the brain waves of the partners in the *alpha range* (more on this later in the chapter) became synchronized when they held hands and the pain diminished. Other brain waves did not become synchronized. In addition, the more the brain activity between the partners synchronized and the more empathy in the partner without the pain, the more the pain subsided.[3] The fact that someone's touch can have an effect in reducing another's pain has been seen in many studies. But the Colorado study confirms that the process is associated with brain synchronization in the alpha range. In later chapters we discuss the importance of coherent brain-to-brain synchronization, or in other words, the benefits of causing coherence to spread to others in the vicinity. But let's step away from looking at how one person's brain becomes synchronized with the brain of another, which may just result in the two brains becoming synchronized at a relatively low level. Let's look, instead, at why it's important for different parts of our brain to be synchronized to a high degree with other parts of the brain.

Coherence: The Neural Basis of Peak Performance

In 1949, Canadian neuropsychologist Donald Hebb wrote the now famous book, *The Organization of Behavior*.[4] It proposed theories about brain functioning that were speculative in their time, but which have now been demonstrated to be true and have come to be known as "Hebb's Rule." It is a rule that says that there must be extensive synchrony or coherence among *distant* brain areas in order to process inputs to the brain, generate appropriate responses, and, in general, be successful in life. Why is this connection between distant brain areas important? Different parts of the brain do different things. One part is responsible for memory, one for moral reasoning, one for processing visual images, and so on. And because success requires many different areas of the brain to contribute to solving problems, the different areas need to be communicating with each other.

How does this communication take place? In recent years scientists have concluded that the catalyst allowing different brain areas to communicate with each other is coherence. Dr. Friedhelm Hummel of the Department of Neurology at the Medical Center at Hamburg University states that the brain areas "strengthen their connections by repeated synchronous [or coherent] activation."[5] When we perceive something in the way we should perceive it, Hummel says that large numbers of neurons in different parts of the brain are "firing in synchrony."[6] In other words, they are firing in the same way at the same time. When there is this synchronous firing or activation *between distant brain areas*, we don't just see random shapes with our eyes; instead, a part of the brain is communicating with another part and we recognize that the shapes are persons, and the lights have colors, and the letters form words, and so on.

On the other hand, if a sufficient number of the brain's neurons are not in synchrony (that is, not coherent), then the necessary connections won't be there, and we won't process information correctly or analyze or perceive things as well as we could. If there is a significant lack of order in the brain, we may then have one or another form of dyslexia or agnosia where, for example, we recognize a fork as something to eat with, but think it's a spoon, or we can't distinguish between red and green, or determine left from right, or count the syllables in words. And if the disorder is not so pronounced, many are coming to the view that our thinking is just not as clear or profound as it could be. Harvard Medical School Professor of Psychiatry Robert W. McCarley says that "synchronized [brain] rhythms characterize conscious thought, perception and problem solving" and that "our brains need a coherence of firing to organize perception and analysis of data from the world around us."[7]

The Kind of Coherence Most Important to Success

Hummel and his colleagues from Hamburg University were interested in more than just validating the general principle that synchrony or coherence between different areas of the brain was important to success. They designed a test to determine what kind of brain coherence in ordinary subjects was most crucial to enhanced brain performance. They measured the brain waves of the subjects in their study by placing twenty-eight electrodes across the scalp to sense the activity of many different brain areas. The subjects were then given a task to determine if a configuration of dots they were shown visually matched a configuration of raised dots in a Braille text that they touched. Our sight and touch centers are in different parts of the brain so the researchers theorized that there would have to be good communication between those distant brain areas to be successful in quickly determining a match. There are four lobes of the brain, and the test measured the communication between the occipital lobe in the back of the brain, which is responsible for vision, with the activity in the parietal lobe at the top of the brain, which is associated with touch. They found that those subjects with the greatest *alpha brain wave coherence* between these distant brain areas were most successful at the task. Conversely, where performance was not successful, there was the least amount of alpha wave coherence. The researchers' hypothesis, borne out by their research, was that the more coherence in the brain, and especially alpha coherence, the better the performance.[8] To scientists there is a technical difference between brain wave "synchrony" and brain wave "coherence," which is explained in endnote 8 of this chapter, but they are the same for practical purposes.

In summary, looking at brain waves over time, we can see if there are similar oscillating or vibrating patterns. The extent to which oscillating brain wave patterns remain similar over a given time period (similar in frequency, amplitude, and phase) provides a measurable estimate of the brain wave coherence.

Using the EEG to Measure What our Brain Cells are Doing

Neurons are nerve cells and serve as the working units of the brain. Neurons are continuously active, receiving and sending endless streams of electrical and chemical messages. And, while the electrical activity of individual neurons is too small to be measured across the skull, what can be measured is the *collective* activity of the neurons in particular areas of the brain. This measurement is known as electroencephalography or EEG.

To record the EEG, small electrodes are attached at different places to the scalp of a subject, and these electrical signals are then amplified and recorded as brain waves. The brain waves are typically analyzed both for their amplitude and frequency. The different frequencies are a measurement of the number of waves or oscillations in a one-second period and are labeled in what is known as hertz or Hz. It makes sense that when there are more waves per second, there is more brain activity, as can be seen in the chart opposite.

Waves that have a frequency of less than 4 Hz, or fewer than 4 oscillations per second, are called delta waves; waves of 4–8 Hz per second are called theta waves. These are the very slow waves often associated with sleep or drowsiness. Then there are waves of 8–12 Hz, which are called alpha waves. Alpha waves are associated with relaxation, but also with heightened alertness and with higher brain functioning. It makes sense that people would do their best when relaxed and highly alert. With alpha waves it is also important to distinguish between slow alpha, sometimes called alpha1, which is between 8–10 Hz, and fast alpha, sometimes called alpha2, of from 11–12 Hz. The slow alpha waves have generally been found to be most desirable. Then there are waves with a frequency of 13–30 Hz, which are called beta waves, and waves from 31–100 Hz, which are gamma waves. These are the fastest waves but can be associated with anxiety states. Certain of the information in the chart below is from the work of Dr. Fred Travis, introduced later in this chapter. The chart summarizes the research showing the association of particular waves with particular mental states.

Type (band) processes	Frequency (Hz)	Brain location	Cognitive and Physiological
Delta	4 or less	Frontal (adults)	• Occurs in sleep for adults • Indicates continued attention
Theta	5 to less than 8	Various locations	• Common in young children • Indicative of drowsiness in adults • Associated with working memory • Depressants increase theta
Alpha1	8–10	Frontal	• Increases during internal tasks • Associated with higher blood flow in brain • Associated with transcendence in meditation, which is traditionally understood as meditation's goal • Associated with being simultaneously alert and relaxed
Alpha2	11–12	Occipital and Parietal	• Decreases during external tasks • Associated with lower blood flow to the brain • Associated with mindfulness meditation and other "open monitoring" meditations
Beta	13–30	Various	• Associated with concentration and also anxious thinking • Associated with concentration and focusing meditation types • Increased beta can be caused by caffeine and stimulants
Gamma	31–100	Various	• Associated with sensory processing • Associated with short-term memory • Associated with REM sleep • Too much is associated with anxiety

To summarize, what we have known for some time is that different mental states such as deep sleep, dreaming, waking, or meditation will have a predominance of a specific frequency of brain waves. For example, in a sleep state, we see delta waves predominating. The higher frequency beta and gamma waves are dominating when the person is actively concentrating, and between those two extremes, if theta waves are dominating, the person can either be drowsy or in a quiet mental monitoring state. And again, if slow alpha waves are dominating (alpha1), the person is normally relaxed as well as alert, which is important for high-performance functioning.

Inducing Brain Coherence

The relationship between brain wave coherence and improved performance is starting to become a popular area of research in what is part of the new science of consciousness. Perhaps not unexpectedly there are even devices being marketed to electrically stimulate the brain in an effort to generate coherence. We'll see in coming chapters that meditation is the best-known way to generate brain coherence, specifically Transcendental Meditation. But let's first look at one other approach that has been shown to at least produce some brain coherence, and the practical effects of doing so.

In a 2017 study at Boston University, researchers used electrodes to give an electrical charge to two areas of the brain at the same time (the medial frontal cortex and the lateral prefrontal cortex), while measuring the slow theta brain waves of the subjects in the study.[9] The researchers found that by electrically stimulating the two frontal areas of the brain at the same time, it increased the brain wave coherence between the two areas at the theta frequency, and the participants in the study learned faster and made fewer errors, and when they did make errors, they corrected them more accurately. Conversely, the researchers could disrupt the brain coherence by sending electrical currents at different times, and the subjects then made more errors and learned more slowly. The researchers did the experiment repeatedly with the same results. At one time they disrupted the brain wave coherence during the learning test and saw the performance decline. Another time, during the task they switched the stimulation from "dumb" to "smart," increasing the coherence and within just minutes, they restored brain coherence and higher performance. The change was dramatic enough that after seeing their results, some of the students in the study asked if they could wear the electrodes during exams.

This study of theta coherence (theta waves are very close in frequency to slow alpha waves) shows that coherence in bands other than alpha can also be highly beneficial. This is a delicate area, however. Applying electrical charges to the brain is not what we consider a natural technique and safety issues have been noted even when the technique is applied in a university or research setting. A 2015 review article published in *Frontiers in Neuroscience*[10] noted that the subjects of the various studies have noted side effects of electrical stimulation, including mild headaches, nausea, and fatigue, and the negative side effects of repetitive electrical stimulation, and the long-term effects of even a single session are still unknown.

Abnormally Low Brain Coherence and Mental Disorders

Just as coherent brain activity is becoming recognized as being associated with higher levels of performance, as we might expect, a lack of normal coherence in brain wave functioning is associated with many brain disorders. In 2006, researchers at three prominent brain institutes in Germany published their comprehensive review of the substantial body of research linking a lack of brain synchrony to brain disorders such as schizophrenia, autism and Alzheimer's disease. They concluded that "there is consistent evidence across studies that disorders of schizophrenia, autism, and AD [Alzheimer's disease] are associated with a reduction of neural synchrony that involves both local as well as long-range synchronization."[11] Another review of the available studies in 2008 by researchers at a university in Istanbul lists four studies showing reduced alpha coherence in Alzheimer's patients, as well as three studies showing reduced theta wave coherence and two studies showing reduced beta wave coherence.[12] If brain wave coherence and especially alpha coherence is critical to high performance, it may not be surprising that dysfunction would be associated with a marked decrease in coherence.

There is one caveat here. Looking at brain disorders and coherence can provide unexpected results. One 2007 study, for example, found that, as expected, people with autism had lower brain wave coherence than normal in the frontal area of the brain in the alpha1 range of 8–10 Hz (again, this is the brain wave pattern that appears to be highly important for high mental performance), but at the same time they had greater coherence than normal in the theta range.[13] One explanation for this result seems to be that disorders in a part of the brain may be compensated for by another part of the brain becoming more coherent than usual. The brain and body want to heal themselves, and when one part of the body is threatened, it can result in another part of the body strengthening itself to compensate. Similarly, the brains of sight impaired people are now known to actually compensate by increasing the connections (increased connections means increased coherence) in other areas of the brain to help those with vision loss hear better or otherwise deal with the environment. And people who are depressed often show temporarily increased coherence in some parts of the brain to compensate for the reduced functioning in the area connected to their depression (see Chapter 7).

Researchers have also looked at epilepsy and motor functioning in Parkinson's patients and how they were associated with a lack of brain coherence or synchrony. Epilepsy and Parkinson's are complex disorders that are difficult to understand just through brain coherence research, resulting in some uncertainties in the area.[14] With epilepsy, for example, when there are seizures some say there is increased *local* brain coherence (sometimes called brain power, which we remember is different from the *distant* coherence necessary for high performance), but a disconnection of the local area with other parts of the brain.[14] Other research simply shows a lack of brain coherence during a seizure.[15] When a person has an epileptic seizure, the electrical activity of the brain is in a very excited state and it may be likened to the heightened electrical activity during a lightning storm. The brain is in a seriously overloaded and overactive state. We might expect then that a highly excited state would result in so much electrical activity that in some local areas we would find coherence, but as the research shows there are still reduced connections between the seizure area and the distant areas; as we've seen, *distant* brain coherence is crucial.

Continuous Brain Wave Coherence

We can get some indication of the importance of brain wave coherence from the studies just referred to on higher performance on a sight and touch test, or the better student performance while wearing an electrode cap, and the reduced pain from a husband's touch. But these studies just scratch the surface. What if instead of some momentary coherence during touch or when wearing electrodes, we could cause the brain to continuously be more coherent? Just as we have homeostatic systems, immune systems, and innate chemical generating systems that work continuously to generate inner orderliness or coherence and fight disease, what can we expect from continuous brain wave coherence?

One preliminary study was the subject of a book, *World-Class Brain*,[16] by Harald Harung, Ph.D., a researcher who teaches management and world-class performance at Oslo Metropolitan University, and Fred Travis, Ph.D., mentioned earlier, Director of the Center for Brain, Consciousness, and Cognition at Maharishi International University in Iowa. They looked at the brains of thirty-three world-class athletes and twenty top managers and compared their brains to those of control groups of athletes who were less successful and to mid-level managers.

The elite athletes were from the National Olympic Training Center and Norwegian School of Sports Sciences and had placed in the top ten in major competitions like the Olympic Games and the World Cup. The control group of athletes competed regularly in competitions, but did not normally place in the top 50 percent in Norwegian championships. Top managers in Norway were cho-

sen based on the selections of the former head of a top manpower
company and the editor of a weekly management magazine.

Harung and Travis measured brain wave coherence in the prefrontal cortex, as well as the strength of the alpha1 brain waves
over the whole brain, as well as another measure of the brain's efficiency that indicates whether the brain gets active at the appropriate times. These three measures were combined into a Brain Integration Scale. The research showed the world-class athletes and top
managers had significantly more coherent and efficient brains. As
the authors state:

> Typically, the athlete who performs best is the one who is
> calmest, who has greater presence of mind in frantic situa-
> tions. He or she isn't distracted by the pressure or chaos, but
> instead is more inner-directed.[17]

In Chapter 1, we briefly introduced the ancient Vedic system of
natural medicine, popularly known as Ayurveda, whose strategies
focus on creating coherence in the mind and body. Like any system of medicine, Vedic medicine deals with health and disease,
but it sets a higher standard for health than Western medicine.
According to the Vedic tradition a healthy person is not just free of
disease, but maximizing his or her potential and enjoying life—a
person who is more fully alive. The Vedic tradition has many strategies for generating coherence depending on the person and the
disorder. We'll look at its most important strategies beginning with
meditation, which this tradition considers the supreme healing
practice because of the vital role of brain coherence in both mental
and physical health.

Part II

MEDITATION

Chapter 3

Super Coherent Brain Waves from Transcendental Meditation

Th=here are three types of brain wave coherence—local, distant, and global. When there is coherent activity of neurons (brain cells) close together in a local assembly, this is local coherence, which is usually described in the research as a finding of increased "power" in the area. We can also measure "distant" coherence as Dr. Hummel did (Chapter 2), meaning measuring the brain wave coherence between distant areas of the brain. This, again, is the coherence that is necessary for the integration of diverse information and is the basis of higher performance. Finally, there can be "global" coherence which is when high levels of coherence across *all* areas of the brain are seen. This is rarer and even more profound than distant coherence among several brain areas.

Dr. Alarik Arenander has a Ph.D. in neuroscience from UCLA. He is a long-time brain researcher and also a long-time TM meditator and TM teacher. For the past twenty years he has spent most of his time researching brain wave changes during meditation and traveling around the world demonstrating the brain wave activity that occurs during the Transcendental Meditation technique to

government, military, education and business leaders. He told Jay
in an interview:

> The key issue in the last ten years or so in the community
> of brain researchers is what is known in the scientific com-
> munity as "communication through coherence." Stimuli flow
> through the brain all the time from internal desires or mem-
> ories or from external events, and these stimuli have to be
> dealt with appropriately for effective thinking and behavior
> in life. In addition, there are so many inputs that the brain
> has to do what it does very quickly.
>
> So we have these billions of brain cells and trillions of syn-
> apses in the brain, and they form units or assemblies that are
> all oscillating. And, most importantly, only coherent oscillat-
> ing assemblies of brain cells can effectively communicate with
> each other. It is only when cells work together in the same
> rhythm that effective information flow occurs in the brain.
>
> And what is interesting is that there is a fundamental mode
> or rhythm of brain functioning and the most basic one occurs
> every 1/10 of a second. That means if you look at the brain
> over the entire day, you find that everything going on in the
> brain falls into one of four global types of oscillation func-
> tioning, which occurs every 1/10 of a second. So right away
> we see that the 10 times per second fluctuations associated
> with slow alpha waves is crucial to how the brain naturally
> organizes information.
>
> Different frequencies of the brain all make their specific con-
> tributions to brain functioning. However, we should note
> that over half a century of research on TM shows that coher-
> ence among alpha waves, and in particular slow alpha1 oscil-
> lations measured at distant areas of the brain, are crucial to
> effective brain functioning.

Super Coherent Brain Waves from TM

In measuring EEG coherence, most of the early researchers would choose a particular frequency they were interested in (such as a frequency in the alpha range) and then analyze the EEG waves between different areas of the brain at that frequency to see if they were in step or in phase with each other. Coherence can range from 0, where there is no relationship between the phases of the EEG waves measured at two different places on the scalp, to a value of 1.0, where the two signals have a stable relationship over time and are talking to each other.

The first research on TM and brain wave coherence was conducted in the early 1970s by Dr. Jean-Paul Banquet, a neurophysiologist at Massachusetts General Hospital. He found that the TM technique produced a unique orderliness in the functioning of the right and left hemispheres of the brain. This is distant coherence that allows the two hemispheres to work in concert allowing the person to be both intuitive or artistic as well as scientific.[1]

Banquet's findings were then replicated by Dr. Paul Levine at Maharishi European Research University, who used a mathematical formula to measure EEG coherence accurately. What Levine found was truly amazing. During TM practice he found extraordinarily high, sustained levels of coherence. If you compare these high levels of coherence to the wide range of normal coherence in the population, we can consider this a *super coherent state*. Levine's most common finding was an increased EEG coherence in slow *alpha* waves (alpha1) during the practice of the TM technique, but also coherent theta waves, which continued to be exhibited after the meditation session.[2] The chart below displays peaks of strong coherence between front and central parts of the brain during sleep *(left)* or TM *(right)*. In this graphic, for a peak to be displayed, the coherence must be *above* a value of 0.95 (remember that 1.0 is perfect coherence) for a period of several seconds, so any peaks in the chart indicate remarkably strong coherence.

In the first set of the charts below from Levine's work (*Figures 1 and 2*), the relatively few peaks of coherence during sleep are in the delta frequency band, the marker of deep sleep. In contrast, during a twenty-minute TM session, the meditator of only two weeks has sustained coherence, and it is in the alpha1 range. While we think of sleep as being a very settled experience, we can see that with the loss of consciousness during sleep there is a very different pattern of coherence that is typical, compared to the state experienced during the TM technique.

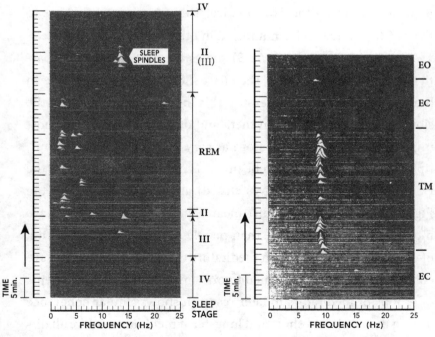

Fig. 1 **SLEEP (NON-MEDITATOR)**   *Fig. 2*   **2-WEEK MEDITATOR**

During TM practice, the meditator is deeply relaxed yet alert and fully conscious. In this unique state of restful alertness, we see brain coherence, especially in the 8–10 Hz alpha wave frequency area (the slow alpha or alpha1 frequency range). For the meditator of two weeks, the experiment begins at the bottom of the chart on the right while the subject sits with eyes closed. At that time, there is some coherent activity before meditation, but no evidence of high coherence. Remember, over a 0.95 value is necessary for the computer analysis to display a peak.

After a few minutes, the individual in Figure 2 (*chart on the right, previous page*) starts to practice the TM technique. At the start of meditation, we notice two things. First, high coherence, as reflected in the EEG recordings, actually begins the *moment* the technique begins. Second, this rapid onset high alpha coherence is sustained during the TM practice. This experience is unique to the TM technique and is not found in other meditation practices.

The chart opposite (*Figure 3*) shows the brain waves of a particular five-year meditator. The chart shows a super coherence in brain wave functioning at least in this individual, primarily in the slow alpha range but also in theta and other bands. What is most important is that the meditator has very strong coherence at multiple frequencies even when he or she is not meditating. This is the EO (eyes open) and EC (eyes closed) areas at the bottom of the Figure. The illustrations don't mean that all meditators will have more brain wave coherence than people who don't meditate. And, of course, some four-month meditators will have more brain wave coherence than five-year meditators. In addition, measurements of groups of meditators in later research shows similar coherence during meditation in short and long-term meditators. We're all different. But we can say that practice of the TM technique reliably

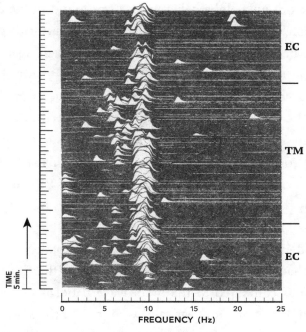

Fig. 3   **5-YEAR MEDITATOR**

increases brain wave coherence outside of meditation where we want it most.

How Long Does it Take to Experience Brain Wave Coherence?

Studies by Drs. Travis and Arenander at Maharishi International University in Iowa confirm that individuals experience high levels of brain coherence during TM practice in only a matter of months, and often in just weeks.[3] A study led by Dr. Michael Dillbeck and published in the *International Journal of Science* looked at fifteen subjects and measured their brain activity before learning TM and two weeks after learning. The testing after two weeks showed a significant increase in frontal alpha coherence.[4]

And it is not only alpha coherence as was found in the earlier studies. Drs. Travis and Arenander measured twenty-two people at baseline before learning the TM technique, then again after two, six, and twelve months of TM practice.[5] This study showed that there is coherence in alpha and other frequencies in what is known as the prefrontal cortex of the brain, located just behind the forehead. EEG coherence in that area increases to a high level after only two months of practice, and then remains at that high level when evaluated six and twelve months later. People vary at how quickly they see significant brain wave changes from TM, but many will see the changes right away.

Yet another study looked at the brain wave patterns of students who had been meditating less than a year (the short-term meditators) as compared to the brain wave patterns of students who started TM at an early age, and who, by the time they were in college, had already been meditating for eight years on average (the long-term meditators).[6] In the chart opposite, the dark bar represents the measurement of brain coherence of the short-term meditators just before starting their TM practice (while these students were sitting with their eyes open), and the lighter bar shows the significant increase in the brain coherence once they close their eyes and start TM.

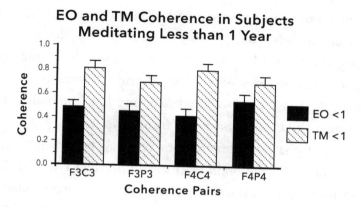

The chart below from the same study shows the brain coherence in the long-term meditators, reported in the study. Their brain coherence is naturally much greater than that of the short-term meditators during the period when they are just sitting with their eyes open, and then coherence increases again once they start the TM practice.

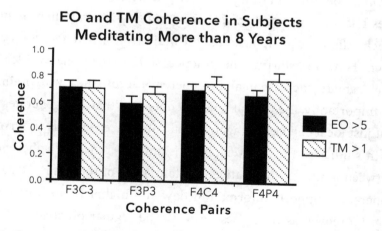

This front part of the brain, where Drs. Travis and Arenander see especially pronounced coherence, is highly important, since it is responsible for analytical and creative thinking, and for distinguishing between right and wrong. It is also the part of the brain that allows us to pay attention and focus on goals, and in general regulates our behavior by taking in data through the senses and making decisions. The prefrontal cortex is said to be the brain's conductor or chief executive. It has extensive physical connections with all the other areas of the brain, and both influences these other areas and takes information from them.

The next chart *(opposite)*, from research by Travis and colleagues illustrates the brain wave coherence that typically develops in meditators. It shows the slow alpha brain wave coherence in a new meditator across three different mental states. In this chart, the dots represent the various scalp sensors for recording the faint EEG signals from the brain. The lines connecting dots indicate the degree of correlation or coherence. More connecting lines means more coherence. There is a low baseline level of alpha coherence when this new meditator sits with his eyes open *(left pictures)* before beginning the TM practice. When he closes his eyes but does not start meditating *(middle pictures)*, there is not much difference in alpha across the brain from when his eyes were open. However, starting the practice of TM *(right pictures)* leads to a dramatic increase in alpha coherence across the entire brain.

Importantly, the typical kind of coherence that TM generates is not just local coherence (again, local coherence is usually referred to in studies as EEG power), but distant coherence, or coherence between a number of relatively distant areas of the brain. Distant coherence supports information flow and higher brain functioning. Moreover, as time goes on, with the regular practice of TM, meditators can exhibit what is known as *global coherence* or total coherence. That is where the brain waves are coherent at every location across the brain. Dr. Arenander told Jay:

With TM meditators, after a while there is alpha coherence across the whole brain, and in addition, the longer the person meditates the very high levels of coherence are found extending into other frequencies as well, until the whole brain is communicating in a highly orderly state. And we see this often enough, so it is not just a rarity. This is what happens to the brain as it evolves and becomes fully functional.

Alpha EEG Coherence Maps

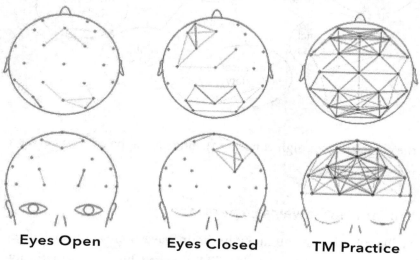

| Eyes Open | Eyes Closed | TM Practice |

Reference: *Cognitive Processing* 2010; 11(1): 21-30.

Brain Wave Coherence and Practical Benefits

The following figure (*next page*) shows research from four studies on advanced TM meditators demonstrating a high correlation between coherent alpha waves and performance. The "*p*" factors in the figure show the statistical confidence in the findings. For example, a "*p*" value of .01 for concept learning means that the study showed that there was only one chance in a hundred that

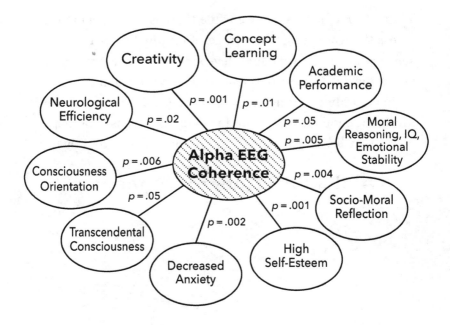

the correlation of high concept learning and alpha coherence was a matter of chance.

William Hathaway's Experience

William Hathaway found out his brain waves were abnormal when he was young, but practicing TM changed his life dramatically. The doctors gave William's mother too much anesthesia during his birth. When she wasn't experiencing contractions, the doctors used forceps. If forceps aren't applied evenly or are applied with too much force, it can cause compression of the head and hemorrhaging, which it did for William. The left side of his head was injured, leading to problems with coordination and learning disabilities. William says he had attention deficit disorder (ADD), and difficulty memorizing things, and learning vocabulary and mathematics. He had an EEG test of his brain waves, and later in life his parents told him the doctors found problems and that his EEG was "chaotic." He wasn't a good student in high school, and although he enjoyed reading and especially writing, he had trouble studying and had a rebellious streak. After high school William moved to California. His interest in writing led him to talk his way into a job as a copy boy at the *Oakland Tribune*, and he worked his way up to a cub reporter. At that point he realized he should go to college if he wanted to advance his career. However, he still had trouble concentrating and disciplining himself to work, and he flunked out after a year at the University of Colorado. Then after military service as a Green Beret in Panama and Vietnam, a friend told William about Transcendental Meditation.

William learned the TM technique in 1968. When he started, he still had trouble concentrating, but after TM instruction, William says that almost right away—within a couple of weeks—he felt much more relaxed and his thinking and ability to concentrate became better. He had been using marijuana extensively before, during, and after military service, and that just dropped away. He had been taking notes for a book about the Vietnam War, and after learning to meditate he began working on his book in earnest. Then after about a year he heard about a program at Columbia University in New York, and as a result of the changes meditation had brought about, he decided that he was better prepared for the discipline of college study. Based on an essay he submitted, he was accepted into Columbia's writing program. His life progressed from there, and he says his meditation program was the ordering force. He received his M.A. in English from the University of Washington, wrote his Vietnam novel (which received a Rinehart award given to promising first authors) and seven other books, and he became a Fulbright professor of creative writing at the University of Bonn and the University of Oldenburg in Germany. Along the way, his enthusiasm for TM caused William to become a trained TM teacher. He told us:

> My EEG now shows normal, orderly brain waves with no sign of damage. TM healed my birth injury and gave me access to my talent and mental abilities.

No EEG Slow Alpha Coherence in Other Meditation Practices

It is important to note that, with the exception of certain Zen Buddhist priests (described below) and a single Qigong meditator, other meditation practices have not been reported to result in EEG slow alpha coherence, distant alpha coherence, prefrontal alpha coherence, or global coherence. A 2010 article by Drs. Travis and Shear in *Consciousness and Cognition*,[7] supplemented by a 2019 report by Dr. Travis,[8] analyzed the published brain wave research on all meditation types where brain wave data could be found. The meditation practices included loving-kindness-compassion meditation, Zen-3rd ventricle, Zen (Zazen), Diamond Way Buddhism, mindfulness meditation, Qigong, concentrative Qigong, Sahaja Samadhi Meditation (Art of Living Foundation), and Transcendental Meditation. Many of the studies involved individuals who had been meditating for many years. The most common finding for the meditation practices other than TM was increased theta, beta, or gamma activity. According to Dr. Travis' research, mindfulness studies generally report increased theta and beta activity, and any increases in alpha activity are alpha2 increases in activity, but not alpha coherence. The increased alpha activity (activity, not coherence) from mindfulness is also in the central and posterior (back) of the brain, not the frontal area. Increased alpha2 power (at times from mindfulness) is associated with decreased blood flow to the brain and shows up in central and posterior areas of the brain which govern the motor and sensory systems, whereas the frontal region where TM has a significant effect, controls reasoning, creativity, and executive functions.

One study reported by Travis and Shear in their *Consciousness and Cognition* article[9] showed increased theta coherence in Sahaja meditators and one study showed higher frontal alpha1 coherence in Zen Buddhist priests. The priests' technique was to focus their attention on what is known as the "third ventricle" of the brain during meditation, and the priests reported "transcending the physical and mental realm" during their practice. The reason for the different brain wave findings is due simply to the techniques all being different.

What explains then why focusing or concentration techniques may sometimes feel good or why the Zen Buddhists were able to generate alpha1 coherence? Travis and Shear state that getting some results from focusing type techniques is likely the result of a concept called "automaticity." That concept is familiar to researchers and postulates that focused attention type meditations, when practiced for a long period of time, can transform themselves into a much more effortless type of meditation as the technique naturally evolves in the practice. Concentration and focusing techniques are difficult to practice, but the mind naturally wants to settle down. As a result, it can happen that after some period of time (and generally a lengthy one), there will be moments when the mind relaxes and starts to practice the concentration or focusing type meditation without the focus and slips into a deeper state that is more successful. Still, if we want to systematically produce coherence, we want a technique that itself is effortless and doesn't rely on the mind getting bored with a focusing technique and slipping into a more natural procedure.

Chapter 4

You're *Not* a Terrible Meditator— You Just Need a Different Technique

Talk show host Michael Feldman of the NPR show "Whad'Ya Know" was interviewing author and *The New York Times* columnist Patricia Marks in 2015. Marks said she paid a lot of money for someone to teach her to meditate and the experience was awful. She hated meditation. Feldman agreed. He said, "I'm a terrible meditator." He said he learned "the thousand petal meditation, and not one petal opened." Presumably neither Feldman nor Marks has since tried a different meditation technique because of their bad experience. Others, however, have a good experience with meditation and find immediate or almost immediate benefits. So, is it the person or the program that's the problem?

Calm, Headspace, Breathe, Mindfulness, TM: Which is Right for You?

If you look on the internet, you'll find writers saying that there are no rules about how to meditate. Just find one you like. They say you should expect meditation to be difficult, but sit there and do it, and

51

eventually there will be benefits. We don't consider this very good advice, and we think you'll see why.

If you're looking to get started with meditation, or you want to switch programs to find a better one, most people probably either take the advice of their friend even if the friend doesn't do it regularly, or they just try something that they found on the Internet. You can try meditation inexpensively with a number of apps, which probably costs only a small monthly fee. But one problem with this approach is that you're likely to only try one or a few meditation apps before you give up if the meditation doesn't seem to be working, and if you are only going to experiment with one or two, which should it be? In 2017 there were 1,300 meditation apps,[1] and that number is likely to be far greater today. So, should you choose an app for Calm, Headspace, Breathe, or Mindfulness, and if what you choose isn't working, should you switch after a few days, weeks, months, or years? Of course, if you switch, how do you know you just didn't give the first one enough of a chance? After all, "it's not supposed to be easy."

Vidya Cicchini tried many different meditation programs over almost a twenty-year period. Vidya entered West Point in 1976 as part of the Academy's first class with women in it. She graduated, was commissioned an officer in 1980, and then served in the military for five years. Now a nurse, Vidya says she began experiencing severe anxiety from the moment she set foot on the West Point campus. After military service she began more than 20 years of therapy and heavy medication, and she began trying different meditation practices as a means of gaining relaxation and getting rid of invasive thoughts. Her stress, she said, had manifested in "overwhelmingly invasive thoughts and suicidal ideation." She was

still regularly going to her local VA Medical Center and had severe
mood swings when she learned Transcendental Meditation in July
2015. Vidya had been meditating about eight months when Jay
interviewed her. Vidya said:

> Over almost twenty years I tried all the other meditation
> techniques: Siddha Yoga, Forest Zen, Japanese Zen, Buddhist
> and Christian contemplative, mindfulness meditation. TM
> [Transcendental Meditation] is the best!
>
> I tried all these other practices and was only partially suc-
> cessful. Some of them worked, but again only partially. With
> mindfulness I had a lot of trouble with it, and I just didn't
> find it very helpful. I couldn't actually settle down and relax.
> It didn't get rid of all the thoughts in my head. It wasn't what
> I wanted.
>
> TM was different, and it worked from the very beginning. It
> is much deeper than the other practices and really helps me
> put my body into a restful state and then at the same time, it
> clears out my head. I really look forward to the calmness it
> brings, and I seem to tap into inner resources that I did not
> know I had. The mood swings that were prevalent in my life
> are gone. I've acquired a new ability to respond to situations
> in a healthy way, instead of feeling confused or angry and
> reacting in that state. My physical health has improved too. I
> have more vitality, and 50 percent of the chronic pain is gone,
> and I can recover from illness in days instead of weeks or
> months. I think this should be a program in every VA Med-
> ical Center. I see mindfulness-based meditation courses all
> the time. But I have tried all these meditation techniques and
> they just aren't the same as TM.

TM is Easy

Let's go back to the common teaching that meditation is difficult. Those who say this may seem to be making a realistic statement since we associate things that are worthwhile with being difficult and requiring lots of effort. However, the opposite is actually true when evaluating meditation practices. Simple and effortless is not just good, it's necessary for meditation to be maximally effective and generate coherence. If you choose a difficult meditation practice, you may very well have the same reaction as Michael Feldman, and like Michael you'll conclude that you're a terrible meditator. But contrary to the common advice in this area, you're not terrible at meditation, the problem is likely the technique.

Vidya's experience that TM was easier (and more effective) than other techniques she tried is a common experience. David Connors worked for UCLA for 10 years as a construction manager overseeing everything from parking lot and road repairs to construction of laboratories and offices. Age 44 at the time Jay interviewed him at the end of 2016, he was then working as a business analyst for UCLA. David learned Transcendental Meditation after trying a half dozen other popular meditation or mental techniques. The ones David tried included mindfulness meditation; HeartMath, a guided meditation; hypnosis; and brain entrainment. Because of his lack of success with these practices, he said he "didn't think he was going to be able to do TM," and he was very skeptical about his teacher's statements that TM was easy and that anyone could do it. TM has been successfully taught to children age ten and older, octogenarians, those who are highly anxious or depressed, those with severe PTSD, people who suffer from panic attacks, and more.

54

David finally decided to start after seeing many testimonials for TM on the Internet and watching several YouTube videos. He said he also had a positive feeling about TM after learning about non-profit organizations making the TM program available without charge to so many children and other groups in need. He said the fact that these non-profit organizations were making TM freely available to such organizations fit with his own core values. He finally decided to give TM a try to deal with the stress in his life. David said:

It was as simple and effortless as advertised. It's actually remarkable. You go into TM thinking it's this little technique for reducing stress, and that alone would make it worthwhile, but you actually have no idea of the gifts you will receive. It was incredibly relaxing right from the start and that benefit alone would be worth it, but it's so much more.

In mindfulness I was taught to focus on my inner and outer breath. But you can only do that for so long. And because you can't keep doing that, it sets you up to fail. With TM there is no concentration or focusing like that, and the technique really changes you mentally and physically. My health improved exponentially. It's not yet 100 percent, but I've only been meditating five months and I am confident it will get to 100 percent.

I also make better decisions. I don't get angry or overly emotional in situations. I'm more compassionate, kinder, gentler, and, again, incredibly more relaxed. My relationship with others has improved as well as my relationship with myself. I'm clearer and more flexible. You don't know when you start, but it is a true experience of abundance or maybe fulfillment on a level you would never expect.

Classifying Meditation Techniques

To simplify our understanding of how TM differs from other meditation practices, it is helpful to classify meditation techniques into general types. One way of course is to classify them based on whether they create brain wave coherence. From the research, TM appears to be the only meditation that does this. But let's see why TM does this and other meditations don't by using a classification based on how the techniques are done, which was suggested by Drs. Travis and Shear, meditation researchers who are also long-term TM practitioners. They propose that there are three basic types of meditation. The first is where the meditator strongly concentrates on a mental object or idea. The second (using less effort than in concentration) involves contemplating or imagining pleasant experiences, or giving focused attention to some object, or dispassionately monitoring the object or the thoughts that enter the mind. This second type, which includes mindfulness meditation, generally involves focusing the attention on present moment sensations or the body or breath or the stream of mental activity (as David Connors from UCLA described) followed by a more receptive state of open-monitoring of the mind's activity.[2] David's experience, like that of Vidya Cicchini, was that the practice wasn't easy and that the benefits weren't comparable to those from TM. The third type is the easy and effortless TM technique, which does not involve focusing or trying to monitor the mind or body's activity.

While David and Vidya didn't get much if anything out of the techniques they tried before finding TM, this doesn't mean that no one will benefit from mindfulness and other focusing or monitoring techniques. Research shows that some people do benefit from mindfulness and other meditation practices, and they have their advocates, but we say the practical benefits will be much more modest than those from TM. To understand more fully how TM differs from other techniques, an analogy may be helpful.

Tony Nader, M.D., the international head of the TM organizations, has a Ph.D. in brain science from MIT in addition to his medical degree. In a 50-minute YouTube video (go to youtube.com/watch?v=y7hun3_SCeA), he compares TM to mindfulness and other techniques. He first explains that consciousness can be likened to an ocean.[3] Like the ocean, our consciousness has different levels. The surface of the ocean can be turbulent with many waves or it can be relatively calm, but the ocean also has a deep, silent level. Using this analogy, consciousness is like the ocean with a surface level that can be very active, and a deep level that is silent.

When we meditate using a focusing or monitoring technique, Dr. Nader says our awareness stays on the surface level of the ocean of consciousness. When we put our awareness on the surface level, such as on sensations in the body or our breathing, we are causing the mind to be aware of something. This is, for example, what mindfulness does. Being mindful of something is being aware of something, and this can have benefits since focusing on one thing, to the extent we are successful, may prevent the mind from focusing on negative things, and in the process calm the mind and relax you at least temporarily. Other techniques that focus on positive emotions like kindness can also have benefits. Dr. Nader explains that whatever we put our attention on grows stronger in our life, so there may be benefits from continually putting our attention on being kind. But focusing the attention on positive qualities, or on sensations in the body, or on our breath or on being mindful of things, is putting our awareness on the different waves at the ocean's surface, rather than diving to the silent, perfectly calm depths of the ocean of consciousness. This is the inner source of our silence and calmness, an inner source of fulfillment.

The word "transcend" means *to go beyond.* Transcendental Meditation gets its name because we go beyond thinking at the surface levels of consciousness (the level of the waves) and learn how to dive within to the silent depth of the ocean of consciousness. This is the profound level of silence and calmness that we want to cultivate. In his YouTube video, Dr. Nader says that in the ancient Vedic tradition from which TM derives, this experience of the silent depth of consciousness is sometimes called a state of *samadhi*; in Japanese and Buddhist traditions it may be called *satori* or *nirvana*, and it has other names in other traditions. To some, this experience may sound intriguing, but whether or not that is the case, in scientific terms it is important because the experience brings maximum coherence to the brain. Brain wave coherence increases as the mind settles down and coherence is greatest when we transcend thoughts and experience that completely calm state of mind. Because what we give our attention to grows stronger in our life, regular TM practice results in our becoming increasingly calm (even in the midst of turbulent surroundings), and the brain becoming increasingly coherent. Moreover, because the brain is the control center of the body, order in the body grows as well, resulting in the prevention of illness and the improvement or elimination of numerous physical disorders.

If concentration, focusing, and monitoring techniques don't work as well as the TM technique, why do so many techniques involve concentration or an effort to focus on or monitor something? In ancient traditions, it's well understood that the goal during meditation is to quiet or silence the mind, and as a result many meditation practices involve trying to quiet or settle the mind by holding it still. However, trying to keep the mind still by, for example, focusing on your breath or monitoring body sensations are active processes that involve effort, no matter how many times someone may describe it as a "passive" process. It keeps the mind on the surface level and does not allow the mind to *systematically* experience a quieter and more coherent state. Any effort to hold the mind still or to focus is a form of activity, which is counterproductive to transcending to a completely settled state with no activity.

Dr. George Kolodner, medical director of the Kolmac Outpatient Recovery Centers (drug abuse rehabilitation centers), says he was introduced to the Transcendental Meditation technique in 2014 by a popular book on the subject, Dr. Norman Rosenthal's *Transcendence*. In an interview in 2017 for the monthly publication *Enjoy TM News*, he said:

> [TM] sounded like a simple way to help manage the stress of everyday life, so I got the training and have been practicing regularly ever since. For me, it has not only improved my ability to respond to stress but has also stimulated my mind to move in more creative directions. It is so effortless that I thought that it would be ideal for my patients in early recovery, who usually find that focused-based meditation techniques are too difficult.

One other interview for this book indicates the value of the TM experience of going inward to the depths of consciousness. Jane Smith (not her real name) from Missouri, learned the TM technique in April 2018. Previously she had practiced mindfulness meditation regularly for about four years, and then off and on for another few years. Jane says that mindfulness, done regularly, helped promote a better ability to focus and she experienced "some level of stillness" during the technique. She said she felt somewhat calmer when she was doing mindfulness than when she wasn't, but that "any calmness during the mindfulness technique didn't carry over enough into everyday activity." She said it also didn't help her to feel centered and cope with daily stress. Jane's conclusion was that while she got benefits from mindfulness, even after years of practice she had not really gotten what she was hoping for.

Then she decided to learn TM from an acquaintance who said she could teach Jane the technique. That person, although not a TM teacher, had previously learned TM. But when Jane tried meditating from her friend's instruction, it didn't work any better than mindfulness, so she dropped it. Finally, Jane heard that qualified TM instruction occurred over four days (an hour and a half to two hours each day), and when two friends told her TM had "saved their lives," she took the official TM course. Jane was interviewed about ten days after she learned TM. She said:

> What I've noticed from TM so far is that it is so much easier. Almost right from the start of the practice, I feel a settling and a calmness that is different from anything I experienced with all the years of mindfulness. I feel I am still in the process of learning TM, and am not as deep as I can get, but the calmness already comes more quickly with TM and is deeper than what I personally could ever achieve with the mindfulness technique. With mindfulness I couldn't get into that zone.

Another important point is that it is very important to be correctly trained in TM by a qualified instructor of the program, who can then check your practice. A few years back, I was given some informal training by a well-intentioned acquaintance. I then did attempt what I thought was the correct technique for TM, but not seeing any different benefits from my mindfulness practice, I didn't continue with it. I think it is extremely important to have the correct formal training by a qualified TM instructor. This is what I have now and there is a big difference.

TM is Easy Because It's Natural

If TM doesn't involve concentrating, focusing or monitoring, how does the mind experience its maximally silent and coherent state? It happens *naturally*, and what natural means in this context is important to understand. In teaching TM beginning in the early 1960s, Maharishi Mahesh Yogi, the founder of the TM program, recognized a simple but profound understanding. This is that the mind doesn't wander aimlessly. As a result, we don't have to tame the mind or focus it or concentrate during the practice in order to settle the mind.[4] Instead, Maharishi said that the mind moves purposefully in search of greater satisfaction. For this reason, for most of us it is easier to listen to music than to a lesson on algebra because the music is more satisfying. The *natural tendency of the mind* is to move to (and stay on) what is satisfying, and this natural tendency governs mental functioning whether you're engaged in activity or in meditation. The more satisfying something is, the more you're attracted to it. The TM technique uses this natural tendency of the mind. Everyone enjoys being relaxed and settled, and, given the right inward direction, the mind will naturally move

61

toward a most settled state because that state is so satisfying. With TM there is no attempt to direct, control, or focus the mind; no trying to observe a candle or focus on the heartbeat or the breath (passively or otherwise); and no attempt to keep repeating a word or thought or *mantra* (discussed below), or monitor all thoughts and sensations that come to mind.

Over time, as the person continues to meditate, the mind becomes not only more settled, but more satisfied from within. That is the real source of our ability to be mindful of things. The same natural tendency of the mind to wander in search of greater satisfaction is operative whether we're meditating or engaged in activity outside of our meditation practice. If the mind is not calm and satisfied, it will wander aimlessly. If it is calm and satisfied, it will naturally stay on the tasks at hand.

Patricia Glispin had the experience of naturally becoming more mindful as a result of her TM practice. She is the head women's basketball coach at Clark University in Worcester, Massachusetts, and is one of the few coaches in the history of Division III women's basketball to win over 500 games. Coach Glispin was inducted into the New England Basketball Hall of Fame in 2009. However, the pressures of coaching for almost thirty-five years had taken its toll. In her interview, she said:

> Until a year or so ago I was very stressed out, and worried about every little thing, like buses being late for games. I couldn't even sit down during a game. I was up the entire game, pacing the sidelines. And as a result of the stress, I was really tired all the time.

Coach Glispin had tried different meditations, but she says they
were difficult to do and didn't change her stressed out condition.
Finally, at the urging of a body worker she used, but very skeptical
about getting results, she tried Transcendental Meditation. For her
the TM results were gradual, but highly effective. Coach Glispin
was interviewed in May 2018, which was thirteen months after
starting TM. She said:

> I'm much, much calmer now. TM, once you get the hang of
> it, is just so gentle and relaxing. The other meditations were
> not easy. With TM, I've had huge benefits across the board—
> happier, healthier, much less stressed out, and I think gentler
> with people. Also, I'm much better able to focus on things.
> During the day I can stay on task much better and get a lot
> more done. It's interesting because I have also gone to some
> of these mindfulness clinics they have here. And trying to be
> mindful of what is going on or what you are doing is hard
> work. With TM it's completely different. You really become
> focused on the task at hand and become naturally mindful
> of what's important just as a consequence of being more
> relaxed. It's a monumental difference.

TM is said to make us naturally mindful. That means being mindful without losing spontaneity.

The TM Mantras

There is a second part of the TM practice that makes it easy and
effective. That is the *mantra*. The word *mantra* means *a sound whose
effect is known*. In TM, a mantra from the ancient Vedic knowledge of India is selected for each meditator. The mantra has the
dual effect of facilitating the inward direction of the mind toward

an increasingly silent state and promoting orderly mind and brain functioning. Mantras are a special category of what are known as Vedic sounds, and we'll discuss the healing power of Vedic sounds in the coming chapters. But for now, what is important to understand is that meditation practices are all different, and the mantras (if there are mantras) that are used to meditate are also very different. And as we've seen, different meditations will vary greatly in the benefits they produce.

It is important to understand that there is a major difference between the sounds we enjoy in popular or classical music and the mantras used in the TM technique. We enjoy music for the meaning of the lyrics or the feelings it arouses in us, and we may like the beat or rhythm. But those aspects of music draw the attention outward, whereas the mantras used in TM are valued for their ability to draw the attention inward, and their ability to quiet the nervous system and produce a settled, coherence effect. If we focused on the meaning of the sounds, it would interfere with the effectiveness of the technique. The TM technique would become a contemplative practice, not one whose goal is transcending.

Maharishi Mahesh Yogi, who founded the TM program and introduced it in the West, said this about the mantras in his book *The Science of Being and Art of Living*:

> Because each personality has its own quality, it is extremely necessary that each man should have selected for him a special quality of thought whose physical influence will be conducive and useful to himself and the world at large.

> The influence of a spoken word that is carried by the waves of vibrations in the atmosphere does not depend upon the meaning of the word. It lies in the quality of the vibrations

that are set forth. Therefore, where it is necessary to produce vibrations of good quality that produce an influence of harmony and happiness, it also is necessary that the quality of vibration should correspond to that of the individual.[5]

The TM teacher chooses the proper mantra based on objective criteria and his or her training in this aspect of the teaching. Because of the delicacy of the nervous system, and the positive or negative effects of sound vibrations on the body, the selection of a mantra is not an area for self-experimentation. The TM mantras, coupled with the proper technique of how to use them, produce the results.

Olena P. has been an accountant for more than the past thirty years. She works for a large financial institution in Des Moines, Iowa. Olena had a number of health issues, and she decided to go for treatments to The Raj, an Ayurvedic health clinic in Fairfield, Iowa (see Chapter 16 for the effects of her treatment). While at the Raj she also learned TM, and she was interviewed about a month later. Olena had actually been doing a mantra meditation before learning TM but found TM to be very different. Olena said:

> I did the Kundalini Yoga meditation prior to TM. With the Kundalini meditation you recite mantras to yourself. The mantras are phrases and have a melody to them. In the Kundalini practice, the mantras you get depend on what you want to achieve, like mantras for calmness or better concentration. I did it for six months and I thought it was good; it worked, but not like TM. With the Kundalini meditation, I still had fatigue and it wasn't easy or as calming, and when coupled with my morning practice of the Kundalini Yoga movements it was taking about two hours, which I couldn't afford.

When the doctor at The Raj recommended TM, I talked to my son, and he said he had heard good things about it, and he encouraged me to learn while at The Raj for the Ayurvedic treatments. Now, after learning TM, I am so much calmer and honestly am feeling the joy of life again. This is an experience I haven't had for many years.

So, I know this is the right meditation for me. Before TM and my treatments at The Raj, I would get stressed in situations, but now I don't feel stressed like before. I feel in control. I'm no longer tired like I was before. I get more accomplished during the day and I am calmer in family situations that used to be stressful, so I get along better with family. Life is so much better. I would like to get my son, my husband and my niece also interested.

A Holistic Approach is Ideal

Unlike a form of meditation or mental technique aiming for a specific result, the TM program produces an overall or holistic change in the way the body functions. Many years ago, the value of a generalized or holistic approach was described by psychologist Abraham Maslow in his book *The Farther Reaches of Human Nature*. He said:

If you think of physical health, and if you ask the question, "How do you get people's teeth to be better? How do you get their feet to be better?" or their kidneys, eyes, hair, etc., any physician will tell you that the best thing to do is to improve the general systemic health. That is, you try to improve the general (G) factor if you can…then these procedures, in one single blow, will improve their teeth and their kidneys and their liver and their intestines and everything else; that is, the whole system will be improved.[6]

The Bottom Line in Meditation Practices and
Brain Waves / How TM is Taught

The practical benefits of TM meditation are described more fully
in the next chapters. The important thing for now is that among
the known meditation practices that have been researched, only
TM consistently results in a highly coherent style of brain functioning that includes slow alpha coherence. Moreover, because of
the effortless nature of the TM technique, it does so even from the
outset of the meditation practice.

If you learned to meditate from a friend, or a book, or CD, you
haven't learned Transcendental Meditation. TM is a revival of an
ancient practice that is taught in a one-to-one initial instructional
session. The teaching is done through a certified TM instructor,
typically at a TM center, which can be located at tm.org. During
the instruction, the new meditator is given his or her mantra, and
taught how to use it. Based on the meditator's experience, further
instruction is given. Books don't know your experience and would
not be effective in teaching this particular technique.

TM's effortless meditation can be done by anyone. The technique has been taught in over 120 countries to over six million
people of every race, religion, and culture from every walk of life.
Children can learn when they are about ten. It's successful with
highly stressed PTSD sufferers. It's been successfully taught to
the elderly in nursing homes. It's been taught to patients who are
severely depressed. It's practiced by businesspeople, generals in
the Army War College, and middle school, high school and college students. It will work for anyone who can follow the simplest
instructions.

Appendix A to this book consists of selective studies on TM and
mental development.

Appendix B provides more information on how TM is taught, as well as its cost and a list of some advanced programs. TM may be the only meditation program with a thirty-day money back guarantee if you are not satisfied.

Chapter 5

What the TM Research Shows: Whole Body Coherence

Evaluating Research

Everyone teaching a meditation technique, whether it is TM, mindfulness, Qigong, or Zen meditation, will have a rationale about how their technique works, and everyone will have anecdotal reports to support their claims of benefits. We have to exercise care in evaluating programs based on anecdotal or personal accounts, which can be unreliable. Researchers are often skeptical of personal accounts because there is a well-known expectancy factor. That means that where there are high expectations about a program, it may lead to overly positive reports about it. This is known as the *Rosenthal Effect*. In addition, many people won't admit that they're spending time in a program that doesn't really seem to work so they may exaggerate the benefits.

We also have to be careful in evaluating research in an age where almost everyone touting a meditation program will have some research to back up their claims. But research studies may have been done on very small samples, or in ways that bias the results. So how do we evaluate the research and personal accounts we may see on the Internet and those in this and other books?

Ideally, we should evaluate different programs or techniques in multiple ways. We should look at the personal accounts to see if they appear genuine but discount such evidence somewhat because of the Rosenthal Effect. We should also look at what the research says, how much research there is, and whether it is published in peer-reviewed journals (discussed below). Collectively, the research on any particular program should show significant physiological changes during the meditation practice, as well as practical benefits in daily life.

The TM research shows physiological changes during the meditation practice as well as changes in daily life. The physiological changes and practical benefits have been well documented with more than 600 research studies having been conducted at more than 200 independent research institutions in 27 countries. Importantly, almost 400 of these studies were peer-reviewed before publication. That means the articles were submitted to scientific journals and reviewed by experts in the field of study to determine if the research was of a high enough quality to be published in the journal, and the articles were only published if the peer reviewers had confidence in the research findings.

Published studies are also of different kinds. There are case studies, which are simply reports about an individual or group of individuals who are followed over a period of time. However, because there is no control group to compare that group to, case studies are not considered to have statistical validity, though they can provide a useful illustration of what is possible. At the other extreme, there are randomized control trials (RCTs), which are generally considered the gold standard for a research design. These studies are conducted so that as many sources as possible of potential bias in the study are removed by the study's design. For example, a typical study objective is to determine if a specific treatment or drug makes a positive difference in those being treated. In this situation we want to avoid a tendency that people have to report that they are doing better as a result of the treatment. To avoid this potential bias, the study needs a control group, meaning that the experimental treatment to be studied should be compared either to a placebo, or to another treatment or another group who doesn't get the experimental treatment. That way we have a benchmark for comparison. And the best controlled studies will have people with similar characteristics randomly assigned to the new treatment group and the comparison group(s) so, for example, not all the young people or the healthy people will be in one group and the old or unwell in another. Random control studies are not always done, however, because they are expensive and take a considerable length of time to conduct.

A final means of analyzing research is by what is known as "meta-analysis." This analyzes the data from many studies and combines the data in order to discover trends and see the overall picture since even individual studies may not have a sufficient number of participants or could have other defects.

Many of the TM studies, and especially the newer ones and those funded by outside research groups are *random assignment* control studies. For example, to date the National Institutes of Health (NIH) and the Department of Defense (DOD) have provided more than $28 million of funds for TM research, typically random assignment control studies, which itself is a good indication of the quality of much of the TM research.

The Initial TM Research on Changes During the Meditation Session

The initial research on TM was done by author Dr. Wallace. He learned the TM technique in 1964 while he was an undergraduate in physics at UCLA, and he continued his research while getting his doctorate in physiology at UCLA. Wallace had many occasions in those days to visit with Maharishi, who encouraged the study of the changes in the body resulting from the TM practice. Maharishi said that because the mind and body are so intimately connected, the profound mental effect of turning inward during the TM practice would produce profound physical changes.

Wallace's first major research was in 1969 on relatively new TM meditators, and even he was surprised by the results. His research showed distinct changes in the physiology during the TM practice—changes that had only previously been seen in Zen monks who had been meditating twenty or so years. Wallace's research was published in the early 1970s in *Science, Scientific American* and the *American Journal of Physiology*,[1] which are among the most respected scientific journals in the United States.

Dr. Wallace's early research was surprising from at least two perspectives. First, he was studying a mental technique, but it produced physical changes. TM practitioners are seated comfortably in a chair with their eyes closed, and there is nothing remarkable about what is happening as far as anyone can tell by just observing the situation with the naked eye. But the mind and body are so closely connected that the profound effects that meditators were experiencing in consciousness showed up in physiological tests as Maharishi had predicted.

The second surprise was the magnitude of the results. During the TM session, Wallace found that the meditators experienced not only brain wave changes, but a profound state of rest. Oxygen consumption declined very rapidly (Wallace found a 16 percent reduction and later studies have shown a reduction of from 4 percent to 30 percent).[2] There was a marked increase in skin resistance, indicating relaxation;[3] a reduction in heart rate and respiration rate; and a significant decrease in blood lactate levels, with high concentrations of lactate associated with anxiety and high blood pressure.[4] Subsequent research showed startling decreases in respiration that became barely susceptible to monitoring on laboratory equipment.[5] The conclusion from these findings was that TM produced a unique state of what is called *restful alertness*, where the mind and body are deeply rested yet the mind remains alert (unlike sleep).

Later research showed that TM lowers the level of the hormone cortisol in the body, sometimes known as the stress hormone.[6] In response to a threatening situation such as an impending car accident or someone attacking you, the adrenal glands will release adrenaline and cortisol into the body to help us deal with the situation. These chemicals give us the energy and strength to deal with threatening situations, even the stress on the body of our medications or of eating too much sugar. Problems arise, however, when we have too many stressful encounters, or stew on a problem as anxiety-prone people tend to do. Then the body continuously releases cortisol, and this keeps it in an overly active state. This in turn can cause serious problems, including increased anxiety, increased blood pressure, suppression of the immune system, and even unhappiness. Studies have also found that cortisol is highest in those who are rarely happy, and lowest in those who were almost always happy.[7]

Finally, just as cortisol is the stress hormone, which we want less of, serotonin is often considered the happiness hormone, so it's one we want more of. Serotonin is a hormone and neurotransmitter, which transmits messages to the brain from one nerve cell to another and regulates how we feel. Serotonin levels are said to determine whether a person feels happy or sad, hungry or satisfied, and low levels of serotonin are associated with panic attacks, obesity, violence, sleep disorders and various types of addictions. Because it is difficult to directly measure serotonin levels in the brain, it is common for researchers to study what is known as 5-HIAA, which can be measured in the urine and is the major byproduct of serotonin. Several studies by researchers in the U.S. and Europe have found a significant rise in the urinary excretion of 5-HIAA as a result of TM practice.[8]

The Entire Body is Gaining Coherence

How should we understand all the TM research? As deeply resting as the TM meditation session is, which itself would have very practical applications, the TM state is different from the sleep state in a number of important respects. Mentally, the meditator remains alert during the TM session. He or she would hear outside noises and could respond to interruptions. The meditator feels settled and at ease, while remaining alert, and while he or she may not realize it, *the entire physiology is gaining a highly coherent state.*

For example, the decrease in the breath rate and in oxygen consumption during the TM session doesn't cause a deficiency in the oxygen that is supplied to vital organs and tissues of the body. This is because the body is operating more efficiently during the TM session as compared to other waking states. If there were oxygen starvation during the TM technique, it would show up in compensatory "over breathing" in the minutes following meditation but this does not occur. Similarly, while heart rate slows during the TM practice, there is no shortage of blood flow through the body. We might expect that if the heart beats more slowly, there would be reduced blood flow, but researchers have found increases in blood flow to parts of the brain and in the forearm. Even hormone levels are becoming more balanced as a result of the meditation practice, so we aren't in an overly amped up state caused by daily pressures or traumatic events.

The physiological changes from TM result in practical benefits in almost every area of life. The changes show that the body as a whole is becoming more orderly or coherent and is functioning in a more efficient and balanced way. A person who is overly anxious with high blood pressure would likely have his anxiety and blood pressure reduced as a result of TM practice, whereas TM should make a person who lacks energy and has low blood pressure more energetic and his blood pressure may normalize. A person with low cortisol wouldn't likely have his cortisol reduced. A person with normal serotonin levels wouldn't likely have his serotonin increase. This is what coherence does. It gives the mind and body what they need. This overall enhancement of the body's coherence is the general systemic change that many believe is the best way to remedy any single disorder, and it has the potential to remedy them all.

The Carry Over Effect

The important thing about meditation is the effect it has in our activity. During the practice of TM itself we want to generate a highly coherent style of brain functioning that includes slow alpha coherence. But we don't practice meditation simply to achieve a calm and coherent state of mind during the brief meditation session. TM is not an end in itself. As we suggested earlier, we want coherent brain waves all the time so that whatever we do is effective, and the coherent brain is continually inducing coherence in the physiology to fight entropy and disease. The way the mind and body work is that what we do over and over becomes ingrained. This can be good or bad. We may become habituated to the pharmaceuticals we are taking, and then they start to work less well. Or if we are in a combat situation, the constant anxiety and need to be hyper alert cause the body to secrete certain chemicals and habitually function in a hyper alert, or fight-or-flight, manner. This contributes to the PTSD epidemic among our returning veterans. But with TM, the calm and coherent state during the practice is good for the mind and body. As we continue to practice TM we become more calm and coherent throughout the day. All of us who are busy need to repeatedly experience a relaxed and coherent state to prevent the stressful experiences of life from becoming ingrained in the physiology. If we don't allow the body to regularly experience a coherent state, entropy grows, and the inner disorder becomes deep rooted and will harm us over time. Conversely, as inner coherence grows, the brain and body grow in their ability to prevent disorders and reduce or eliminate those that are present.

Chapter 6

The Coherence Effect in Overcoming Stress and Preventing Disease

The findings of an important annual health survey were reported in *Forbes* magazine in 2014. The state of health in the U.S. was compared to ten other industrialized nations—the U.K., Germany, the Netherlands, Switzerland, Sweden, Australia, Canada, France, Norway and New Zealand. The United States came in last. And it was last even though it has the most expensive health-care system.[1] The United States gets very poor scores on all three indicators of healthy lives—remaining life expectancy for someone who is age 60, mortality amenable to medical care, and infant mortality. A subsequent 2017 report shows life expectancy in the U.S. is falling even farther behind other developed countries.[2]

The Unexpected Truth About Conventional Prevention

There are two counterintuitive findings about these reports. First is how much individuals spend on health care in the United States, and second is how the United States compares to other countries in the provision and receipt of *preventive* care. The prevention of disease is the most important factor in healthy living, and Americans' relative lack of health would seem to indicate that the United States is at or near the bottom in prevention. However, just the opposite is true. According to the *Forbes* magazine survey, the U.S. fares best on the provision and receipt of preventive and patient-oriented care.

So, what is the cause of our relatively unhealthy lives, especially when we are first in preventive care? The answer is that what we are doing in the U.S. in the name of prevention is not effective. We say that because Americans actually have very little knowledge of how to maintain and enhance the body's coherence, and we are disrupting our coherence by not eating right and working ourselves to death. Work is especially problematic in the United States where Americans have a work ethic that is second to none. A report last year by the International Labor Organization showed that U.S. workers averaged nearly 2,000 hours of work every year (40 hours per week x 52 weeks = 2,080 hours), which means a lot of weekend and overtime work. It also means we work nearly 350 more hours per year (nine more weeks) than Europeans. According to the non-profit American Institute of Stress, this increased workload is the main cause of workplace "stress," accounting for 46 percent of all on the job stress. And stress is the main disruptor of the body's coherence and, consequently, our unhealthy lives. Stress increases the risk of heart disease by 40 percent, the risk of heart attack by 25 percent, and the risk of stroke by 50 percent.[3] The Institute says that 40 percent of stressed people overeat or eat unhealthy foods, 44 percent lose sleep every night, three out of four doctors' visits are for stress related ailments, and that stress is the basic cause of 60 percent of all disease and illness.[4]

What is Stress (and Why are There so many Misconceptions)?

Stress is something we need to define more fully so we understand how we can best overcome it and the disorders it produces. Conversationally, we may speak of "the stress of the job" or "the stress of a divorce," using the term "stress" to refer to external events that are potentially stressful. However, more accurately we should reserve the term for the internal bodily reactions to those situations that disrupt the body's naturally coherent state. The external events that are potentially stress producing in the body are known as "stressors" or just stressful situations, to which individuals react very differently. One person in a given situation may suffer a stressful reaction, that can precipitate chronic disease, whereas another handles the situation with ease. And the extent to which you can handle the external disruptors depends on the extent of the body's coherence.

How Stress is Typically Eliminated

With all the potentially stress-producing situations we encounter in life, a good question is why we don't have even more stress related disorders—more ulcers, anxiety, heart disease, depression, insomnia, and so on. Although our bodies incur a heavy stress load on a regular basis, stress is a physical abnormality, which the body normalizes or heals whenever it is given the opportunity. When we become ill, we may relieve the symptoms with medicines, but Sir Hans Krebs, a Nobel Laureate in physiology, says "The physician and the patient can do no more than assist nature, by providing the very best conditions for your body to defend and heal itself."[5]

The rest we gain during sleep is an important requirement for "assisting nature" and allowing the body to heal itself by gaining a measure of coherence during sleep. And sleep is so crucial that it is part of every physician's prescription for virtually every disorder. Insufficient sleep can lead to obesity, diabetes, suppression of the immune system, anxiety, depression, and other disorders. Sleep is important for the prevention of and at least the partial elimination of stress related disease.

However, while we have naturally eliminated a lot of stress through sleep, the statistics on stress related disorders tell us that most people are not winning their fight against stress and have come to accept being stressed as "normal." We manage our stress with an increasing number of pharmaceuticals as we get older and think nothing of a full medicine cabinet to deal with our many disorders. And many of us are medicating ourselves with alcohol, illegal drugs, or misuse of pharmaceuticals, especially pain killers. This is an approach that relies on one or more medicines for each disorder, as opposed to changing our lifestyle and habits so that we can give the body the coherence it needs to alleviate and prevent disorders.

Natural Remedies that Work and Those that Don't

Today, natural remedies have gained popularity for relieving stress and addressing almost every disorder. One website advocates almost a dozen natural ways to alleviate stress, including exercise of almost any kind, which can increase endorphins and put us in a better mood; massage to eliminate toxins; warm baths to increase circulation; aromatherapies to soothe the mind; talking to someone about your problems; keeping a stress diary; organizing your environment; and mindfully coping with your anger. Some of these strategies may be beneficial, while others will likely do *nothing* for your stress.

Stress is an internal condition, something physical, so it should be obvious that talking about your problems, keeping a stress diary, organizing your environment, or even practicing being mindful of your anger can't heal an existing physical disorder. It is not that these things can't be helpful in some ways. They may help you understand your stress or even help prevent a greater buildup of stress, but they don't change the abnormal level of chemicals or other physiological disorders, the internal abnormality that we call stress. Consider mindful coping, for example.

Mindfully Coping with Your Anger

One website describes how to use mindfulness to cope with anger.[6] It cautions that being out of control when you're angry can cause tremendous harm to you and your relationships. And as a result, it recommends several strategies when you feel anger.

- Become aware of the sensations in your body, your heart rate, and/or breath rate.

- Breathe into the physical sensations or count out ten breaths if you like.

- Stay with the sensations and try to understand the feeling you are having.

- Notice your thoughts and try to let go of them, and if you can't, then watch the way your feelings and thoughts feed each other.

- Step back from what you are experiencing and notice you are the observer of your thoughts and emotions.

The instructions caution that coping with anger is challenging, but the idea is to keep these steps in mind so you can react to a stressful situation in the future with minor frustration and not outright anger.

The problem with the mindfulness strategy (and other coping strategies) is, first, its complexity and lack of clarity ("breathe into the physical sensations" and step back from what you are experiencing and "notice you are the observer of your thoughts and emotions"). How do you breathe into the sensations, for example? Second, when you lose your cool or really fly off the handle, it is an overshadowing experience that doesn't allow you to step back and just be an observer of your emotions or remember to apply the six coping steps. On the other hand, if the body's internal state is more coherent (that is, more balanced and relaxed), you naturally will find yourself standing back from the situation and not getting overshadowed by anger, anxiety, or fears. The internally relaxed and orderly state is not produced by learning coping skills, keeping a diary, or talking to someone. Practicing standing back does not cause you to be naturally relaxed.

Josh Griffith, the writer of several popular TV shows, had what is a common experience for those starting TM. You naturally step back from situations and don't lose your cool in the first place. Josh said in an interview:

> I can now very easily, when it's happening and I'm in the middle of that so-called crisis or something that's going to cause me major anxiety, I am able now to step back and go, "Whoa—hold on. Let's look at this. What can you do to avoid this? How can you deal with this?" It's given me a life-coping skill that has been remarkable. No matter what's thrown at me I can step back and look at it and go, "What's the best way

to go? What am I going to do next?" as opposed to the feeling, "I can't function, I can't deal with this....I don't know how to handle this," and the anxiety then would lead to depression where I would just not want to do anything. I've never been able to step back like that before.

Coherence is the Opposite of Stress

Physical anti-stress strategies such as exercise, yoga, massage, and aromatherapy can have a significant effect in healing when done properly. They have a physical effect and, therefore, can work because stress is a physical abnormality. The Vedic health strategies (Ayurveda) recommend exercise, yoga and aromatherapy, and we cover this in greater detail in the coming chapters. However, in the ancient Vedic system of health, for centuries the paramount strategy for human development, and for overcoming what we now know of as stress, is meditation, revived in this age as Transcendental Meditation. Allowing the mind and body to gain a coherent state is the antidote to stress because the coherent meditative state is the opposite physiologically of the disordered stressed state.

We should expect that if the brain and body are gaining a coherent state, many disorders would be prevented before they become serious health problems. But this is ordinarily hard to measure scientifically. There are, however, several important prevention studies. One small study by medical researchers in Spain was published in 2014 in the *International Journal of Yoga*.[7] It studied nineteen subjects who regularly practiced TM, some of whom also practiced an advanced program available to TM meditators called the TM-Sidhi® program, which is discussed in Appendix B. The meditators had practiced their technique for an average of seven years at the time of the study, and they were compared to

83

16 healthy subjects who were not practicing any form of meditation or relaxation technique. The laboratory tests showed the TM meditators had significantly more white blood cells. They had significantly more of the white blood cells known as T-cells, which destroy virally infected cells and tumor cells and are sometimes likened to soldiers who search out and destroy targeted invaders. The TM meditators also had significantly more white blood cells known as B-cells, which secrete antibodies, and more natural killer cells (NK cells) that neutralize bacteria and viruses or attack cancerous tumors. While the TM group had very significantly greater white blood cells, this is a small study and not a definitive one. However, many studies show that chronic stress compromises the immune system so whatever we can do for stress should help us in this important area.

Perhaps the most important studies on TM and the prevention of illness were those conducted by Drs. David Orme-Johnson and Robert Herron. Orme-Johnson, a psychologist associated with Maharishi International University, conducted an extensive five-year study that looked at insurance data to determine the medical visits of over 2,000 TM meditators as compared to non-meditators of comparable age, gender, and profession, who had similar health insurance policies.[8] Over the five-year period, the TM meditators consistently had fewer than half the doctor visits and hospitalization than the non-meditators, and the differences between meditators and non-meditators was greatest for people over forty. The meditators had significantly fewer incidents of illness in seventeen medical treatment categories, including 87 percent less hospitalization for heart disease, 87 percent less for nervous system disorders, 73 percent less for nose, throat and lung diseases (including virus caused diseases), 65 percent less for metabolic disease, including diabetes,

Health Insurance Statistics:
Fewer Hospital Admissions in All Disease Categories
through the *Transcendental Meditation* technique

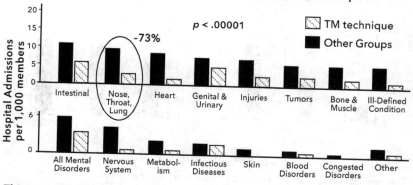

This study of 2000 TM practitioners over a five-year period found reduced hospital admissions – lower in all categories of disease for TM. They are 73% lower for Nose, Throat, and Lungs diseases, which includes diseases caused by viruses in the same family as the coronavirus.

Reference: Orme-Johnson, D.W. Medical care utilization and the Transcendental Meditation program. *Psychosomatic Medicine* 1987; 49: 493-507.

and 55 percent less for cancer. The significantly better results for the TM group also extended to blood disorders, intestinal disorders, infectious diseases, and genital and urinary disorders.

A subsequent Canadian study of senior citizens published in 2011[9] and conducted by Dr. Herron, also associated with Maharishi International University, compared the health spending of 1,418 Quebec health insurance enrollees who practiced TM with the same number of controls who were matched for age, gender, and region. The study looked at medical costs (adjusted for inflation) for all treatments for both groups for the eight years before the TM group learned the technique and for the six years following their start of TM. Both groups were composed of persons who had high medical costs each year. The medical costs of the two groups for the eight years before the one group started TM were not sig-

Decreased Hospitalization and Doctor Visits in All Age Categories

through the Transcendental Meditation technique

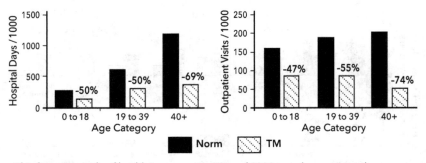

This five-year study of health insurance statistics of 2000 people practicing the Transcendental Meditation technique found that their medical-care utilization was lower than the norm in all age groups, with the greatest reduction in older adults.

References: *Psychosomatic Medicine* 49 (1987): 493-507

nificantly different. But after starting TM the medical costs show the TM group got significantly healthier. In the six years after the TM group learned the technique their costs decreased an average of 13.8 percent per year compared to what the control group was spending on health care.

Overcoming Job Burnout and the Stress of Growing Up

Work doesn't have to be the stressor it is. Josh Griffith, mentioned earlier, went from being burned out on the job to having the enthusiasm of a new hire. Josh was the head writer for the popular daytime TV shows *Days of Our Lives* and *The Young and the Restless*. In 2013, he was having serious stress issues at work, and he started looking into meditation practices. Jay interviewed Josh in early 2016 after he had tried other techniques and had been practicing TM for a year. Josh said:

I saw a celebrated doctor on television and decided to try a meditation he said would help. He said to sit in a chair and close your eyes and then ask yourself four questions: "Who am I? What do I want? What is my purpose? Why am I here?" And you would just repeat those four questions. And he said don't answer them, just repeat the questions and you would repeat those for ten or fifteen minutes. So, I tried that. I did it for about a year, and sometimes I sort of modified it to my own way of doing it, and I made up sort of my own series of words that I would do in the evening. It was kind of helping, but then the work issues got worse and I was still feeling the same way that I had before.

Then Josh saw an interview about TM on television, and he decided to try it. He said:

In the world of daytime TV, you're having to create five shows a week. As head writer [*The Young and the Restless*] I was responsible for all the stories that aired. I walked away from it a few years ago because I felt burned out. It was too much. It was too much of an output, and I didn't feel the quality of the output was something I could be proud of. It was taking such a toll on me that I walked away.

Then I started doing TM. I thought I was a meditator before starting TM. Boy, was I wrong.

I was offered the head job on *Days of Our Lives*, and I agreed to take it because with TM I already felt sort of a creative energy bubbling back inside of me. So, I stepped back in and it was sort of the case where I felt like "I'm back at the beginning of the career."

I felt like I had the energy that I had when I first started doing daytime. I was able to come in and the ideas flowed nonstop, whereas before I didn't know if I would be able to finish this. I was thinking "I don't know what I'm going to do—I've hit a wall." TM allowed me to generate so many story ideas that it was, in a way, sort of like a rebirth. You know I've had a 30-year career. And the changes happened within a month of practicing TM. I feel like I'm starting [my career] now. I feel like a 25-year-old again.

You know, I even got both my daughters into it this past year as well. And they are in their 20s. But again, they were both like, "Wow! I wish I had had this before I turned 15. It would have been, my life would have been much different."

Stress can also ruin young lives. William R. Stixrud, Ph.D., is a leading expert on child education and development. He is a clinical neuropsychologist and Assistant Clinical Professor of Psychiatry at the George Washington University School of Medicine. He has authored articles on children with epilepsy, impaired brain development, and self-esteem issues, and Transcendental Meditation's effect on students with ADHD. In an interview about TM and education available at davidlynchfoundation.org, Dr. Stixrud said:

I talk about TM because children can do it very easily, and when they do it 10 minutes twice a day, they have a core, a center of peacefulness and happiness inside that they can access. And the more they do it, they find they are less reactive to stress, and when they do get stressed, they get over it faster, they generally sleep better, and they eat and get through life [better]. Kids simply need antidotes to these tremendous stressors including drug and alcohol abuse and sleep deprivation.

Much more important than what they're taught and what they learn is really having brains that work in a healthy way and being in an environment where kids feel safe.

If you think about it, what are the real dangers as kids grow older and get into adolescence? They're things like making bad decisions, losing motivation, kids getting depressed, kids developing eating disorders, or self-injury, kids abusing drugs and alcohol. These are really worrisome things. And all these things are highly related to stress. And if we see Transcendental Meditation correctly as a beautiful tool, a very easy tool, for normalizing the stress response and providing deepest rest, then all these things get better.... My feeling is there is nothing more important than helping kids develop nervous systems that work well, that can learn well, and that feel great.

Chapter 7

From Anxiety, PTSD, and Depression to Calmness and Inner Fulfillment

Overcoming Simple Anxiety

At the time of his interview, Bryan Dietzman was a casting associate for The Asylum, a film production company in Los Angeles, which produced the *Sharknado* franchise films. Bryan started TM in late 2015 because of the anxiety in his life. He said:

> I was having a lot of stress and anxiety with work and I had started seeing things on Facebook and elsewhere about TM and am also a fan of Jerry Seinfield. I saw TM come up a couple times on his shows, and I saw Jim Carrey talk about it. And I'm also a fan of Russell Brand. I watch a lot of his videos and he talked about it, and I decided to start.

> I did mindfulness a long time ago in Philadelphia and eventually faded away from my practice of it. That was probably early to mid-2000s. A friend of mine there had turned me on to mindfulness, and when I kept up with it, it did help. I didn't find it as easy to keep up with it as I do with TM. I had read Jon Kabat-Zinn's book [Kabat-Zinn is the founder of

mindfulness] and had a couple of his CDs and would listen to some of his guided meditations and that always helped me, but I pretty much had to be at home in a room with a CD playing, whereas now I can pretty much do it anywhere I can close my eyes.

I started taking the bus to and from work and I meditate on the bus every day. TM's a lot different than I expected I think because of the name Transcendental Meditation. That word Transcendental seemed like there was so much involved to get you to this point of transcending. That's just how it came off to me, but then I found out how simple it is.

And particularly when I do the group meditations. There is a noticeable difference. We have them once a week—a group at the TM center and when I can get there, it's a noticeable difference.

The most noticeable benefit has been with my anxiety. I guess I'd never really experienced or identified anxiety before, and I started to think it was stress, but it didn't feel like normal stress to me and finally it just hit me like "Wow. I think this is anxiety. I'm having anxiety." But at the time my life wasn't that stressful. I was doing my job and things were going well, and I thought "why do I have all this anxiety?" And probably I did TM a month at least before I realized that my anxiety was gone.

So, yeah, it's working. And definitely my stress level has gone down and how I deal with events in my life is better. I'm less reactive and I don't get as stressed as quickly.

We asked Bryan if others have commented on the changes in him after he started TM. Bryan said:

I have one friend who I didn't even know was into TM, and I brought it up, and she was like "Oh, I've been doing that since

91

I was a teenager." I had no idea but when she said that it made sense because she's one of the most clear-headed, down-to-earth people I know. Anyway, she said that she could tell a difference in me. I guess I should make it more of a point to ask others. There's not a lot of people who know I'm doing it actually.

A study published in 2020 was conducted principally in Italy at a research laboratory in Lucca and the Department of Medicine and Surgery at the University of Pisa and published in 2020 in the journal *Brain and Cognition*. This study is important because it was a random assignment study that measured not only perceived depression, anxiety and stress, but also changes in the subjects' brain functioning as measured by magnetic resonance imaging (MRI).[1] The researchers found significant changes in the TM group of nineteen subjects in their perceived depression, anxiety, and stress levels after just three months of TM practice, with no changes in the control group of fifteen subjects. And new feelings of well-being were directly related to measurable changes in brain activity, those being greater functional connectivity, an indication of coherence, between different brain areas. There were no changes in brain activity found in the control subjects who did not learn TM. The researchers concluded that "TM may effectively counteract dysfunctional brain changes associated with increased anxiety and stress."[1] Although the brain connectivity element was looked at in this recent study, the finding that TM produces measurably increased well-being in a short period of time corroborates many earlier findings.

Depression, anxiety and stress symptoms
significantly decreased as brain connectivity increased in TM subjects

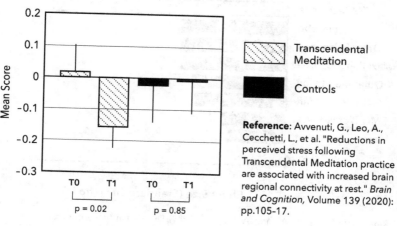

Transcendental Meditation

Controls

Reference: Avvenuti, G., Leo, A., Cecchetti, L., et al. "Reductions in perceived stress following Transcendental Meditation practice are associated with increased brain regional connectivity at rest." *Brain and Cognition*, Volume 139 (2020): pp.105-17.

The most extensive early study on TM and anxiety was conducted in 1984 by Dr. Kenneth Eppley of the Stanford Linear Accelerator Center, Stanford University, and his colleagues. They completed an analysis of 99 studies comparing TM and other meditation or relaxation technique on trait anxiety (a meta-analysis). Trait anxiety is long-term anxiety involving excessive worrying and fears in many situations. Dr. Eppley designed his study to compare TM to other forms of meditation and to Progressive Relaxation and biofeedback, which were then popular. Eppley's finding was that TM produced significantly greater effects than the other programs, in fact approximately twice the effect, of the other forms of relaxation he looked at.[2] He told us:

> TM produced a significantly larger effect than other forms of meditation and relaxation in the reduction of trait anxiety. The difference was too large to be accounted for by expectations or placebo effects. We also looked at the source of the

Effectiveness in Reducing Trait Anxiety
Meta-analysis of 146 studies

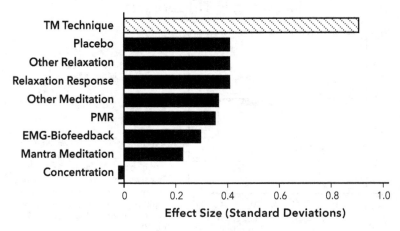

Reference: Eppley, K., Abrams, A., Shear, J. (1989). Differential effects of relaxation techniques on trait anxiety: a meta-analysis. *Journal of Clinical Psychology*, 45 (6): 957-974

studies and the attitudes of the researchers. Some [researchers] were highly favorable to TM, others were neutral or negative. The effects found in the studies were not related to the experimenter's attitudes.

Another analysis of TM's effect on anxiety was published in *The Journal of Alternative and Complementary Medicine* in 2014.[3] This was also a meta-analysis focused on only the most well-designed studies, and it also compared TM to other programs seeking to reduce anxiety. All the studies randomly assigned the study participants to either the TM group or the comparison group(s). The groups compared with TM included the relaxation response, Tao meditation, a mantra meditation other than TM, simple relaxation, muscle relaxation, just sitting for twenty minutes with the eyes closed, health education, and corporate stress management practices, including deep breathing and self-awareness exercises. The analysis was of sixteen studies involving 1,295 participants. Again, TM was found most effective and, as perhaps would be expected, those persons with the highest anxiety levels, that is, those with chronic anxiety, veterans with PTSD, and prison inmates, had the greatest reductions in their anxiety. Persons with high levels of anxiety are found to fare much better using TM as compared to other techniques, including comparisons of TM and mindfulness.[4] More than fifty studies in total show TM reduces anxiety.[5]

Other Comparative Studies on TM and Relaxation

An early comparison of TM and the "relaxation response" technique was undertaken by a Pennsylvania psychologist who investigated changes in skin resistance. The technique was popularized by the book of the same name and developed by Herbert Benson, M.D. Benson argued generally that all meditation techniques produced a relaxation response that was beneficial, and then, surprisingly, he cited the TM research for the supposed benefits of his relaxation response procedure. The relaxation response that was studied involved just repeating the word "one" or some other word or phrase over and over, which is characteristic of focusing or concentration techniques. In the Pennsylvania study, there were twenty-six subjects, half of whom learned TM and half who learned the relaxation response. Skin resistance, a common measure of relaxation, was measured three weeks after the subjects began their respective techniques. The mean rise in skin resistance for the relaxation response was 25 kilohms, whereas the mean rise for the TM group was 137 kilohms, or about five times as great indicating how much more relaxing is TM as compared to this other technique. The study found that only one subject in the relaxation response group was able to reduce his need for tranquilizers, whereas all ten subjects taking tranquilizers at the time they learned TM reduced their usage. The relaxation response group said that after six weeks they became "extremely bored" with the practice, whereas in the TM group all were still meditating after eight months.[6]

A similar early finding was made at Princeton. A researcher there decided to teach both TM and the relaxation response to a group of subjects and compare the personality traits of those who might prefer the TM technique with those who might prefer the relaxation response. The researcher administered a personality inventory to 26 subjects, after which half were first taught the relaxation response and the other half taught TM. Then, two weeks later, each group learned the other technique. However, to the researcher's surprise no comparison could be made of the types who would prefer one technique over the other, because all 26 subjects preferred TM. It didn't matter whether the subjects were rated "high-anxious," "low-anxious," "extroverted," "introverted," "dependent," or "independent;" they all preferred TM.[7]

Pamela Peeke, M.D., M.P.H., is WebMD's lifestyle expert for its 90 million members. She also serves as chief medical correspondent for nutrition and fitness at Discovery Health TV. She is spokesperson for the American College of Sports Medicine's Exercise is Medicine initiative and is Assistant Clinical Professor of Medicine at the University of Maryland School of Medicine. Peeke started TM in 2014 after failing to get results from the relaxation response technique. Speaking on a video posted on the website of the David Lynch Foundation (davidlynchfoundation.org), she said:

> It's a miracle because I can meditate. I'm a Type AAA personality. I make Soledad [Soledad O'Brien, also a TM meditator]

look like she's hypothyroid [sluggish and lethargic]. I'm the best thing that ever happened to TM because if I can do it, anyone can do it.

I am their [the group teaching the relaxation response] most spectacular, most famous failure....I couldn't relax to save my life. You could have given me half a billion....I still couldn't make it happen [with the relaxation response].

Then I went to the Bethesda [TM] center and I said "I have rules. If I see candles, I'm out of here. And I'm not changing my religion. I kind of like mine. It's a little flawed, but it works. We're not sharing [holding hands]. No circles are forming. Stay away from me." And then a small miracle took place. It fit like a glove. And I haven't stopped and it's been a year and a half. It's fantastic.

Anxiety with Panic Attacks

Jason, age 39, produces and edits trailers to market television programs and films. He says he has had anxiety since he was in his teens, but it got worse as he got older. He told us:

I've had anxiety for as long as I can remember. But there is a difference between being anxious and knowing the cause is stress at work or money issues, and what I experienced, which is an unexplainable force causing irrational attacks, panic attacks.

Panic attacks are a category of anxiety that are especially severe and can be disabling. They can result in the abrupt onset of intense fear or discomfort. The attacks usually reach a peak within minutes and can result in a pounding heart, sweating, trembling, chest pain or discomfort, chills or heat sensations, fear of losing control, and even fear of dying. They can easily be mistaken for a life-threatening situation and many who have them may rush off to the hospital.

Over the years Jason saw therapists and was prescribed Zoloft and Lamictal for what he was told was a type 2 bipolar disorder. Then, a number of years ago a therapist he was seeing got him interested in meditation, and he started reading about it. Jason said, "Mindfulness is a mainstream buzzword these days, and I got interested." Jason practiced mindfulness for a while, the type where he would close his eyes and focus on his breath or some other part of the body. He said that at times he was successful in doing that and tuning out other thoughts, but he said the practice was difficult, and it didn't reduce his panic attacks. Then he read a book by film director David Lynch called *Catching the Big Fish* where David writes about his enthusiasm for Transcendental Meditation. Jason was a film school graduate and David Lynch was one of his heroes, so Jason got excited to learn TM. Jason had been practicing TM for about two months when Jay interviewed him in May 2017. Jason said:

> In my case, things had gotten to a point where I would wake up in the morning and have a panic attack over whether I would have a panic attack that day. I didn't want to be in a social situation where it would come on and I would have trouble extracting myself from the situation. Then I started TM and that made me realize how difficult mindfulness was in getting me into a settled state. It was hard to believe how easy TM was, and it worked from the beginning.
>
> It was almost immediately after starting TM that the panic attacks stopped. I just don't have panic attacks anymore. I may at times have some mild anxiety about things, but that's all. It made me really eager for my wife to start TM. I started

before her, but she was very interested and started a month after me, and she loves it as well.

With mindfulness, while at times the practice seemed good, it didn't have effects that carried through to the rest of the day. It didn't lead to any reduction in my anxiety, and now it just seems like something that distracted me from TM.

Jason also remarked about changes others were seeing in him. He said:

My wife notices the difference for sure. And my parents visited me recently and my dad was like "I can't really describe what it is, but you look good and seem very clear and more together. Something about you is really better."

PTSD

PTSD is a kind of anxiety sometimes characterized as a disabling anxiety resulting from traumatic experiences. It was first brought to the public eye as the after-effect of combat in returning military personnel, but it can result from any traumatic experience, including a divorce, a death in the family, losing one's job, a bankruptcy, being bullied at school, a serious accident, or being a victim of a violent act. Often individuals with PTSD can't stop thinking of the event and may relive it in flashbacks or nightmares. The high level of anxiety is often accompanied by insomnia, depression, alcoholism, and substance abuse.

For those who have been in combat, the hyper-vigilance required in a combat zone leads to veterans not being able to relax, being constantly on the lookout for dangerous situations, not being able to sleep, and being easily startled. The anxiety attacks can be triggered by sights, sounds, and other sensations that cause the unwanted memories and feelings to surface. Pavlov's dog experiments are used by some to explain how PTSD surfaces. Each time Pavlov fed his dogs, he rang a bell and after a while the dogs began to salivate just from the ringing of the bell even when no food was presented. Those with PTSD become conditioned to respond as if in danger because of a trauma from the past.

The problems veterans experience can simmer under the surface and erupt years later. But traumatic events can affect everyone, and some estimates say that PTSD affects almost 13 million adults in North America and twice as many women as men. Worldwide the number is staggering as a result of the refugee situation in the Middle East and the effects of years of war in Africa, which are estimated to result in 100 million Africans suffering from PTSD. It is estimated that from 60 percent to 75 percent of individuals in North America will experience a traumatic event in their lifetime and are potential PTSD sufferers.[8]

At the time Dan Kester was interviewed for this book in early 2016, he had been meditating for just a few months. He was an executive at a community college in Arizona and had recently retired from the Air Force after 38 years from his role as a Senior Master Sergeant. Dan said he "had issues with post-traumatic stress disorder as a result of the Iraq war and other traumatic experiences." He was having one of his worst days in years when he happened to meet two TM teachers who encouraged him to learn the technique and told him they had scholarships that would be available to cover the cost. Dan said:

Well, it's interesting the way my psychologist explained my PTSD. If you come from a rough childhood, as I did, you grow up thinking that the world is not a very safe place to be. But as you get older, you usually can say, "hey, that was just a one-off experience." But after my childhood, I became a fire fighter, and in that you see a lot of accidents. I had three babies die in my arms on my very first day in the fire department. So, you see a lot of trauma and a lot of death, and it reconfirms that the world's not a safe place. Then you go into combat like I did in Iraq, and when people are trying to kill you, you realize that it's definitely not a safe place and you end up with PTSD. Others could have a nice upbringing and go to Iraq and they can rationalize that Iraq is dangerous, but it's supposed to be, because its war. Maybe they don't come back with PTSD. That's kind of how he explained it.

For me, the PTSD manifested as traditional fight-or-flight. I would feel threatened and sometimes it wasn't even a physical threat; it was things at work where I would feel threatened and would go into instant fight-or-flight. I'd either want to quit my job or I'd want to go bang on someone's office door and confront them. Neither one was good.

In my job now, like many institutions, the school had some difficult issues, and I came in about that time to clean things up and try to get us to pass various audits so it's a very stressful position that I'm in. Normally I would have cleared out by now or probably done something to get myself fired by now if I hadn't had TM.

TM kind of took the edge off of those feelings. They didn't go away completely, but it sure helped when I did my TM. I've done two meditations today and I can feel a huge difference. Everything is better with TM. My relationships are better. I've never really had any big problems with relationships, but things don't get me reacting like they used to.

My wife liked what happened to me so much that she decided to spend the money to do it. It was free for me and then we both liked what it was doing, and we decided to get our 10-year-old into TM, and he meditates now as well. I can already see in our son a positive difference in his behavior.

The Conventional Gold Standard Treatment for PTSD

The conventional therapy that has been considered most effective in treating PTSD is what is known as Prolonged Exposure Therapy (PET), which is endorsed by the American Psychiatric Association and the Department of Veterans Affairs.[9] PET is one-on-one therapy, which can be expensive, but is generally considered superior to group therapy. PET is typically administered once a week for ninety minutes over a three-month period.[10] PET involves a trained clinician discussing the events of the patient's trauma and exploring the patient's thoughts and feelings to help the patient feel less distress when recalling the trauma and help decrease the unwanted traumatic reminders. Another aspect of the treatment encourages patient interactions with "safe" things the patient has been avoiding in order to help him overcome these fears. The therapy gets patients to relive their traumas so that ideally they see them in a better light. In Pavlovian terms, it seeks to wean the patients from re-experiencing the trauma by prolonged experiences of the traumatic situation in a controlled environment.

Of course, many patients don't want the stress of reliving their traumas, and although PET is said to be the best of the conventional therapies, it sometimes increases PTSD symptoms, and it is estimated that 60 percent to 72 percent of patients retain their PTSD diagnosis after PET therapy.[11]

TM's Effect on PTSD found to Exceed the Gold Standard PET Therapy

TM's effectiveness in small studies on PTSD led to a major $2.4 million study on TM and PTSD funded by the Department of Defense and published in 2018 in *Lancet Psychiatry*, a leading scientific journal.[12] The study was conducted by the VA San Diego Health-Care System and the Maharishi International University Research Institute. The study surprised many of the long time PTSD researchers since it compared TM to PET, which had been considered the best therapy for PTSD, and TM produced better results.

The study involved 203 veterans, most with severe PTSD symptoms. The veterans were randomly assigned to either learn TM, or participate in PET, or receive health education (a total of three groups). PTSD was measured using a clinician-administered questionnaire providing what are commonly known as Clinically Administered PTSD Scores (CAPS), considered the best measurement device for PTSD. The results were that 61 percent of the TM group compared to 42 percent of the PET group had significant reductions in their CAPS scores (significant reductions in their PTSD), compared to 32 percent in the health education group. Other studies on TM and PTSD have made similar findings, but these were not random control studies.[13]

TM's Effects on PTSD Compared to Mindfulness-Based Stress Reduction

Research shows the TM effect on PTSD also compares favorably to the effects of mindfulness. A 2018 report on mindfulness stress reduction programs for PTSD[14] mentions four PTSD random control studies. Two of these studies found no results on PTSD from mindfulness and the third and fourth studies found only temporary results that didn't last. In the third study, mindfulness significantly reduced PTSD symptoms from the beginning of the study until the completion of treatment, but the PTSD symptoms then increased significantly from the completion of the treatment to the final assessment at a 6-week follow-up.[15] The last of the four mindfulness stress reduction studies involved 116 veterans who were taught mindfulness meditation and also received psychological education about PTSD and its symptoms. This group was compared to group therapy. Similar to the prior study, the researchers reported that in a two-month follow-up, those in the mindfulness group were no more likely than those in group therapy to have overcome their PTSD diagnosis.[16]

PERSONAL EXPERIENCES IN OVERCOMING PTSD

Law Enforcement Officer

Michael Ortiz retired with severe PTSD after more than twenty years as a New York State Trooper and Drug Enforcement Agent. His more complete account of his experience with TM is posted in a video that can be found at the website of the David Lynch Foundation. To summarize his story, at the time he retired he was having trouble sleeping and dealing with stressful situations; he had flashbacks of his years of trauma as a trooper; he exhibited signs of paranoia; his marriage was deteriorating; and he was getting drunk and taking drugs to avoid his problems. His wife Deborah was concerned about his behavior and after many other interventions failed, Deborah and Michael started TM. Michael said:

I tried help from every other area and didn't get it. I was
having a slide projector [reliving past traumas]. I was still
craving to go get drunk. I was still having the craving to use
drugs, prescription and illegal drugs. And I will be honest
with you as I sit here today, with the TM it has all gone away.
And I only tried TM for her [his wife Deborah].

Deborah added:

We did it together [started TM], and I was just blown away.
I saw light coming from his eyes that I had not seen for I
don't know how long. And I was floating on air. Since TM
we actually have a future. I knew he was going through some
tough stuff, and I didn't want to walk away since I didn't want
to leave him in a place that was so dark. TM has absolutely
changed our lives. It is the greatest gift we have been given.

Changes in an Army Infantryman

David learned TM in a small TM-PTSD research study. David was
in the Army Infantry with the 101st Airborne Division in Iraq in
2003. Near the end of his tour of duty, he was injured in a suicide
car-bomb attack, and after his return to the U.S. he was diagnosed
with PTSD. David was prescribed medications to deal with his distress, but he didn't like their effects and never took them for long.
His life after the military began fairly normally with work and
going back to school, but after a few years, David said, "I snapped."
He recognized something was very wrong with the way he was
functioning, and, in a video at davidlynchfoundation.org, he said:

I began to withdraw myself from life. I began abusing drugs
and drinking to try to control my PTSD. I went back and
forth to the Veterans Administration to try to get help, but all

they wanted to give me were the mind-numbing medications they prescribed while I was in the Army.... This went on for almost three years....

Then while driving David heard a radio ad that reported a research study with physician Norman Rosenthal was seeking veterans to take part in an examination of the effects of Transcendental Meditation on PTSD. David signed up and said the following on the David Lynch Foundation website:

> The first time I meditated I experienced this relief from the constant anxiety attack my life had become. When I meditated, it stopped. I just felt completely relaxed for the first time in five years. Since I first transcended, I knew my life had picked up again. The new sense of awareness that I had after I started practicing [TM] regularly twice a day had me ecstatic!

Changes in a Navy Veteran

Ms. K was a 32-year-old Navy veteran who participated in the San Diego VA TM program described earlier in this chapter. In statements posted as an addendum to the 2018 PTSD study by Dr. Sanford Nidich and others published in *Lancet Psychiatry*, Ms. K said:

> Shortly after my Navy career [ended] I began to experience many difficulties in my well-being. It all began with an onset of paranoia and escalated to full blown PTSD. I would drink alcohol to excess to numb the pain of loneliness.... I was afraid to venture out of my house or drive or do anything that included interaction with people.

During her first TM meditation, Ms. K reported that her practice was "easy," "peaceful," and "pleasant," and over the four-day course of instruction she experienced feeling "calmer." She said:

Through TM I began to trust, blossom, and most of all I began to heal. I began to come out of my nightmares and face the battle I had ahead. I began to attend the sessions faithfully. I began to drive, and I started community college. I got the courage to apply for a job in a hospital. This program has given me my life back.

Depression

More than a dozen studies show TM reduces depression.[17] The most recent was the study described earlier in this chapter that showed reduced depression, anxiety, and stress that was associated with changes in the actual functioning of the brain. The largest study was published in 2009 in the *American Journal of Hypertension*.[18] It was a random control study of 298 university students who were assigned either to learn TM or to a wait-list control group. The overall group was studied as well as a subgroup of 159 students

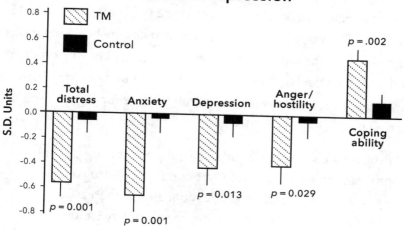

Increased Coping Ability / Decreased Depression

Reference: Psychological Distress, and Coping in Young Adults, *American Journal of Hypertension*, Vol. 22 , Issue 12 (2009), pp. 1326-1331.

who were at risk for hypertension due to, for example, their family history or being overweight. TM resulted in significant reductions as compared to the controls in depression, anxiety, and anger, and significant improvements in coping ability, and the improvements were also correlated with decreases in blood pressure, showing the physical effect of the program.

Two other random control studies funded by the National Institutes of Health (NIH) showed an average 48 percent reduction in depression for the TM group within three months of starting TM, and a random control study done by TM researchers in collaboration with the U.S. government and the West Oakland Health Center showed significant decreases in depression in the TM group and an increase in depression to the controls who took a stress management course.[19]

Gary Kahn (not his real name by request) is a 1995 graduate of the University of Minnesota and an occupational therapist. Jay spoke to Gary in June 2016, about three weeks after he started practicing TM on a regular basis. He had learned the technique in early 2015, but he said he was very sporadic in doing it despite believing it was right for him. Then, however, he developed a serious drug problem and said that after "bottoming out" at the beginning of May 2016, a few weeks later he entered a daily drug treatment program, and he started practicing TM regularly.

> I started a daily seven-hour a day out-patient drug treatment program on May 24, 2016. I was coming off a drug and there was a big increase in my depression, and an increase in anxiety. So, my baseline at starting my recent twice daily TM practice, my baseline was very, very low as far as my mood and my depression, an 8 out of a 10 scale.

And after a few days of TM I immediately felt not an initial huge increase in mood, but like a progressive increase in happiness. Does that make sense? And after about four days of it, I'm like, "wow—what am I feeling?" It was kind of surprising to me that I felt an increase in mood. I am being medicated at the same time, but I've been on medication for a while for depression. But for me after four days of it I was really better.

And my motivation! I just kind of took over my life again. I became more motivated as far as writing goals and actually keeping track of my goals, and more motivated to take care of myself, self-care, and more motivation to exercise.

Tim, in his mid-60s, is a veterinarian. He had been meditating about nine months when interviewed in mid-2016. He had a very mild form of depression, which he hasn't had since starting TM. He said:

A couple of people remarked about changes they've seen in me since learning TM. They said they've noticed I'm not nervous or uptight. And, yes, I'm easier about things, and feel a lot better about myself.

I will admit I did have suicidal thoughts at one point. I wasn't taking any medication. It was never that serious. Just day to day stuff that got a little heavy, and now I'm more just taking it in stride.

My dad had depression and he never talked about that, but he would say he had depression and I understand kind of where he was coming from now. And I haven't had that kind of thought since I've been through the TM course.

The brain research on coherence and depression is interesting and is somewhat counterintuitive to what we might think. In 2007 researchers in Finland at the Helsinki University Central Hospital found there was actually more brain coherence in both alpha and theta bands in patients with major depression as compared to the normal patients in their study.[20] However, the Finland researchers said that this unusual occurrence (unusual because they acknowledge that incoherent brain function is normally associated with depressive states) is an adaptive and compensatory mechanism as the brain tries to cope with its disorder. Similarly, in 2017 researchers from the Saban Research Institute at Children's Hospital in Los Angeles found a thickening of the cerebral cortex (increased brain connections) in depressed patients, again to compensate for the reduced functioning caused by the depression.[21]

These studies don't indicate that coherence in the brain causes depression. What they show is that for some people, the brain's natural response to disorders like depression is to gain coherence, at least for a time, to help the person handle his depression. As the Los Angeles researchers state, the more new brain connections (indicating coherence) that develop, the fewer the symptoms of depression.[22] This is not unlike how those with other impairments compensate and adapt to overcome or at least alleviate their disorders. The brains of blind people compensate by rewiring themselves to enhance not only the senses of hearing, smell, and touch, but even memory and language.[23] The researchers discovered increased connections between different parts of the brain, which they said was the brain adapting and compensating to allow the blind persons to interact more effectively with the environment in light of their loss of vision. Again, increased connections between different areas of the brains means that distant areas of the brain are firing in a synchronous manner and at least parts of the brain become more coherent to adapt to the absence of vision. The brain and body naturally want to gain coherence and sometimes will do so out of necessity to protect against various disorders.

Lasting Happiness Means Being Happy for No Reason

Let's get back to how we become happier and what that really means. It's obvious that those we interviewed who were able to overcome anxiety, panic attacks, PTSD, and depression became happier in their daily lives once they were free of these disorders. But even when we overcome our gross disorders, we'll want to become still happier. How TM fits into that goal is important. There is a popular book called *Happy for No Reason* by Marci Shimoff. The title tells us a lot about the common experience of TM meditators. We generally think of happiness as something that comes as a result of an event or experience—getting a high grade, getting into a good college, getting a desired job, falling in love, and so on. But the nature of life is that good events just don't happen all the time. There will also be mistakes, losses in business, family discord, and illness. This book is describing something different from the happiness (or sadness) that is occasioned by external events. The happiness being described by TM meditators is independent of outside events. The meditators in this book describe a peace and calm (and sometimes bliss) during meditation that continues after the TM session and results in inner satisfaction or an elevation in our mood during the day.

Each person has a baseline level of happiness that is not related to the events of the day. With TM, the meditator's baseline happiness increases as he or she continues to practice the technique and their physiologies become more coherent. This elevated baseline happiness doesn't diminish a person's abilities or will to succeed. The meditator becomes more capable of succeeding, and with that comes an increased enjoyment of daily activities.

Chapter 8

Overcoming Heart Disease, Addictions, and Insomnia, and Leading a Joyful Senior Life

We've seen in the prior chapters that those who have anxiety, PTSD, depression, and other mental disorders often find quick and lasting relief through TM. We might expect that these mental disorders can be helped by a mental technique, but TM also heals many physical disorders. Because the mind and body are so intimately connected, as the brain becomes more coherent as a result of the TM practice, it heals stress related disorders in the body. This is an important understanding about this new science of consciousness.

Reducing Heart Disease Risk Factors

Heart and blood vessel disease, also called cardiovascular disease, is the leading cause of death in the United States for both men and women. According to the Center for Disease Control, about 610,000 Americans die from heart disease each year, which is approximately one in every four deaths. In the U.S., someone has a heart attack every 43 seconds.[1] Heart disease includes numerous problems that are often related to a process called atherosclerosis, which is when plaque builds up in the walls of the arteries, restricting blood flow and leading to blood clots, which can cause heart attack or stroke. Other heart diseases include heart failure where the heart isn't pumping blood normally, leading to insufficient blood and oxygen in the body; arrhythmia, which is an abnormal rhythm of the heart; and heart valve problems when the valves don't open or close properly.

The risk factors for heart disease are those physiological and behavioral measurements that enable physicians to predict the probable occurrence of heart disease and heart attacks. According to the National Institutes of Health, some of the most important risk factors which have been highly correlated with the occurrence of heart disease are: (1) hardening of the arteries (atherosclerosis) reducing blood flow to the heart, (2) hypertension or high blood pressure, (3) hyperlipidemia or high levels of cholesterol combined with very low-density lipoproteins, (4) cigarette smoking, (5) diabetes and prediabetes, (6) obesity, and (7) poor lifestyle choices.[2] The TM technique has been shown to be effective in reducing virtually all of these risk factors and in increasing blood flow to the heart.

Increased Blood Flow to the Heart and Reversing the Effects of Heart Disease

When the flow of blood to your heart is reduced, it prevents the heart muscle from receiving enough oxygen. A reduced blood flow is usually the result of a partial or complete blockage of your heart's arteries and is sometimes known as "myocardial ischemia" or "cardiac ischemia." A severe blockage of one of the heart's arteries can lead to a heart attack, and may also cause serious, abnormal heart rhythms. Treatment involves improving blood flow to the heart muscle, and may include medications, a procedure to open blocked arteries (angioplasty), or bypass surgery. A recent pilot study suggests that TM may become another standard treatment.

A study with funding from the NIH and the Department of Cardiology at Columbia University Medical Center and co-directed by Robert Schneider, M.D., medical director of Maharishi International University's Institute for Prevention Research, was published in September 2019 in the *Journal of Nuclear Cardiology*.[3] The research involved 56 African American patients who had coronary artery disease, including those with a recent heart attack, coronary artery bypass, or angina. Of these, 37 of the patients completed the before and after blood flow evaluations. The study was a groundbreaking proof of concept study that combined TM with other lifestyle changes (e.g., exercise and counseling). The study randomly assigned the patients to four groups, a rehabilitation group (diet and exercise changes), a TM group alone, a TM and rehabilitation group, and a usual care group. When TM was added to rehabilitation, the patients had a remarkable 20.7 percent increase in blood flow to the heart. The group that only used TM had a 12.8 percent increase in blood flow, and the cardiac rehabilitation group improved their blood flow by 5.8 percent, while the usual treatment group did not improve and actually had decreased blood flow to the heart of 10.3 percent. The researchers say it is not known precisely how TM increases blood flow, but they speculate that reduced levels of stress hormones and possibly inflammation may improve the functioning of the cells lining the coronary arteries.

Hardening of the Arteries

Healthy arteries are critical to avoiding heart attacks and stroke. High blood pressure, high levels of cholesterol, diabetes, and obesity all damage the arteries. High blood pressure, for example, is where the force exerted on your arteries is so high that it creates microscopic tears in the artery walls that then turn into scar tissue, which hardens the arteries. The arteries also get narrowed by fatty deposits and plaque that builds up in the artery walls. When the arteries harden and narrow we have a greater risk from blood clots. The blood can carry these clots through the body unless they get lodged in narrowed and *inelastic* arteries that block the passage of blood through the body. A heart attack is the result of a blood clot where the blood is blocked to the heart and a stroke is the result of blood being blocked to the brain. The number one killer of Americans is heart attacks caused by sudden clots in the heart's arteries. Obviously, if we could heal our damaged arteries or prevent undue damage, it could have an enormously beneficial effect on our health.

In 2000, the journal *Stroke* published an article on the effectiveness of TM on reducing hardening of the arteries or "atherosclerosis."[4] Amparo Castillo-Richmond, M.D., of the University of Illinois Chicago led researchers from UCLA, the Charles Drew University of Medicine and Science in Los Angeles, and Maharishi International University. Castillo-Richmond and her team studied African Americans who were at risk for cardiovascular disease and examined the effects of the Transcendental Meditation technique on hardening of the carotid arteries that carry blood to the brain. African Americans are twice as likely as others to die from cardiovascular disease.

The study was a random control study where 60 hypertensive African Americans were randomly assigned to either the Transcendental Meditation program or a health education control group. Tests were conducted before the TM group learned the technique and again after an average period of approximately seven months of meditation. Using ultrasound, researchers measured the distance between the inner and outer wall of the carotid artery, what is known as the intima-media thickness or IMT, which is an index for measuring the inner diameter of the vessel, the inner tube through which the blood flows. IMT is considered an excellent predictor of heart attack and stroke. The results demonstrated an impressive reduction of 0.098 mm in wall thickness for the TM group (a reduction in wall thickness means the diameter of the vessel is larger and the blood can more easily flow) after the relatively short period of TM meditation (seven months). The control group showed an increase of 0.054mm in wall thickness. Put in perspective, the authors state that a decrease of IMT of 0.098 is within the range of reduction one could expect from lipid-lowering medications or an intensive lifestyle modification program.

This is the first controlled research showing that a stress reduction technique, unaccompanied by change in diet or lifestyle, can reverse atherosclerosis. Of course, if there is a longer duration of TM meditation, or if TM is used along with exercise and a better diet or other lifestyle changes, the combined results should point to an even greater reduction in deaths.

High Blood Pressure

High blood pressure is another of the principal heart disease risk factors. Over one-third of the adult population of the United States has high blood pressure. About 90% of these cases are reported as essential hypertension, a condition for which the precise cause is unknown. However, many researchers feel the unknown cause of essential hypertension is nothing other than the fast and stressful pace of life today and the body's often prolonged physiological response to stressful situations. The current treatment is primarily symptomatic, that is, prescription drugs that temporarily lower the blood pressure but do not cure the cause of the disorder.

Over the past twenty years, scientific studies have confirmed the beneficial effects of the TM program on blood pressure. Over $28 million has been given in grants by the US National Institutes of Health and other government agencies to study the TM technique, particularly in the area of blood pressure. These studies were carried out in collaboration with major medical schools and hospitals. They repeatedly show that TM significantly reduces both systolic and diastolic blood pressure, particularly in patients who have recently developed the condition.

A study published in 1995 in the journal *Hypertension*[5] looked at the effects of TM in a study involving 127 African Americans living in an urban setting with an average age of 67 years. The subjects were randomly assigned to one of two experimental groups, a TM or a Progressive Muscle Relaxation (PMR) group, or to a third "usual-care" control group. The usual-care control subjects received instructions for weight loss, salt restriction, alcohol moderation, and exercise. The average blood pressure of the TM group prior to the study was 145 mm Hg systolic and 94 mm Hg diastolic. After just three months, the TM group reduced their blood pressure an average of 10.7 mm Hg systolic and 6.4 mm Hg diastolic, which was a significantly greater reduction in both systolic and diastolic blood pressure compared to the PMR group and the control group.

Another paper analyzed 17 studies involving over 900 participants and compared the TM results with other stress reduction programs for treating high blood pressure.[6] *(see chart below)*.

The study used the "meta-analysis" tool described in the prior chapter to evaluate the different studies. This method is considered reliable since it takes into account the number of subjects in a study, and codes for the strength of the research design (e.g., in the best designed studies subjects are randomly assigned to the

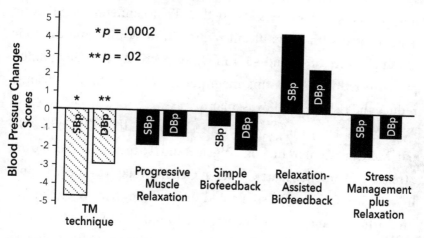

Stress Reduction Programs in Patients with High Blood Pressure
Meta-analysis of 17 studies

Reference: Rainforth, M.V., Schneider, R.H., Nidich, S.I., Gaylord-King, C., Salerno, W., Anderson, J.W. (2007). Stress reduction programs in patients with elevated blood pressure: a systematic review and meta-analysis. *Current Hypertension Reports*, 9 (6): 520–528.

different study groups), and other factors and comes up with a quantitative index called an "effect size." The results showed that compared to other stress reduction programs, TM significantly reduced both systolic and diastolic blood pressure while none of the other treatments, including simple biofeedback, progressive muscle relaxation, and stress management training, showed any significant results.

Independent Verification of the Blood Pressure Research

In 2008 skeptical researchers at the College of Medicine at the University of Maryland reviewed nineteen studies on TM and blood pressure and selected nine to analyze further since these studies compared TM to control groups that were randomly selected and had adequate data.[7] The researchers state that their analysis of all nine studies, including the studies with subjects having relatively normal blood pressure, showed that Transcendental Meditation is associated with a significant reduction in systolic and diastolic blood pressure of –5 and –3 mm Hg respectively. Sustained blood pressure reductions of this magnitude are likely to significantly reduce the risk for cardiovascular disease.

C. Noel Bairey Merz, M.D., Professor of Medicine at Cedars-Sinai Medical Center in Los Angeles and Director of the Barbra Streisand Women's Heart Center at Cedars-Sinai was the principal investigator for an NIH-sponsored study of the effectiveness of TM on cardiovascular health. She has also found TM to have beneficial results on lowering both high blood pressure and blood glucose levels and advocates more widespread use of TM to control stress related disorders. After her research, she said:

We are gratified that our research demonstrating the efficacy of TM on blood pressure is being recognized and hope that this consensus will result in its wider use in clinical practice.[8]

High Cholesterol

The effect of the TM technique on high cholesterol was investigated by Cooper and Aygen in 1978. They studied twenty-three high cholesterol patients and controls matched for age, gender, diet, weight, and their cholesterol levels at the commencement of the study. Twelve of the subjects participated in the TM program for eleven months; their serum cholesterol significantly dropped, while the cholesterol level of the non-meditating controls did not change. The observed decreases in the TM subjects' cholesterol levels were significant compared to their own base line and to the controls.[9]

Suzanne Steinbaum, M.D., a cardiologist and Director of Women's Heart Health at Lenox Hill Hospital in New York City, summarized her experience in dealing with patients having multiple risk factors for heart attack and stroke.[10] She said:

It's only very recently that we've understood the impact of stress in the formation of heart disease. The fight-or-flight response releases stress hormones, and increases blood pressure, cholesterol levels, and inflammation. All of this leads, in turn, to heart disease.

When I prescribe a medication for heart disease, I'm happy if I get efficacy of treatment at about 30%. But now I know that if I treat heart disease with something like Transcendental Meditation, I can get as much as 48–66% improvement with treatment.

I very clearly say to my patients: "Let's treat blood pressure. Let's treat your cholesterol. Let's treat your stress. And the way we're going to treat these is with Transcendental Meditation practice."

SOME HIGHLY REMARKABLE REPORTS

Deb Scott started Transcendental Meditation in 2011 when she was the chief information officer at a medical facility in southern Arizona. A cyber security expert who spent over thirty years in the military or in a civilian status serving the military, Deb started TM because she said, "the job was horrifically stressful" and affecting her health. Deb had digestive problems, high blood pressure and elevated cholesterol. She was also motivated to learn TM because her instruction was free. Deb was able to learn without charge as part of a "provider resiliency" program that made the technique available to "wounded warriors" and those providing them with health care. Before starting TM, Deb's blood pressure was averaging around 150/90 and her LDL cholesterol (bad cholesterol) had climbed to about 230, which is well above normal—over 190 is considered very high. Like most people who practice TM for a number of years, Deb experienced multiple benefits.

Deb told us that "from the time I started TM, I have not had an abnormal blood pressure reading." Typically, she said her blood pressure is now in the low 120s and high 60s, and her cholesterol is in the 180s, which she said is the lowest it's been since she was 25.

Deb actually found another job after learning TM, and while she said that the job "was also a very important job serving the military and was also very stressful," she found that she was much better able to naturally cope with the stress of work. Through church groups Deb had previously done a visualization kind of meditation and one where she would repeat phrases usually from a poem or a prayer. She said she did those for many years whenever she was under stress. We asked her how the results compared to TM, and Deb said it was spiritually helpful, "but oh my goodness, it wasn't anything like TM for the physiological help."

Deb also had suffered from claustrophobia for many years, and recently had to have an MRI, which can be a problem for those with her condition because the procedure involves being put inside a long full body tube. Deb said:

> As soon as they started I panicked, and they had to stop. Then the nurse asked if there was anything she could do because otherwise they were going to have to cancel the MRI. I told her I could meditate for a few minutes. Then they put the tube over my head and I meditated the entire 55 minutes I was in there. For me it was amazing.

In a follow-up just before the book was published, Deb told us, "TM is still the best gift I have ever given myself."

Jay interviewed a top executive at a Fortune 500 company in late 2016. He asked not to be identified by name, and we will just call him Gary. He started a guided meditation called Headspace around March of 2015, which he did for a few months with some success. Then he read about TM, and he and his wife learned TM around June of 2015. After experiencing TM, they stopped their Headspace meditation and have been practicing TM ever since. Gary explained TM as a "deeper level of clearing my head" and he said that TM "seemed more powerful." Gary said he was "infinitely more peaceful and calm now [after TM] as compared to what I was a year ago." He also said:

> I'm better able to concentrate and concentrate for longer periods of time and see things with a lot more clarity, and now I don't think anything is really a big deal. Just learning to pace myself. The only regret I have is that I didn't do this 30 years ago.

In passing, Gary also said "my blood pressure has also come down a little bit," something that was clarified by his wife, who was also on the phone at the time of the interview. Gary's wife said his blood pressure was actually down 20 or 30 points from 150 to 160 (systolic) to 120 to 130. She also said:

> The first thing I noticed was that he [Gary] has been able to sleep better, and he really waits a moment before he answers.... He's completely not judgmental; he's cool-headed most of the time, really so mellow and nice. And that little issue with high blood pressure, that's disappeared completely.

The blood pressure changes in Deb Scott and Gary are more than should generally be expected. High blood pressure can be caused by stress, by being overweight, by an excessive intake of salt, or by genetic factors, and the different causes probably account for different success rates. If being overweight is the cause, TM may not help as much as if the cause is stress, unless TM helps give you the discipline to exercise, eat better, and lose weight. In all events, TM alone can sometimes be effective in reducing blood pressure, and sometimes it is used as an adjunct to medication or diet and exercise. TM also can help lower the required dosage of medication.

Tobacco Use

As many as half the people who use tobacco die from it. The World Health Organization estimates that each year tobacco use causes about six million deaths (about 10 percent of all deaths) and that in the twentieth century about 100 million deaths worldwide were caused by cigarette use. The Centers for Disease Control and Prevention describe tobacco use as the single most important preventable risk to human health in developed countries. Smoking is a key risk factor for heart disease, and causes 440,000 deaths a year in the U.S. today. It also is a major cause of pulmonary disease (including emphysema and bronchitis) and cancer, especially lung, mouth, and pancreatic cancer. The effects depend on the number of years that a person smokes and on how much the person smokes.

Subjectively, the simple story of why people smoke is that they like it. They like the feeling it immediately produces, and then they compulsively smoke because nicotine is addictive. According to the National Institute of Drug Abuse, nearly 35 million users of tobacco know it is harmful and want to stop each year, but can't. Approximately 85 percent of those who try to quit on their own fail, most within a week, and conventional smoking cessation programs have a poor record. For example, replacement therapies have been popular because for some time it has been thought that the cause of cancer and disease from smoking is not the nicotine, but the burning of tars and gases that are released from burning tobacco. However, even replacement strategies have limited success. A research review of different nicotine substitution programs, such as nicotine gum, inhalers, sprays, patches, and tablets, found that the percentage of smokers who were abstinent after twelve months or more ranged from about 12 percent to 25 percent depending on the program.[11] The Surgeon General has recently concluded that nicotine itself is both addictive and unsafe, especially for young people, for whom it adversely affects brain development, and those who are pregnant.[12]

TM, however, has been found to be effective as a natural means of reducing or stopping smoking, actually more effective than other approaches despite the fact that it is not designed as a tool to stop smoking. TM teachers wouldn't normally even know if a new meditator was a smoker and TM teachers don't admonish meditators not to smoke. A comprehensive analysis of TM's effectiveness in reducing cigarette use compared to other methods was published in a special double issue of the *Alcoholism Treatment Quarterly* in 1994.[13] That study also used meta-analysis to evaluate the different approaches in different studies. Published meta-analyses often use a quantitative index to evaluate the different approaches called an "effect size." In measuring changes in behavior an effect size of .80 is considered a big effect of the program, while an effect size of .50 is considered a medium treatment effect, and an effect size of .20 is a small effect. The meta-analysis to evaluate smoking cessation programs compared 16 TM studies to 115 studies on other approaches. For TM the average effect size was .87 (a big effect) and considering only the better designed TM studies, it was .97. By comparison, the effect size for counseling programs was about .20 (small) and for pharmacological treatments about .30 and for the best of the conventional approaches, which was prevention education programs, about .40 (less than a medium effect).

Effectiveness in Decreasing Cigarette Use

Meta-analysis of 131 studies

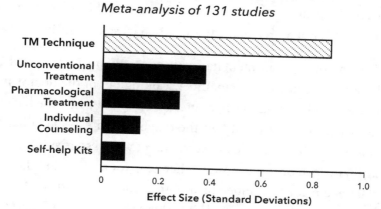

Reference: Alexander, C.N., Robinson, P., & Rainforth, M. (1994). Treating and preventing alcohol, nicotine, and drug abuse through Transcendental Meditation: A review and statistical meta-analysis. *Alcoholism Treatment Quarterly*, 11, 13-88.

TM's effectiveness is likely a combination of the natural relaxation that comes with the practice and its ability to provide satisfaction from within. Meditators like feeling relaxed and over time many stop using artificial substances.

Michael Cuddehe, age 72, was one of those who wanted to stop smoking, but couldn't quite do it on his own despite a strong motivation to do so. Michael started smoking when he was twelve. He says his father gave him a hard time about smoking when he was young, so initially he only smoked intermittently. Then, on his sixteenth birthday, his father relented and gave him a birthday present of a carton of cigarettes and Michael became addicted. In those days in high school in Plattsburg, New York, there was a smoking lounge, and at breaks and at lunch he would go to the lounge and smoke. After a while he was smoking a pack a day, then two packs, and by the time Michael was twenty-two, he was smoking four

127

packs a day. He saw a doctor at that time who told him that if he kept smoking, he would die of emphysema, and the doctor warned him that it is not a pretty way to die. Michael said in an interview:

> The doctor's appointment had a big effect on me. I was scared by what he said, and I remember walking out of the doctor's office and throwing my cigarettes away. That's when the battle began because I still had the craving, and especially if I was out having a couple of beers. Then I would start smoking again for two or three months, then stop for a while and then start again for a number of months. That went on for five years. Then in 1973 I started TM. There was a pretty dramatic shift internally as a result of TM, and I never again had the desire for cigarettes. I never smoked again.

The American Heart Association says the risk of heart disease is strongly linked to family history. So, because Michael's father died of heart disease that is a genetic factor increasing Michael's risk for heart disease. In Michael's case, however, his TM practice is a protective factor. Michael has been practicing TM continuously since he learned in 1973. He liked it so much he even became a TM teacher. Jay asked him about his current risk factors for heart disease when he interviewed him in May 2017. Michael said, "I just came from a doctor's checkup. My blood pressure reading was 110/60. I also have no cholesterol problems, and I don't need to take any medications. My father on the other hand was taking twelve different medications when he died of heart disease."

Insomnia

Sleep is crucial to good health. It is a natural means of restoring coherence to a tired brain and body. Yet about 70 million Americans sleep poorly according to the American Academy of Sleep Medicine. A December 2014 press release from researchers at Brigham and Women's Hospital in Boston states that our web-based culture is making sleep worse: glowing computer screens from nighttime web surfing, and emailing and movie streaming are said to be disturbing to sleep because the screens on smart phones, tablets and computers emit wavelengths of light that vibrate in a way that signals the brain to wake up rather than sleep.[14]

The literature on insomnia also suggests a pressing need for a simple, natural method of relieving sleeplessness as an alternative to drugs. Barbiturates and sedatives interfere with the dreaming phase of the sleep cycle and often result in a more lasting medical problem known as drug-related insomnia. The problem is that people develop a tolerance to sleeping pills, so that eventually even huge doses can't produce a healthy sleep. When the pills are abruptly withdrawn, nearly total insomnia results, and disturbed sleep with frightening nightmares may follow. Almost every sedative, if used regularly, will eventually aggravate the insomnia it is intended to address.

As indicated in some of the earlier interviews, TM is one natural antidote that works for many with insomnia although some changes in diet and nighttime activities are also important as discussed in coming chapters. Just as the technique relieves anxiety in daily activities, for many people it also relieves the "midnight anxiety" we call insomnia.

An article in *Anxiety, Stress and Coping*[15] published in 2007 reported on a study of employees in the automotive industry who

129

learned TM compared to a control group (random assignment) that was similar in job position and pretest characteristics. The TM meditators improved their sleep significantly more than controls. A 2017 study of 143 veterans who learned TM found a 26 percent improvement in sleep in just the first month of TM practice.[16] And an early small study in 1972, at the University of Alberta in Canada found that the insomniacs in the study averaged an hour and a quarter to fall asleep before TM and after thirty days of TM practice, the time it took to fall asleep dropped to fifteen minutes, and it remained constant at about fifteen minutes during the entire first year of meditation.[17]

Tim, the veterinarian from Chapter 7 who had been meditating for nine months, said:

> I used to wake up anxious in the middle of the night about something. And I couldn't go back to sleep. That kind of wears on you. Now if I do wake up in the night for whatever reason I can usually go back pretty quickly. So yeah, it's [TM] definitely improved my sleep quality.

Jace Badia, a disabled Iraq veteran, made this statement in 2017 after starting TM:

> TM has taken the stress out of my life. It has allowed me to relax. The anger is gone, the irritability is on a lesser scale, and I'm sleeping. I used to get three hours of sleep a night, but since I started TM I'm often getting eight to ten hours a night.

Jeanne Pettenati from Bethesda, Maryland, writes children's books about famous people (*Galileo's Journal* and *Arturo [Toscanini] Takes a Bow*). She also had serious sleep problems before starting

TM in about 2010. Before TM, Jeanne said she would lie in bed rehashing the day for at least an hour and often for several hours before falling asleep. The problem was compounded because like many people she also couldn't sleep very well through the night. When Jay interviewed her in May 2018, she said:

> After I started TM, my sleep changed pretty quickly, in just a few weeks. After TM I found that when I put my head on the pillow, I was able to let go of things and be settled, not as much churning in my head. And it started to be more like a half hour before I could get to sleep, not several hours like before. Also, I would previously wake up maybe every two hours, and I started sleeping through the night. With TM I started getting seven hours of solid sleep, which for me was unprecedented.
>
> Before TM, I was also taking melatonin maybe five to six times a week, and now I can count on one hand the number of times I've had to take it in the past five or six years.

Jeanne has been meditating twice a day now for ten years. She said, "I'm a lot calmer and better able to focus on one thing at a time without getting distracted." As with many of those mentioned earlier in the book, this calmness and greater ability to focus is the natural ease and mindfulness that TM produces.

Reduced Use of Illicit Drugs

For illicit drug use the meta-analysis of 19 TM studies involving 4,524 subjects (3,249 meditators and 1,275 controls or participants in other programs) compared TM to 51 studies using more conventional approaches for combatting drug use. The TM results were even better than TM's results in stopping cigarette use. For example, the effect size of the nineteen studies for preventing the use of illicit drugs for TM was .74 compared to a very small effect of .06 from the DARE program (TM was 12 times more effective than DARE). In populations actually being treated for substance abuse the effect size for TM was 1.16, a very large effect.[18]

Effectiveness in Decreasing Drug Abuse
Meta-analysis of 70 studies

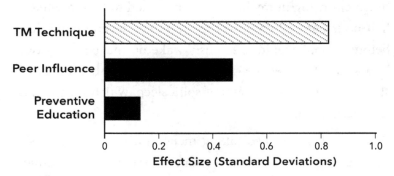

Effect Size (Standard Deviations)

Reference: Alexander, C.N., Robinson, P., & Rainforth, M. (1994). Treating and preventing alcohol, nicotine, and drug abuse through Transcendental Meditation: A review and statistical meta-analysis. *Alcoholism Treatment Quarterly*, 11, 13-88.

Mike Love, lead singer for the Beach Boys, advocated for TM's usefulness in avoiding drugs and alcohol. In an interview with the *Portland Tribune* a few years ago, he said he learned TM in 1967 and credited doing TM every day for forty-five years as the secret to his vitality and to surviving life on the "rock and roll highway." He said:

> It gives me rest and relaxation in pursuing activities and combats fatigue. It gives you a sort of high without having to resort to alcohol and drugs. That's been a big benefit to my life.

You have the clarity and energy to entertain the types of activities we do with traveling and rehearsing and performing. When you meditate, all those feelings of grogginess and irritation and fatigue are eliminated. Your biochemistry changes. It's very simple but amazing stuff.

A Joyful Senior Life

Jerry Yellin is one example of a lifetime of benefits derived from Transcendental Meditation. A pilot in World War II, he learned Transcendental Meditation in the mid-1970s and led a very active and fulfilling life until his death in 2018 at age 93. Jerry authored three books, including *The Blackened Canteen*, written when he was 83 (2008); and *The Resilient Warrior*, written when he was 86 (2011). In his late 80s, he also wrote one screenplay about his experiences in World War II and learning to appreciate the Japanese people who he previously considered the enemy. Jerry was the inspiration behind the formation of Operation Warrior Wellness, a division of the David Lynch Foundation that teaches TM to veterans with PTSD, often at no charge. He lectured on the benefits of TM for veterans, and played golf most days into his 90s. Jay had this conversation with Jerry in early 2017.

Jay: Tell me your experience with TM.

Jerry: I put the uniform on of the United States military in August of 1942. I was inducted into the Army Air Corps. When you put the uniform on you learn two things. The first is that you're willing to give your life to protect everybody else's, and they're willing to give their life to protect you. And also the purpose of the war is to kill your enemy.

133

I was 19 years old when I graduated from flying school and I was three weeks into my 21st year when I landed a P-51 on Iwo Jima on March 7, 1945. There were 90,000 soldiers fighting on this small island, and there were 28,000 bodies rotting in the sun: 21,000 Japanese and 7,000 American. And another 21,000 Marines were wounded. It was horrific.

Jay: I am sure it was.

Jerry: That's not all. I flew 19 combat missions over Japan in a P-51. Each mission was eight hours long, and I flew with 16 guys that I came to know very well, and none of them survived. Five were killed in training, and 11 were killed by the Japanese.

The last of the original 16 were Phil Schlamberg and Jerry Yellin. We were on the last combat mission of World War II, and Phil Schlamberg was the last man killed in combat in the war. He was 19 years old, and I was 21. And when I came home, I went to his mother's house and I brought part of his wings and his lieutenant bars, and she didn't want to have anything to do with me. I was in their house in December of 1945 and she said to me, with a heavy Jewish accent, "It should have been you who was killed, not my son Phillip. I hope you never sleep a night in your life like I can't sleep." And I never slept. I thought about suicide. I thought about taking my life, I stopped flying for the New Jersey National Guard because I knew if I continued to fly airplanes I was going to die by chance or by choice and every night I spoke to these 16 guys.

Then I got married in 1949 and we moved 15 or 16 times including to Israel, and I was a basket case for 30 years. Then my wife and I saw Maharishi Mahesh Yogi on the Merv Griffin Show in June of 1975 and she said to herself, "I'm going to learn TM." And my son graduated from the University of Pennsylvania in 1975 and he was interested, and he said, "Mom, wait for me to learn TM." So, Steven and Helene learned Transcendental Meditation.

Jay: Did you see any changes in them? Is that what made you start TM?

Jerry: I didn't see any differences in them at all. Not at all. But I still was thinking about starting. And I had a guy that I worked with, named Mo. We were running a real estate trust in Coral Gables and I said, "Mo, I'm going to learn Transcendental Meditation," and he says, "Oh, I learned. Don't give them $150. You learn a word and say that word. It's a mantra, and you just close your eyes and just say the mantra. I'll give you a mantra." He said, "just sit down in a quiet place and say Shalom, Shalom, Shalom."

Jay: Out loud? Shalom?

Jerry: No, to myself. I kept saying it to myself—Shalom. So, I'm doing this and saying Shalom to myself. I told Helene that I was doing it, and she told Mike Scalari, who was a TM teacher in North Miami Beach, and he kind of went ballistic and he called me and he said, "That's all wrong—that's not what you're supposed to do." Mike introduced me to a TM teacher, and I went through the program, and what they taught me was really different and not just the mantra, the whole technique. This was in August of 1975, and I had an instant change to my life.

Jay: Like what?

Jerry: Instantaneously. The changes in my life went from dark and dreary to green and light. Everything was just changed, and I was different. I looked at life differently.

For example, I had never, ever played golf to enjoy myself, not until 1975 after learning TM [Jerry was a championship amateur golfer and his son, Steven, is now a well-known golf instructor, formerly with David Ledbetter]. I played golf to kill them. It was my goal. It was my alcohol. I just went out there to kill—not only the golf course but the people I played against. I was a killer. A gambler. That's how I made a living.

Then my whole life turned around 180 degrees. It was then that I saw the difference in my wife and my children since they started TM, and in me and my relationships. I felt like a worthwhile human being. Previously, I didn't know why I lived and all those people were killed and died. I had no purpose in life, and all of a sudden I had a purpose.

I settled down into becoming quite an expert in the real estate world. I had clients like Bank of America, Bank of California, Wells Fargo. All of these guys became my clients. I was their number one advisor in the real estate investment trust (REIT) area. And I became a joyful human being. I just lived a beautiful life.

Jay: And how are things today?

Jerry: I'm 92 and I still meditate. In my mind TM is the only unmedicated solution to stress. Our government today—

there are 22 veterans from Iraq and Afghanistan that commit suicide every day. That's more than 8,000 a year. And the government is buying pharmaceuticals—antidepressants and antipsychotics in particular—for $8 billion dollars a month, and the antidepressants and antipsychotic drugs are addictive drugs and they cause more harm than they do good. We could teach them TM for less than $1,000 fee for a lifetime.

Jay: I understand from Steven that you are still playing golf.

Jerry: I play almost every day that I'm home. 18 holes. I'll be home in time to take a days' rest, and then I'll start playing. I also run every day in a pool for 30 minutes, and I intentionally don't eat as much as I used to. I have a 65-year-old girlfriend now [Jerry's wife passed away a few years ago], and she says, "I'm much too old for you, Jerry. I can't keep up with you."

Effects on the Elderly: A Comparison with Other Techniques

An important study, published in 1989 in the *Journal of Personality and Social Psychology*,[19] was conducted by researchers who sought to compare Transcendental Meditation's effect on elderly persons with a mindfulness training program (MF) and a mental relaxation technique (MR). The study used ten or so different measures of health and relaxation and evaluated the results of three different techniques compared to a control group that was tested on each of the measures but received no technique.

The mindfulness program involved was not the mindfulness-based stress reduction program discussed in other sections of this book, but a guided or focused attention technique that involved a word production task. The subjects were instructed to think of a word, take its last letter and find a new word beginning with that letter. It also involved a creativity task that asked the subjects to think about any topic in a new and creative way. The mental relaxation technique (a relaxation response technique) was included as part of the program to test the hypothesis that TM is simple relaxation, and that a relaxation technique not requiring TM's use of a mantra would be just as successful as TM. The instructors in this relaxation program had the participants mentally repeat a familiar verse, phrase, song or poem of their choice as is done in the relaxation response technique. That is vastly different from the TM technique and also ignores the value of the particular TM mantra or sound used in the TM practice, both of which have a coherence-generating effect. TM is not mere repetition of a phrase.

The study involved 73 residents of homes for the elderly, with an average age of 81. They were randomly assigned to learn either TM, mindfulness (MF), or the mental relaxation technique. TM had significantly better results than the other two programs. Substantially more TM subjects reported feeling relaxed during the practice than immediately before, as compared with the mindfulness and relaxation subjects (the scale used showed relative scores on relaxation of 94.4 for TM, 41.7 for mindfulness, and 55.6 for the relaxation practice). The TM subjects did better on two measures of mental flexibility, as well as on a test of word fluency, on systolic blood pressure, and also on behavioral flexibility. The scores on a scale measuring the overall evaluation of the program were 75 for TM, 38.5 for mindfulness and 40 for the relaxation subjects. The TM group felt less old, more able to cope with inconveniences, and less impatient.

Part III

RESONANT SOUNDS

Chapter 9

Healing Through Vedic Sounds or Vibrations: Sometimes There are Dramatic Results

The evidence to date is that sound or vibration healing can work, and sometimes the healing is dramatic. For example, there are extraordinary accounts on the Internet of at least short-term cures that have popularized the potential of using music or sound for healing. In one instance a father living in Boston had suffered from a stroke and was unable to speak. He was frustrated by his inability to tell his son that he wanted to see his beloved Red Sox play that weekend. Although he couldn't speak, to both his surprise and his son's, he got his message across by singing "Take me out to the ball game...." And Alzheimer's patients who are not normally responsive to speech or who do not recognize their families have become temporarily responsive by hearing songs that were significant in the patients' lives, or by having them perform simple musical exercises. Music, as rhythmic sound vibration, plays a major role in our lives, but are these just isolated examples, or can sounds predictably heal, and if so, which ones?

The History of Using Sound for Healing

Almost everyone enjoys music. On average, some say we listen to it several hours a day. We listen to unwind; we listen when jogging and on the way to work; we listen at parties and weddings; we listen in church; and we listen in movies and sporting events. We do so because the music resonates with us in some way and often evokes our emotions. College fight songs and military marches arouse feelings of loyalty to the institution or the cause. Other sounds may help us sleep, relax, or put us in a romantic mood, a spiritual mood, or even a spending mood. Stores today pipe in certain music, which has been shown to reliably encourage purchases.

The reason music affects the emotions was first noted by neurophysiologist Manfred Clynes. In his 1982 book, *Music, Mind and Brain*, Clynes pointed out that the body's limbic system, consisting of the amygdala, hippocampus, thalamus, hypothalamus, and other subcortical structures in the brain, is the seat of our emotions, the system responsible for whether we feel love, sorrow, compassion, or anger. Because music directly excites the limbic system, it can directly influence our emotions.

While we are starting to understand the science of how sounds affect us, the use of music or sounds for healing predates modern science by centuries. Pythagoras, born in 569 BC, is considered the first great mathematician of Greece (author of the famous Pythagorean theorem in geometry), and he was also a pioneer in understanding the importance of sounds and music. Pythagoras and other Greek philosophers considered music to be an essential part of the "divine order." Pythagoras discovered what is known as the diatonic scale (the seven distinct pitches of do, re, me, fa, sol, la, and ti), which is the basis of most Western music, and he and his followers discovered that music could have great therapeutic value.[1] Pythagoras believed that all creatures, and even inanimate objects, have a sound to them (they vibrate in a certain way), and he believed that certain chords could heal. In ancient Greece, as well as in the ancient cultures of China, Tibet, India, and Egypt, music and vibration were discovered to have cured many ailments by having specially prepared melodies played in the presence of the sick. Pythagoras' university even opened and closed each day with special songs that enlivened the mind in the morning for the day's activity and soothed the mind in the evening to begin the resting process. The Greeks were said to use vibration as an aid to overcome rage, anger, despondency, and other mental disturbances, and sleep and other disorders, and the Egyptians had precise "chant therapies" for epilepsy and other diseases.[2]

The Western Use of Sound for Healing

Music therapy began in the U.S. in World Wars I and II when music was used in veterans' hospitals as an intervention to help the wounded deal with pain. Then in 1950 a professional organization of music therapists was formed to train musicians to use music as therapy. The field began to really take off after a 1993 study of college students strongly contributed to the notion that music could improve the brain. The study showed the students performed better on reasoning tests after listening to a Mozart composition. That led to the commercialization of music products to promote brain development, and a 1997 book called *The Mozart Effect* made great claims for the healing power of music. The Governor of Georgia even proposed that every newborn in his state be provided with a classical music CD.

Now, however, some of the popular claims for the Mozart Effect have been called into question. Five years after publication of *The Mozart Effect*, a study published in the *British Journal of Developmental Psychology*, titled "Listening to Mozart does not improve children's spatial ability: Final curtains for the Mozart Effect," showed no benefits in reasoning from listening to Mozart's music.[3]

In summary, according to Dr. Barrie Cassileth, Chief of Integrative Medicine Services at the Memorial Sloan-Kettering Cancer Center in New York, music therapy today is not considered a curative treatment. But it can be an important complementary therapy with research to support its use in specialized situations like temporarily helping patients with Alzheimer's or speech defects, distracting from pain, helping premature babies gain weight more quickly, and strengthening coordination and motor skills in disabled children.[4]

Vibrations Applied Directly to the Body

A relatively new area of sound therapy that has shown positive results for the temporary relief of pain and the symptoms of several other conditions is vibroacoustic therapy. This therapy was first investigated in the 1970s in Scandinavia.[5] It uses sounds that are heard (the acoustic part of the therapy), but the principal part of the therapy is applying mostly low-frequency vibrations of sound directly to the body (the vibro part of the therapy). The therapy aims to produce a relaxing vibromassage and increase cellular vibrations. It's been said by some that this therapy does not yet have enough studies or experimental reports to confirm its effectiveness,[5] but it has been used at some major medical facilities in the U.S. The treatment has been successfully employed for at least

143

short-term pain management following knee replacement surgery with patients at the Duke University Medical Center,[7] and is being used in an ongoing treatment program at the Clinical Center of the National Institutes of Health.

One other study that increases our appreciation of the potential for sound or vibration therapies to generate lasting changes was reported at a conference in 2006 at Stanford University's Center for Research in Music and Acoustics.[8] The conference discussed the studies of Dr. Harold Russell, a psychologist who at the time of the conference was a research professor at the University of Texas Medical Branch in Galveston. Dr. Russell used both light and sound as stimuli. He showed that certain rhythms of light and sound increased the frequency of brain waves in the subjects, resulting in increased concentration in ways similar to attention deficit disorder (ADD) medications like Ritalin and Adderall. This therapy evaluates the brain waves of his subjects and then uses light and sound at a somewhat higher frequency in an effort to stimulate higher-frequency brain activity.

The forty children who were the subjects in Dr. Russell's studies made *lasting* gains in concentration and on IQ tests and had a reduction in their ADD behavioral problems as compared to a control group. A website about Dr. Russell's work says the ADD subjects achieved an average IQ increase of ten points, and that he is currently attempting to determine if similar results can be obtained with children not having behavioral problems.[9]

The Current Revival in Using Ancient Sounds for Healing

While the ancient philosopher/scientists of Greece and other cultures used ritual music and chanting for their healing strategies, the healing sounds or vibrations from most of these ancient cultures is lost knowledge in the Western world. In Western vibroacoustic therapy, *low-frequency* vibrations are generally thought to be best for temporary pain relief for some, and Dr. Russell's work suggests we can get positive results for hyperactive persons with ADD through high-frequency vibrations. However, other than these uses of particular sounds or frequencies, there does not appear to be Western knowledge of the specific sounds that can heal particular disorders. For example, music therapists in the West who play music to their patients are left to conceive of their own harmonies, in an effort to heal or complement other health strategies.

As authors, we became interested in this area due to our association with Maharishi Mahesh Yogi and his organizations. Maharishi revived India's ancient Vedic knowledge of using sound and vibrations to heal, first with his revival of the knowledge of the Transcendental Meditation technique, which, in part, uses the Vedic sounds called *mantras*. Importantly, as we previously indicated, TM is not just repeating a mantra; correct TM practice involves the mantra and the proper technique of how to use it. The Vedic literature is a vast body of knowledge that may be best known in the U.S. due to the growing popularity of Ayurveda, a system of natural medicine (Chapter Twelve), and Transcendental Meditation. Not so well known is the fact that the Vedic knowledge is also the source of yoga, and the source of a science of using sound vibrations to heal the mind and body and even influence the environment in ways favorable to life and evolution.

The crucial thing about the Vedic vibrations is that they enhance the general level of coherence throughout the physiology, and some are also tailored to address specific disorders. This is not a program of playing some pleasing music or sounds that may lighten the patient's mood or bring temporary relaxation. In the Vedic tradition, specific sounds are selected that resonate with the frequencies of the disordered part of the body to enliven that part of the body and restore order to it.

Set forth below are anecdotal reports and limited research on what is known as Maharishi Vedic Vibration Therapy (MVVT), named after Maharishi who was responsible for reviving this particular treatment. This information is not provided to make or support claims for this form of treatment, but to set forth the treatment's mechanics and its potential, which warrants further examination and research. No specific results should, therefore, be expected and effects, if any, may vary considerably from individual to individual. While MVVT is available in most of the developed world, it is not currently available in the U.S. or China.

Gillorie's Treatments For Chronic Pain and Trauma

Gillorie Myrthil, a 37-year-old woman and jazz drummer at the time of her interview, reports having been in several car accidents that left her with severe neck and back pain, weakness in her entire right side from her face to her legs, and a limp from the weakness when she walked. She had been seeing doctors and chiropractors for many years since the first accident, which occurred in 1997 when she was eighteen. One of her doctors told her she had a pinched nerve in the neck, and she had severe anxiety and PTSD resulting from the traumatic automobile accidents.

For thirteen years Gillorie had been unsuccessful in managing her chronic pain through conventional and complementary approaches, which included chiropractic adjustments and prescriptions for codeine, Neurontin, and Tramadol. Nothing she tried had really worked. Then, while she was in California, Gillorie heard about MVVT while at a TM center; Gillorie is a TM meditator. In January 2010, she decided to try it for her neck pain. She said in an interview:

> I had three sessions that took about 45 minutes to an hour. I lay down and removed a garment so the technician could make a better connection [of the sound vibrations] with my physiology. I could distinctly feel the treatment causing vibrations in the nerves and under the skin. After the last session, I felt a great lightness in the body and relief in the neck and all the extremities. After three sessions I experienced a very major reduction in pain, at least a 50% reduction. Then I went back for more treatments for the neck about a year later and experienced a further significant reduction in pain. So, all in all, there was maybe a 90% reduction in what had been chronic pain for 13 or 14 years.

After her initial treatments, Gillorie went back for similar sessions with the trained technicians, first for relief from a chipped iliac crest bone, which is the largest bone in the pelvis. This injury resulted from what had been a very traumatic incident for Gillorie, and she said she was constantly reliving the experience. She said:

> In connection with this treatment they asked whether there was a traumatic aspect to the injury, and apparently they treat it a little differently if there is. For me, someone close to me was abusive, and I couldn't let go of the situation that

had caused the injury. It had been five years since the event, and I was experiencing a lot of pain and a lot of mental stress. Again, I had three sessions of treatment and this was a big one, a very big change. The pain was reduced maybe 75% to 90% and I was finally able to stop reliving the situation and get past the mental distress.

In some jurisdictions, for legal or other reasons, the treatments may be supervised by licensed persons, but the Vedic technicians are needed to administer the MVVT treatments.

Finally, Gillorie went for another session for anxiety and PTSD in October 2015. Her two motor vehicle accidents left her with severe anxiety in general, and especially about driving a car.

Driving had become impossible—I was so anxious. If I was driving, I would find myself holding my breath and have to pull over to the side of the road every few minutes. Now, since the last vibration therapy much of the general anxiety is gone and I am completely over the anxiety about driving. That is 100 percent gone.

Gillorie's experience, and that of the others below, should not be considered typical. In limited research (discussed more fully later in the chapter), in the initial study of subjects with long-term painful conditions of the spine and joints, 127 of the 176 experienced at least a 60 percent relief of pain following the treatment. Subjects with long-term anxiety averaged somewhat less than a 50 percent improvement. Again, various factors including the severity of the condition makes it difficult to predict results, if any.

Remedying Ben's Ten Years of Arthritis Pain

Based in part on the initial MVVT pain and arthritis study, Ben Gosvig, a middle-aged business executive and a long-term TM meditator who was trained as a TM teacher, decided to give the treatment a try. Ben had degenerative arthritis in his right knee that arose 26 years before his treatment following an auto accident. Over the past 10 years it got steadily worse, and he said he experienced "twinges of pain" almost every time he moved the joint, and especially when walking or climbing the stairs. He had consulted many orthopedic doctors for treatment, and in each case he said he was informed that the condition was inoperable and degenerative. Apart from regular exercise, no treatment could be prescribed, and he was told "the long-term prognosis for the condition was that it would steadily worsen." He had success with MVVT from his first treatment. Ben made a statement first published online, where he said:

> After the first MVVT session all the pain was gone from my knee. I could bend the knee without discomfort and could walk with no hint of pain, even when climbing the stairs. I've not experienced such pain-free movement in many years. After two days, a small percentage of the pain—about 5–10 percent—reappeared. After the second treatment, this pain also dissolved.
>
> My right knee now remains virtually pain free—only the slightest discomfort re-emerges during low pressure weather.

How the Vedic Sounds are Projected

In describing MVVT, the sounds are applied or projected to the disturbed area of the physiology to reset or retune the physiology to its natural rhythmic pattern (i.e., to restore the body's original coherence). This is different from playing sounds to a patient who listens to the rhythms or harmony. With MVVT, the patient never hears the sounds, or if he does, it is not part of the treatment. The patient may feel the vibrations, but even that is not important; they are felt by the physiology. As the European website for this treatment states (mvvt.org), the technician whispers within himself or herself some specific sounds traditionally chosen for the indicated health concerns and then administers them by blowing on and/or touching the affected area of the body. Gillorie Myrthil, the jazz drummer, said:

> The Vedic expert internalized or whispered the Vedic sounds to herself and then exhaled the vibration with her breath [in the painful area]. I didn't really feel her breath, but could feel a transformation in my body. From all my years playing drums, I have a good ability to feel vibrations, and I could distinctly feel the treatment.

Sometimes, as in Gillorie's case, as an adjunct to the treatment, the Vedic technician gives the patient either water to drink, or oil to apply, or an object to wear, in which the vibrations have been infused.

The Science Supporting Using Vibrations to Heal

The discovery that healthy cells are vibrating in a rhythmic manner is being reported a broad range of scientists, including biologists like the UK researchers who studied cancerous prostate cells and chemists like the researchers at UCLA who reported their findings on yeast cells (Chapter 1). In addition, an article in the *MIT Technology Review* ("Vibrating Cells Disclose Their Ailments"),[10] reported the cooperative research of two scientists, an MIT physicist and the Dean of MIT's College of Engineering. These researchers explained that a cell has electrical, chemical, and biological activity taking place inside it, which causes minute vibrations at the cell's surface. The researchers combined laser and imaging technologies, which allowed them to measure the vibrational frequencies of red blood cells that were malaria infected and compare them to healthy cells. They saw the difference between health and disease just from looking at the vibrations of the cells, a technology that they predict will soon allow for the detection of ailments simply from the aberrant vibrations.[11]

Laboratory Research on Using Vedic Sounds

The first Western study we know of on the Vedic sounds was conducted by Hari Sharma, M.D., Professor Emeritus at The Ohio State University College of Medicine, and former Director of the college's Division of Cancer Prevention and Natural Products Research. In 1995, he and his colleagues decided to test the effects of certain Vedic sounds on cancer cells in laboratory cultures. Sharma used Sanskrit recitations from what is known as *Sama Veda*, and he tested the effects on lung, colon, brain, breast, and skin cancer cells. Sharma also tested the effect of rock music (hard rock by the band AC/DC) on the different cells.[12]

151

The results were striking. The Vedic sounds significantly decreased the average growth of all cancer cells. The rock music had the opposite effect. It significantly increased the growth of all the cells. These results reflected the researchers' suppositions at the beginning of the study. They theorized that the Vedic sounds would resonate in a way that would have a coherent effect on the cancer cells and that the rock music would have a disordering effect, either causing no change in the growth or worse. The statistics in Sharma's research showed that the likelihood of the results being due to chance or coincidence was less than 5 in 1000.

Clinical Research on MVVT

The next research on the Vedic sounds was clinical research on actual patients. In 2001, Tony Nader, M.D., the international leader of the TM organization, led the research. Joining him in the study were researchers from Harvard Medical School, the Department of Neurology at North Shore University Hospital on Long Island in New York, and Maharishi International University.

They first studied the *immediate effects* of MVVT on a large group of subjects suffering from chronic arthritis, including osteoarthritis and rheumatoid arthritis.[13] Arthritis is the primary cause of disability in the U.S. Back pain from osteoarthritis and disc disease affects 60–80 percent of all adults in the United States at some time in their life. And the literature suggests that exercise, fitness, use of supports, and educational strategies to prevent back pain have little lasting effect. As a result, physicians principally use drugs to treat the pain, but the anti-inflammatory drugs are risky, causing thousands of deaths and almost 100,000 hospitalizations in the U.S. annually from the gastrointestinal side effects.

Dr. Nader's study had an interesting design. All the subjects had arthritis, and they were placed in two groups. Those in the experimental group received the Vedic vibrations intended to address arthritis, while the control group received a Vedic vibration treatment with different vibrations that were intended to address other disorders like gastrointestinal disorders or nervous system disorders. This is like studies where one group gets the real pharmaceutical and another gets a placebo, without the subjects knowing what they received. Only later would the control group get the real treatment for arthritis.

Of the 176 subjects in the study with painful conditions of the spine and joints, 64 or 36 percent who received the real Vedic vibration therapy specifically designed for arthritis reported a 100 percent immediate relief of pain, and 127 of the 176 reported at least a 60 percent relief of pain following the treatment. For painful conditions of the spine, which was analyzed separately, of the 110 cases, 38 cases or 35 percent reported complete relief of pain, and 81 cases reported 60 percent or greater relief of pain. For those with limited range of motion, there were 21 subjects who received the real therapy, and four subjects or 19 percent reported 100 percent improvement and 14 reported 60 percent or greater improvement in range of motion. There were very much lesser positive results for the control group. For example, whereas 64 out of 176 of the experimental patients who received the real treatment reported 100 percent immediate relief of pain, none in the control group had those results but 19 of the patients reported 60 percent relief. The researchers actually expected some positive effects on arthritis from the gastrointestinal or other treatments (that is, the treatments not specifically focused on arthritis) since all systems of the physiology are interconnected to some degree, so the treatment of one system may produce benefits in another.

The study is remarkable because of the positive results even though the subjects reported suffering from their disease for an average of 10.5 years (the range was one week to 41 years) and trying many other treatments. All the subjects had been under conventional treatment prior to the study, and it was their lack of success with these other treatments that caused them to be attracted to the MVVT vibration therapy. The relief from the pain, which is the most troubling aspect of arthritis, was regularly achieved, and there was also a significant improvement in functioning as indicated by range of motion.

The Important Random Control and Double-Blind Nature of the Arthritis Study

How good is the arthritis study? The study involved the subjects' self-report of benefits (the study treated the subjects and then asked them to report on any benefits), and virtually all the patients practiced Transcendental Meditation. These factors are what we described previously as the *Rosenthal Effect*, which is the possibility that research results are skewed due to the expectation of results in either the patient or the rater. In an effort to avoid or minimize this well-known issue, the researchers designed the study as a randomized controlled study, and also as a double-blind study, the gold standard in research. The subjects were randomly assigned to either the group that would get the real treatment (the Vedic sounds for arthritis) or the control group, which would get the other treatment (the Vedic sounds for other disorders). Randomization in assigning the study subjects to the two groups reduces the bias that could occur in the selection process so that conceptually the group you are assigned to is like tossing a coin. The double-

blind aspect of the study is that the experimental and control subjects, as well as the researchers, don't know which subjects in the
study get the real treatment and which get the placebo. With such a
design, the expectations of the subject and the researcher (that the
subject might get better) are greatly reduced but not necessarily
eliminated.

The subjects in the study were required to have been diagnosed
as having a chronic arthritic condition of the joints or spine, and
they were also required to have active symptoms of pain, limitation
of motion, or stiffness when they came for treatment. The experimental treatment consisted of only thirty seconds to several minutes of treatment by the Vedic vibration specialist.

This study also measured the *immediate* results of the short
treatment as opposed to measuring the effects over a period of several months after the treatment. We might think this is a shortcom-
ing of the study, but testing the immediate effects was actually an
intelligent part of the study's design. Testing the immediate effects
tends to prevent the distortion that some researchers have been
known to take advantage of known as the "regression to the mean."
Those who study disease know that the symptoms of a disease typically vary over time. Patients get somewhat better and then they
get worse, then they get better, and again worse. Moreover, they
tend to see a doctor when their condition is worse. Therefore, if
the doctor prescribes mint tea for all those who come to his office
and the disorders get better after a time, we can't say the mint tea
is the cause because the disorders would tend to become better
after their peak, which resulted in the doctor's visit. Any time
researchers select patients for a study whose symptoms happen to
be at the severe end of their spectrum, there is likely to be a similar reduction in symptoms over time (a regression to the mean),

which could be responsible for the drug or treatment appearing to work when in fact it has little or no effect. In the study, the immediate report of the effects of the treatment prevent the results being influenced by the regression to the mean that occurs over time; the changes were the immediate ones from whatever state the patient was in. Also, the results were substantially better for the patients who received the real treatment for arthritis as compared to the control group. This study was peer reviewed by a panel of independent scientists before being accepted for publication in 2001 in *Frontiers in Bioscience.*[14]

Other Experiences with Pain

Diane Wetherall, a teacher in New York City (also a long-time TM meditator) received MVVT a few years ago. In a statement posted online at the European website for MVVT (mvvt.org), she said:

> I was diagnosed five years ago with bursitis in my hip. It hurt to walk. It hurt to sit. It hurt to go upstairs. It hurt to lie down in bed at night, and it was impossible to sit cross-legged on the floor. For an active preschool teacher that's really essential. The doctor gave me medication, which never took the pain away. The next step was steroids, which I didn't want to use. The first day [of vibration therapy] 85 percent of my pain was gone. After the third session I felt so much better that my two children and I took a water taxi over to Manhattan and walked to Canal Street for a delicious dinner. I never would have been able to walk that distance before. Here's a surprise bonus—my back pain also disappeared!

Terry Nevas from Connecticut, another long-time TM meditator who was trained to be a TM teacher, tried MMVT for gastrointestinal problems she was facing. Like many others who have tried MVVT, she heard about it and signed up for treatments at her local TM center. At the same website (mvvt.org), she stated:

> Earlier this year I was diagnosed with colitis and received traditional medical treatment to remove the inflammation. After a few months the symptoms began to return. During the first [MVVT] session I knew immediately that something really profound had happened to my physiology. I experienced an overall feeling of well-being and bliss throughout my entire body. By the time my sessions were over, I no longer had any symptoms. Four months later, not only have I had no symptoms, but my digestion and elimination are also better than they have ever been in my entire lifetime.

The complete eradication of symptoms that Terry experienced should not be expected. Based on limited research (see chart later in this chapter), it appears that many people will get significant benefits.

The Importance of Resonant Sounds

As indicated above, in the arthritis/pain study some patients received the vibrations intended to heal arthritis, and some received vibrations intended to address either asthma, skin disease, or gastrointestinal or nervous system disorders, but not arthritis. The fact that there are different vibrations for different disorders is, itself, quite surprising and underscores the point about the degree of precision necessary in administering the proper sounds.

In his study, Dr. Nader tells us that MVVT is a very precise phenomenon where even slight variations in the vibrations would cause a dramatic decrease in effectiveness. The analogy he uses to illustrate this is how the electrical resonance of circuits in radios allows us to hear the broadcasts from different stations. A station creates a news broadcast, for example, and then transmits it to the public over a specific frequency. To hear the broadcast, the radio must be precisely tuned to that frequency for the broadcast signal to be received. If there is a synchronicity or coherence between the frequency of the transmitter and the radio receiver, the radio broadcast is heard. Similarly, in MVVT the expert whispers the Vedic sounds (using the correct pronunciation of the Vedic words) to create the right vibration, and then he or she administers or projects the vibration to the appropriate part of the physiology as is done in vibroacoustic therapy (more about this in the next chapters). Again, a synchronicity between the Vedic vibrations and the underlying vibrations of the physiology is believed to be critical for the treatment to work. The theory is that through the phenomenon of *resonance*, similar to the way a tuning fork works, each part of the physiology can be reset to its natural rhythm by administering the correct Vedic vibrations.

Study on Other Chronic Disorders

Another study of the use of Vedic vibration therapy on other chronic disorders was also published the same year as the arthritis study.[15] This study involved 213 individuals with 352 chronic disorders (some had more than one disorder) classified as moderate in severity but having lasted an average of 18.42 years before the sessions of vibration treatment employed in the study.

The average reported improvement in this particular study was 40.97 percent and found that conditions related to neck pain improved the most (average improvement of 51.25 percent); followed by respiratory ailments (average improvement of 48 percent); digestive problems (46.9 percent); mental health, including anxiety and depression (46.34 percent); arthritis (41.57 percent); insomnia (37.38 percent); back pain; headaches and migraines (35 percent improvement); cardiovascular conditions (23.31 percent); and eye problems (21.9 percent). This study showed that the percentage of improvement was not dependent on either the severity of the illness or the number of years the subject had the illness.

An Unpublished Tabulation

The changes resulting from Vedic vibration are believed to be lasting or permanent in many instances. An unpublished analysis was conducted by David Scharf, Ph.D., of Maharishi International University on the initial 7,815 patients who received Vedic vibration therapy in the first five years it was offered from 1999 to 2004. These patients had a total of 13,570 disorders. After three treatment sessions, the average improvement for all disorders in this large sampling was 48.64 percent, and 85 percent reported at least some improvement. Many improved 100%. The treatments also had a lasting effect. An average of six months later the participants were still reporting an average improvement of 47%. The largest average improvement after three sessions of about an hour and a half each was 64% for cardiovascular disorders, which is the leading cause of death in the U.S. for both men and women. The chart below may be useful, because while MVVT can at times produce remarkable cures, the treatments to date have been better for some disorders than for others.

Average Improvement by Disorder Category

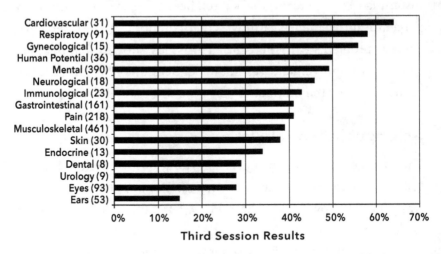

Third Session Results

What Physicians Say

Nancy Lonsdorf, M.D., is a Johns Hopkins Medical School graduate who has been practicing integrative medicine for more than
twenty-five years. She is in private practice in Iowa, but also regularly trains health professionals in Ayurveda at the University of
Maryland and at integrative medical institutes at other hospitals
in the U.S. She is the author of several popular books on Maharishi AyurVeda (the revival of Ayurveda by Maharishi), including
A Woman's Best Medicine. Jay talked to Dr. Lonsdorf about her
experience recommending patients for MVVT treatment. She said,
"There is sort of a bell-shaped curve for the general population
trying anything," and the results will vary in terms of the success
rate. She explained that this could be for a variety of reasons. She
said that "Many of the patients who come to MVVT do so for relief
from long-standing disorders that have not been healed by more
conventional strategies. So, it could be that the patient needed

160

additional treatments." In addition, Dr. Lonsdorf said, "The body is so interconnected, MVVT may not be targeting some area of the physiology that needs to be involved for the treatment to be most effective. This is always a possibility with a treatment aiming at a specific disorder."

As far as she could recall, Dr. Lonsdorf said her experience was that of the 100 or so patients for whom she had recommended the MVVT treatment since 1997, about 25 percent would have had relief of about 75 percent improvement, and 50 percent would have experienced "significant help," meaning alleviation of the disorder or symptoms by about 50 percent. Dr. Lonsdorf said, "Then there are those at both ends of the spectrum where there are no noticeable changes at the lower end and what seem like miracle cures at the other end."

Sometimes There Are Extraordinary Results

Dr. Lonsdorf described one of the extraordinary MVVT results that she saw in a patient. She said:

> Our center in Washington, D.C. became the first, or one of the first, clinical centers with doctors to offer MVVT, which was totally new at the time. We had seen some research that has now come out, but wasn't published yet. In Holland they had done some studies, and given that it had a low potential for any side effect, we offered it, but I really didn't know what to expect.
>
> I had a concern about one of my first patients that elected to do it because he had a skin problem for at least the ten years that I had known him, and he had been to many different doctors and tried many different things. It was severe eczema, and it was very bothersome for him. And in all

those years nothing seemed to effectively treat it. Also, as a result of his skin problems, he was quite irritable because of the constant pain, and discomfort, and lack of sleep. So, I wondered about it, and hoped it would go well for him.

Dr. Lonsdorf said that about a year later she found out how the Vedic vibration therapy had worked. She said:

> I was in my office and there was a knock on the door. I opened it, and he was just standing there. I said, "Oh hi so-and-so," and he said, "Hi Dr. Lonsdorf I just wanted to show you something. I did the MVVT a month ago and I just want to show you my arms." And he put up his sleeves and his arms were totally smooth, and he just said, "look it's like baby's skin. I haven't had skin like this since I was a teenager. The MVVT cleared this up."
>
> He was ecstatic because the poor man had tried everything. That was in 1997 or 1998 and about fifteen or so years later I met him, and of course I had to ask how his skin was, and he said it has been perfect. So, this is not just a placebo or temporary cure for a couple weeks and then it comes back. And he said, "My friend had a similar skin problem and he's also been cured of it." So, that's one of the miraculous stories and as a doctor, I know we just can't expect those results for everyone, but MVVT has had some remarkable effects.

The good effects in treating arthritis in part accounts for the enthusiasm of rheumatologist D. Edwards Smith, M.D., from Albuquerque, New Mexico. Smith was one of the physicians involved in the original research on Vedic vibration therapy. He said:

Nothing in my 30 years of clinical practice as a rheumatologist could have prepared me for the magnitude and scope
of relief within minutes to sufferers of chronic diseases who
participated in the first public demonstrations of Maharishi Vedic Vibration Technology in Berlin, Lille, and Paris
in 1997.

In helping Professor Tony Nader to conduct this double-
blind study, I was amazed to see the surprise and delight
of arthritics free of pain for the first time in years or even
decades. That the study was carefully controlled for expectation convinced me that the phenomenon was real and a
paradigm of shattering significance. Modern medicine is not
going to be the same.

The MVVT treatments are arranged by non-profit organizations.
The treatments require close contact between the patient and the
therapist, and the therapists are all from India. The treatments
are available in most countries other than the United States and
China. Vedic experts who administer the treatment travel to major
cities on a regular basis. Typically, those who want the treatment
sign up at their local TM center. They apply for treatment and are
contacted when the experts from India will be at the center. More
information can be found at mvvt.org, the European website for
MVVT (mvvt.org).

Chapter 10

Vedic Sounds on an App: Integrated Development of Heart and Mind

The knowledge of the applications and practices of Vedic sounds has been kept alive in India principally by being passed down from generation to generation in Vedic families. Because of the precision and refinement with which the Vedic sounds must be pronounced to be effective, those involved in reciting the sounds have to be thoroughly trained, usually from an early age. However, this knowledge was in danger of being lost because of the extensive training required to become expert in the recitations, and due to changes in modern society's mobility and modes of work.

As a result, beginning forty or so years ago, Maharishi organized a major program to create and maintain large numbers of experts in India ("Vedic pandits"), who could accurately continue the tradition of Vedic sounds, which requires reciting while maintaining inner peace and silence. Maharishi organized a network of residential pandit facilities, both for training new generations of Maharishi Vedic pandits and to create places where large groups of pandits can perform their recitations together with the aim of creating peace and prosperity for the world. With the intention to make the unique value of these sounds widely available, an internet-based app, Maharishi Veda App, was launched, containing many of the important recitations.

The Maharishi Veda App

Harris Kaplan has been working with a group in India to help administer Maharishi's Vedic pandit program since 2006. In the 1980s, Harris worked for a publicly traded energy company and gained a deep knowledge of the economics of the industry. He then applied that knowledge to an energy focused, public equity investment fund that he started and managed. His fund took off, and Harris generated top net decile returns, that is, top ten per-cent rankings of all investment funds, for its investors over the fund's life. As a result, after just five years, he decided he had made enough money and he retired from managing money for inves-tors to focus on a life of philanthropy. That ultimately led him to aid Maharishi in supporting the Vedic pandit program, including making the recitations available worldwide.

Jay: Can you describe how Maharishi started the Vedic pan-dit program?

HK: Maharishi wanted to ensure that a powerful Vedic engine for peace, harmony and progress was not lost—the Vedic pandits. At that time, the number of pandits was in serious decline and the understanding of the basis of being a pandit—established in their own inner peace and balance—had been forgotten. A new training program was required to ensure the continued availability of high

165

quality pandits. Working with some of the most senior pandits from all over India, he developed a program both to train boys from the traditional pandit families of India and also to create permanent residential facilities for mature pandits who could perform those much-needed recitations for the welfare of the world. He sent teams to hundreds of villages throughout India where the Vedic families lived and thousands of new pandits began their training.

Where families are interested, young boys of about ten begin training in their local village to learn the basics—Sanskrit and some aspects of the recitations. This is followed by training in residential campuses as the pandits-in-training get to about fourteen years of age. Then after another four or five years, if they want to continue, they are fully trained, fully matured pandits.

Jay: How many of Maharishi's pandits are there?

HK: Over 30,000 pandits have been trained. Many have graduated and have taken positions as pandits around India. We have not had enough funds to keep all these pandits and are delighted that they are making a proper living in their traditional field. But our goal is still to create these large campuses of pandits. Right now, we have about 4,500 fully trained pandits along with pandits in training at our 38 locations. The long-term goal is to have 9,000 Maharishi Vedic pandits in one place in central India and 325,000 pandits throughout the country.

Harris explained that a great many pandits are needed so that the effect of large groups of pandits reciting together can be produced.

Some of the performances require over a thousand pandits reciting those precise sounds at the same location. In the recordings on the app, it is clear that for some of the recitations, there are quite a few pandits involved.

Jay: And what is a typical day like for the mature pandits?

HK: The Vedic pandits have a routine that lasts from sunrise to evening. Twice a day, they all practice yoga asanas, then breathing exercises (Pranayama), then Transcendental Meditation, and the TM-Sidhi program [an advanced meditation program], as well as a shorter meditation in the middle of the day. In the morning and afternoon they do their Vedic recitations and performances [called yagyas]. Of course, they also have their recreation periods, meals and so forth, but the Vedic recitations and performances is their full-time profession.

Jay: Is the experience of listening to the recitations on the app similar to the experience of hearing the recitations in a live setting?

HK: There is a great value in listening to the Vedic sounds, for coherence and otherwise, both live and recorded. There is something special about live recitations, and we would expect that to be the most profound experience, but that does not in any way diminish listening via the app.

Jay: Is listening by headphone to all recitations okay or would some be better to listen to without headphones?

HK: The main thing is the comfort and ease of the listener. Whenever Vedic recitations are heard, the fundamental laws of nature begin to pulsate in the human body, enlivening all its parts and aligning the individual mind and physiology with the universal field of consciousness. If a person is not comfortable while listening, then the person is likely to miss at least part of that experience. For the best experience and results people should go by their comfort.

Jay: Can you play the recitations while doing other things?

HK: It is alright to have a chosen recitation playing in the background. However, if you are engaging in any other activity while the recitations are playing, please note whether you feel any strain at all from dividing your attention—if so, it is best not to continue (*listening while driving a car is not advised*).

Jay: Some recitations seem to be similar in their intended effect to others. Are there any recommendations on which recitations to listen to when getting started? Would some be primers for other recitations, for example, or is it just a matter of preference?

HK: The Vedic expressions all have an overall balancing and nurturing value, as well as some specific beneficial effects. The app has the ability to filter by what are considered the traditional benefits so one can easily look there.

Jay: Some of the recitations refer to the heart. What might they do?

HK: Different Vedic recitations enliven different aspects of the laws of nature. One example is the many recitations that traditionally are associated with the nurturing and nourishing qualities of the heart.

Jay: And, finally, are there instructions on how to listen?

HK: In general, it is best to sit comfortably, completely easy,
not minding anything and if it is comfortable, sit with
eyes closed. It is important not to strain to try to understand the meaning of the recitations. The value of the
recitation is not on the intellectual level. It is the sound
value that is important.

Dr. Fred Travis of Maharishi International University has taken
brain wave measurements of TM meditators who listened to the
recitations live, not on a recording, so their experience may not be
quite the same as those listening via the app.[1] In addition, this was
not the typical group of persons who might listen on the app since
the 37 TM meditators who were measured had been practicing TM
for an average of 34 years. The study analyzed the subjects' brain
waves during a fifteen-minute TM session, and again measured
during the first fifteen minutes of listening to the Vedic recitations.
During both the TM session and the Vedic recitation session, there
was strong slow alpha (alpha1) coherence in the front of the brain.
The coherence was somewhat greater, and there was also theta
coherence during the Vedic recitations as compared to TM.

Care has to be taken in generalizing too much from this limited
research. These were very experienced TM meditators in the Travis study. In addition, the TM session occurred just prior to listening to the recitations, so the coherence from the meditation session
would likely persist over time, potentially leading to the greater
coherence during the later recitations. And, again, the recitations
in the study were live, where the presence of the Vedic pandits may
enhance the coherence of those who were listening (coherence
spreads from person to person, as discussed in the next chapter). A
further caveat with the app is that those with a good ability to settle

their minds and be attentive (like long-term TM meditators) will have more pronounced results from listening to the Vedic recitations. In short, listening to the Vedic recitations is not a substitute for learning Transcendental Meditation. During TM practice there are numerous physiological changes as the entire body functions more coherently.

The Maharishi Veda App has a 30-day free trial and, as of the date of publication, costs about $4 a month. The app is available from the Apple App Store and Google Play Store. It has a "Listening Recommendations" section (click on the Settings logo in the upper right of the page listing the categories of recitations) with additional guidance. For example, what are known as the *Sama Veda* recitations are said to be good for those feeling pressure, as these recitations can promote calmness without sacrificing alertness. The app suggests these recitations may be of help to students before exams and others before important meetings or presentations.

Chapter 11

How the Vedic Sounds Work: The Power of Resonance and the Miracle of Coherence

Therapists who play Western music to patients and those advocating vibroacoustic or related therapies have different theories about how these therapies may work. Some say the patients are distracted from their pain by pleasing sounds, others say the healing is caused by the increased circulation or the relaxation that may come from a vibration massage, and some say the vibrations stimulate nerve endings that can reduce pain.[1] Still others seek to increase brain wave frequency in those with excessively slow brain wave activity,[2] and scientists in Japan have found that certain vibrations can increase neurite growth in damaged neurites (neurites are the tiny tendrils or projections from the main cell body, and damage is associated with various nervous system disorders).[3] Others explain that the body is stimulated by music to release "endorphins" (natural morphine-like chemicals in the body) and thereby decrease pain or increase feelings of satisfaction.[4]

While each of these approaches appear to offer moderate, temporary benefits, and may be useful depending on the particular disorder, these are very different from the approach of Maharishi Vedic Vibration Therapy (MVVT) or the approach of listening to the Vedic sounds. MVVT, for example, uses different sounds for different disorders and the limited research and patient reports indicate it has the potential to produce a permanent or long-lasting correction of a wide variety of disorders.

Vedic Vibration's Approach: The Power of Touch

The researchers who conducted the arthritis study described in Chapter 9 tell us that MVVT is a very precise phenomenon where even slight variations in the vibrations would cause a dramatic change in effectiveness. In MVVT the expert whispers the Vedic sounds (using the correct pronunciation) to create the right vibration for the part of the physiology to be healed.[5] Then the Vedic expert projects the vibration to that part of the physiology by blowing on or touching the physiology. We may wonder how touching a person or having other contact with the hand or the breath can pass the vibrations to the person being treated, because it is not your typical treatment, but there is growing support for related concepts. Today, both massage and touch therapies not involving massage have a growing number of adherents. There is, for example, a Touch Research Institute at the University of Miami School of Medicine, which cites touch and massage as having a healing power that ranges from helping babies grow to decreasing chronic illness in the elderly. And remember the research we cited in Chapter 2 tells us that touch therapies work through a spreading of coherence when one person touches another. In one study, researchers at the University of Colorado at Boulder found that the alpha brain waves of romantic partners became synchronized when they held hands, resulting in a reduction in pain in the female partner. Moreover, the more the brain activity between the partners became synchronized, the more the pain subsided.

One of the most interesting demonstrations of the ability to transfer vibrational impulses by touch comes from the Walt Disney corporation. Disney invented a device that is eventually destined for its theme parks. The device consists of a microphone with a metal casing around it, which is connected to a computer's sound card. When someone holds the microphone by the metal casing and whispers into it, the computer sends an inaudible or vibrational version of the message back to the microphone, which then reverberates on the hand holding the microphone. In the demonstrations of the device, the microphone is not connected to speakers so no one in the area hears the message. But when the person holding the microphone receives the vibration back from the computer (he just feels the vibration but doesn't know the message that produced it) and touches his finger to the ear of a nearby friend, the friend hears the secret message just by being poked in the ear.[6] Even complex vibrational patterns, such as a lengthy sentence, can be transmitted by touch.

The Power of Resonance

But however the Vedic vibrations or sounds are transmitted to the person to be treated, whether by listening to recitations, or by touch or the breath, the healing is based on the principle of *resonance* and is an aspect of coherence. Resonance occurs when the vibrations produced by one source, such as the Vedic vibrations, are the same or similar to the vibrations of an object (for example, the particular tissues or organs). When resonance, or synchronicity, occurs, there

173

is an energy transfer that can be very powerful. For example, an opera singer or a rock musician can hit a note that causes a crystal wine glass to shatter. A video of this can be located on YouTube (search "shattering glass with the voice"). Interestingly, what causes the glass to shatter is not just that the note is sufficiently loud, but also the effect of resonance.[7] The wine glass itself, like all objects, has a natural vibrating frequency based on the shape and composition of the glass (all objects are vibrating as science tells us). If the musician's note is loud enough and matches the frequency of the glass, there is an energy transfer from the vibrations of the singer's note to the glass that causes the effect.

As another example of the power of resonance, it is said that the military is careful when soldiers are marching across a bridge. The bridge can normally carry hundreds or thousands of times the weight of the soldiers. However, if they are marching in step (in a synchronous fashion), and if their particular cadence creates a vibration that resonates with the vibration of the bridge, it is possible for the bridge to weaken or even shatter, like the glass.[8] For this reason, those in command often require the soldiers to march out-of-step when crossing bridges.

Of course, if resonance is necessary, and if someone has arthritic joints, or anxiety, or insomnia, or a cardiovascular disorder, how do we know what vibrations should be applied to reset the naturally coherent rhythms of the disordered area?

The Link between the Vedic Sounds and the Physiology

The principles underlying the potential of the Vedic sounds to heal the human physiology may challenge some of our beliefs about nature. First, for the Vedic sounds to work there must be some association or compatibility of the Vedic sounds and the human physiology in order to induce the coherence effect. In fact, there is a relationship that appears to be highly precise, even mathematical.

To appreciate the relationship between the Vedic sounds and the body, it may be helpful to first take a look at a relationship between mathematics and the body and how mathematics informs us about relationships. In mathematics, there is what is known as the Fibonacci sequence, which appears to be a formative sequence found in the human physiology and other living organisms.

Leonardo Pisano Fibonacci, also known as Leonardo of Pisa, was born in Pisa, Italy, around 1175 AD. He was said to have been the greatest European mathematician of his time. The mathematical sequence he discovered is the numerical pattern: 0, 1, 1, 2, 3, 5, 8, 13, 21, 34, 55 and continuing infinitely. The sequence of numbers is obtained by adding each number to the one before it to obtain the next number. 0+1=1, 1+1=2, 2+1=3, 3+2=5, 5+3=8, 8+5=13, 13+8=21, 21+13=34, and so on. Fibonacci's sequence is important because the Fibonacci numbers are found so often throughout nature that the sequence is said to underlie the laws of growth in the universe.[9] For example, the number of petals on most flowers is a Fibonacci number, as is the number of leaves on a plant. The seeds in a flower head also tend to be arranged in a spiral-like Fibonacci pattern where the number of spirals that curve to the left and the number that curve to the right will be adjacent numbers in the Fibonacci sequence.

175

In addition, the ratio between successive Fibonacci numbers approximates the mathematical constant known as phi, or what is called the "divine proportion" or the "divine ratio," which is approximately 1.61803. The higher you go in the sequence of numbers, the more closely the ratio of the successive numbers comes to 1.61803. For example, 8 divided by 5 equals 1.6, and 13 divided by 8 equals 1.625, with the ratio continuing to get closer and closer to phi, the divine ratio, as the numbers increase. This is also said to be the ratio between sides in the perfect rectangle, the ratio most pleasing in the proportions of architectural structures, and the ratio most pleasing in the connecting parts of the human body.[10]

And it is not just a matter of aesthetics. Shapes that resemble the divine ratio apparently facilitate the transmission of images from the eyes to the brain. For example, we naturally scan images much better from side to side as in rectangular images, rather than up and down.[11]

The divine ratio is also seen by botanists in the growth patterns of plants, by entomologists in the genealogy of a bee, by zoologists in the breeding habits of certain animals, and so on. The ratio has been found by astronomers in the spirals of the galaxies, in spirals such as hurricanes, in the spirals of the cochlea of the human ear, and in tornadoes and numerous other structures in nature, including the DNA. The DNA molecule is 21 angstroms in width (an angstrom is a unit of length equal to one ten-billionth of a meter), and the length of one full turn in its spiral is 34 angstroms, both Fibonacci numbers.[12] In fact the human DNA molecule is said to be one long stack of rectangles in the divine proportion.

Not only is our DNA composed in a pattern that is reflective of Fibonacci numbers, but also the design of the grosser parts of the human body reflect the Fibonacci numbers and the divine ratio.

We have five appendages to the torso in the two arms, two legs and head (all Fibonacci numbers). The five fingers and toes are also the appendages on the two arms and legs, again Fibonacci numbers, as are the five openings on the face (nose, two ears and two eyes) and five sense organs for taste, touch, smell, sight, and sound. And while every individual has physical dimensions that will vary somewhat, the averages across populations tend toward the divine proportion in many of our dimensions. The length of our hands in relation to our forearms (measured elbow to wrist) is about 1.618. The forearm bears a similar ratio to the length of the upper arm. And each part of each finger, from longest to shortest, bears a similar ratio to the part of the finger before it, and so on.[13]

Fibonacci's discoveries are especially interesting because they show us how mathematics can reveal to us a relationship in and among organisms that may not otherwise be apparent. The Fibonacci sequence is a mathematical ratio with importance in understanding the growth of human and other living organisms. In a similar way, the Vedic sounds have a foundational importance in understanding life, and mathematics again reveals to us crucial relationships between the different sounds in the Vedic literature and their effects.

Ancient Understandings About the Vedic Sounds

Vedic scholars hold that there is a known vibrational basis to the universe, not just a general notion that vibrations underlie everything. Maharishi has said that the sounds in the ancient Vedic literature are themselves the vibrations and frequencies at the basis of the entire cosmos, including the human physiology. According to Maharishi, the Vedic literature, including all its treatises about health and human development, was cognized by ancient sages as stated by Dr. Nader in his Foreword. What does it mean to cognize something? A cognition in this sense is something very different from what modern psychology may mean when it speaks of cognition. In the sense used here, a cognition refers to knowledge gained from within the mind itself, or we can say knowledge gained subjectively or intuitively. It is different from knowledge gained by experiment, studies, analysis, trial and error, or discussions with others. Those are objective means of gaining knowledge. However, in the East, it is well appreciated that knowledge can also be cognized or gained subjectively by the evolved or coherent mind. While we may have doubts about the validity of knowledge gained in this way, it may actually be a fairly common experience of great thinkers. Mozart, for example, said that his compositions came to his mind in a spontaneous way "already finished" (the whole symphony playing out in his mind) before he began to write the composition on paper. Mozart said he "didn't study or aim at originality," they just came, and he said, "This is perhaps the best gift I have from my Divine Maker."[14]

So how does the mind cognize some knowledge? The minds of the ancient sages are said to have been able to perceive the most basic fluctuations or vibrations of nature. And what they perceived were not just random sounds or vibrations. These fundmental sounds and verses became an oral tradition of knowledge, which was later organized into written form and are what we know today as the Vedic literature. As Maharishi and Dr. Nader tell us, just as a house comes with a blueprint from the architect to guide our understanding of how the house is structured and how it was built, the Vedic literature is actually *nature's* blueprint to tell us how the body is structured and how it can be rebuilt, or reordered. While this may seem to veer into philosophy or religion, there is now scientific support for this idea.

In the 1990s, Dr. Nader was undertaking an in-depth study of the Vedic literature with Maharishi. In the course of their work together, Dr. Nader discovered something startling about the correspondence of the Vedic literature and the human body. When he looked at the Vedic literature, he noted a remarkable mathematical parallel to what he knew from modern science to be the structure of the human physiology, as well as a parallel between the function of the parts of the Vedic literature and the function of its corresponding part of the physiology. In his 1995 book, *Human Physiology: Expression of Veda and the Vedic Literature.*[15] Dr. Nader gives a detailed analysis of how all aspects of the physiology, from the DNA to the entire physiology, correspond mathematically and functionally to specific texts of the Vedic literature.

For example, the Vedic literature is the source of yoga, which in its highest form is a science for the development of the brain. In looking at the chapters on yoga from the Vedic literature, Dr. Nader discovered how these chapters mathematically correlate with the structure of the brain. The yoga section of the Vedic literature has four chapters, written in Sanskrit, which correspond precisely to the four lobes of the cerebral cortex (occipital, frontal, parietal, and temporal).

Within each of these four chapters are Vedic sounds in the form of Sanskrit verses, and the number of verses in each chapter is exactly equal to the number of folds (called *gyri*) in the four lobes of the brain. The 51 verses in the first yoga chapter correspond to the 51 folds in the occipital lobe; the 55 verses in the second and third yoga chapters correspond to the 55 folds in the parietal and frontal lobes of the brain; and the 34 verses in the fourth yoga chapter correspond to the 34 folds in the temporal lobe. Each of the 195 verses in the four chapters on yoga not only correspond to the 195 folds in the brain, each verse in a chapter corresponds to a particular fold, the longer verses, for example, corresponding to the longer folds in the brain.[16]

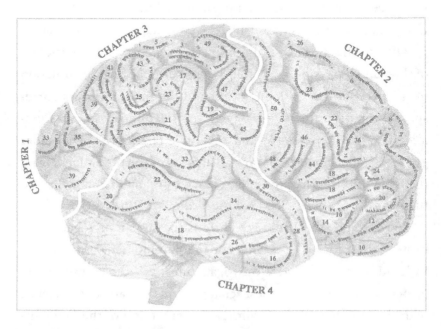

This illustration is reprinted, with permission, from Dr. Nader's book, *Human Physiology: Expression of the Veda and Vedic Literature*, Maharishi Vedic University Press, 2nd Ed.,Vlodrop, Holland (1995).

As another example given by Dr. Nader, the hypothalamus (a section of the brain responsible for governing many of the internal functions of the body) has eight regions, with four nuclei in each (a total of 32 nuclei), which correspond to the eight chapters of *Vyakaran* (another of the branches of the Vedic literature) and its 32 divisions.[17] And the cerebellum, which receives information from the sensory systems and the spinal cord and regulates motor movements, corresponds to the branch of the Vedic literature known as *Vaisheshik*. The cerebellum is divided into ten compartments and has two lobes, a left and a right, and approximately 370 small gyri or folds, corresponding to the ten chapters, two divisions, and 370 verses (Vedic sounds) in Vaishesik.[18] Dr. Nader actually found a similar remarkable correspondence between *all* the principal parts of the human nervous system and the Vedic sounds comprising the principal texts of the Vedic literature. There was such a precise correspondence that it couldn't be due to chance. As with the Fibonacci sequence, mathematics was the key to seeing the parallel relationship between the physiology and the Vedic literature.

So, if each part of the principal texts of the Vedic literature has a functional and mathematical correspondence to a part of the physiology, what does that signify for our health and development? Is this just an interesting phenomenon, or does it have some practical significance? Before answering, there is one more aspect of the Vedic sounds that completes the puzzle.

Sanskrit Equivalence of the Sound With the Form

The Vedic literature is recorded in the Sanskrit language. Sanskrit is the ancient language of India, and it is very different from modern languages. Dr. Fred Travis, mentioned earlier, a professor at Maharishi International University (MIU), explains in an article he wrote that the reason we learn Spanish or German or French, for example, is to communicate with others who speak that language or to understand documents written in the language. But that is not why students who elect to learn Sanskrit at MIU study this language. At MIU, the purpose of reading or speaking Sanskrit is not to communicate with others in the language, but just to enliven the vibrations inherent in the sounds for the purpose of making the body more coherent.

Sanskrit has been said by Maharishi to be a perfect language with a direct relationship between the sound of the words and their meaning. That suggests that if you said the word or sequence of words that means "human" or "heart" in Sanskrit, the vibrations of the words would in some way parallel the vibrations in the human physiology or the heart.

In an interesting study, Dr. Travis had eighteen subjects spend fifteen minutes practicing the Transcendental Meditation technique, which is taught to all students at the university. Then, after a short interval, all the students spent fifteen minutes reading aloud in Sanskrit from a section of the *Bhagavad-Gita*, which is part of the Vedic literature. Then the students read aloud the same section of the *Gita*, but this time translated into French, Spanish, or German. As with their readings in Sanskrit, the subjects knew the sounds of these modern languages and could read the section, but they did not understand the meaning of the words. The study was simply measuring the impact of the sounds or vibrations. The study looked at relaxation and brain wave coherence. The study looked at relaxation and brain wave coherence. The study showed breatlt increased relaxation in the students both during their Transcendental Meditation practice and during the Sanskrit readings. On the other hand, instead of relaxation, the physiological measurements showed increased anxiety during the readings in French, Spanish and German. As for brain wave coherence, during both the reading of the Vedic sounds and Transcendental Meditation there was significant alpha brain wave coherence compared to reading the modern languages.

The Bottom Line

What can be concluded from this analysis? Dr. Nader's research supports Maharishi's statements that the Vedic literature is the blueprint from nature as to how to maintain and repair the human physiology; the Vedic literature is a vibrational replica or counterpart of the human physiology, and as such it provides the key to the healing power of the Vedic health strategies. As Dr. Nader states:

> [Maharishi explains] that the recitation of the sounds of the Vedic literature in their proper sequence will resonate with the same anatomic structures to which they correspond. Their specific sequence will also enliven a specific sequence of neuronal, physiological activity. This will induce the physiology to function according to its original and perfect design. Any imperfections in the form of blocks, stress, lack or excess of activity, or abnormal connections between the various components of the physiology, will be disfavored by reading the specific aspect of the Veda and Vedic literature that corresponds to that area of the physiology which is dysfunctional.[19]

This means that reading, listening to or otherwise applying the sounds or vibrations of particular sections of the Vedic Literature may restore proper functioning of the part of the physiology that is associated with that section of the Vedic literature.

The Miracle of Coherence

As we said earlier, when functioning normally, the human body is almost unfathomably orderly or coherent and thereby perfectly designed for our health and well-being. This is part of what we

183

might call the miracle of the coherence that is at our core. And the laws of nature tell us that coherence has seemingly miraculous consequences, whether we find it in the human body or elsewhere. We referred in Chapter One to the Second Law of Thermodynamics, which says that everything that is not alive becomes progressively more disorderly over time. There is also a Third Law of Thermodynamics in physics, which is an even more important law of nature because of what it tells us about how to create order or coherence. The Third Law states that when the temperature of any substance is lowered, the molecular activity of the substance becomes more orderly or coherent. This is important because temperature is just a technical term for activity. The higher the level of the activity of the molecules in a substance, the greater the temperature. The Third Law, therefore, says that any physical system can become more orderly by settling or calming the system. With the body, we can't just lower the temperature since our body needs to be at about 98.6 degrees Fahrenheit, but calming the mind and thereby making the mind and body more coherent is a functional equivalent. This is one principle behind the success of the Transcendental Meditation technique.

Moreover, the Third Law goes on to say that when a physical system is functioning from its maximally settled or least excited state, the system will be *perfectly orderly or perfectly coherent* in its functioning. When we transcend thoughts at the deepest point of the TM practice, we experience our Self, a perfectly silent, coherent state of consciousness, and it results in a maximally coherent physical state with exceptional consequences for human life. And the Third Law is evident throughout nature, also with exceptional consequences.

The Exceptional Characteristics of Highly Coherent States

Light is produced by the vibration of electrons. The ordinary light bulb produces incoherent waves, and inefficient light, because of the chaotic motion of heat in the filaments. However, coherent light waves can be produced through the *laser* technique, which *coherently de-excites the light atoms to their lowest activity level.* We can say the technique calms the atoms, and as a consequence, the laser light that is produced has waves, which are all in the same frequency, amplitude, and phase resulting in the power and other special properties of the laser beam. A laser light of 1/1000 of a watt couldn't be seen without damaging the eye. Stronger lasers can be built which shatter atoms. And this coherence-generating light technology has changed our world. Lasers are now used in DNA sequencing, fiber-optics, semiconducting chip manufacturing, laser surgery, optical disk drives, laser printers and barcode scanners, as well as in numerous other applications.

Notably, the association of maximum coherence with exceptional new properties appears to be a universal phenomenon. Superconductors, for example, also derive their exceptional properties by creating near perfect coherence through the use of ultra-low temperature (low activity) compounds. A superconducting compound will conduct electricity without any resistance whatsoever (resistance is undesirable because it produces losses in the energy flowing through the material). As just one example, the coherence in superconductivity has resulted in magnetic resonance imaging (MRI) devices, which are non-invasive technologies for probing the body and detecting disease and disorder.

And there is one other feature about coherence that gives us some insight into its importance. Coherence spreads. We've seen that in the study showing husbands creating coherence by touching their wives who were experiencing pain, and thereby reducing or eliminating the pain. But we also see a spreading of coherence whether or not there is physical contact in what is perhaps the most important finding of the new science of consciousness. Over fifty studies, most in peer-reviewed publications, show how coherence from groups of people practicing TM at the same time in the same place produces a coherent collective consciousness that spreads to the surrounding population and can cause reductions in violence, accidents, and other negative expressions. Several books describe this phenomenon in greater detail.[20] This aspect—that coherent elements induce coherence in interconnected systems—and the exceptional characteristics of coherent states, also offers a picture of how Vedic pandits can spread coherence throughout society through their recitations and performances. The sounds in the Vedic literature are said to consist of the first impulses of nature that emerge from a universal field of consciousness that underlies all existence. The fundamental Vedic sounds were once described by Maharishi as "the laws of nature murmuring to themselves."[21] If the sounds are impulses of the laws of nature, it should at least be theoretically possible for the Vedic recitations to have an effect on all of nature, not just on the human physiology.

An important article on the science of consciousness by Dr. Nader, including an analysis of whether consciousness is simply a product of electrical and chemical behavior in the brain or whether it exists without the support of the brain, is "Consciousness Is All There Is: A Mathematical Approach with Applications," published in the *International J. of Mathematics and Consciousness*, Vol. 1, No. 1 (2015) and available online.

Part IV

DIET, DIGESTION, AND IMMUNITY

Chapter 12

Food as Medicine Requires Eating for Coherence (by Knowing Your Ayurvedic Body Type)

Food as Medicine: Its Time Has Come

Many of us grew up with mothers telling us "an apple a day keeps the doctor away," or that carrots were good for our vision. And especially if our mothers were Jewish, we were given chicken soup for our colds. Interestingly, it now appears that at least these particular folk remedies were not just old wives' tales. Modern medicine tells us that apples contain nutrients that are important in heart health and compounds called phenols that may help protect cells against DNA damage; carrots contain a nutrient, lutein, which can help prevent problems such as macular degeneration leading to blindness; and even chicken soup, due to one of its amino acids, can fight the congestion that accompanies a cold.

We know something today of the benefits of food in promoting health due to a growing *food is medicine* movement, and it is starting to attract the serious consideration of mainstream medicine. For years medical schools had no courses in nutrition. And many practicing physicians continue to rate their nutrition knowledge as inadequate. Pharmaceutical companies still largely control what we consider medicine and influence what is taught in medical schools. In many instances these companies have substantial knowledge of the healing power of natural foods and plants, but they have no real interest in promoting food and herbs as medicine. This is due to the fairly obvious reasons that a population that was helping to heal itself with food and herbs would decrease the market for their drugs, and because pharmaceutical companies only sell products on which they can obtain patents. Because you cannot patent what is natural, the drug companies are not interested in selling Ayurvedic or other natural products. Instead, when they find a natural product that seems to work, they try to isolate the active compound in the plant substances and make a synthetic drug in an effort to mimic the natural healing effect or increase its potency. The pharmaceutical companies can obtain patents on their synthetic drugs, but every drug does its collateral damage, which can range from mild discomfort to irritating allergies and rashes to unanticipated tragedies and death.

Ayurveda (the health knowledge from the Vedic literature) holds that the side-effects of pharmaceuticals result from using only part of the plant (the part considered to have the active ingredient) rather than appreciating the holistic value of the plant. The other components in the plant may provide protection from the side-effects of applying the active ingredient only. In addition, Ayurveda holds that healing can come from smaller doses, and that man-made medicines cannot duplicate the coherence-generating potential of what nature provides (see Chapter 1).

How Can Food be Medicine?

To understand how food can truly be medicine, let's first go back to physicist Erwin Schrödinger's analysis from Chapter 1. He tells us what it is about food that keeps us alive. As pointed out in that chapter, Schrödinger analyzed the nature of living systems in his classic book, *What is Life?* He said:

> How does the living organism avoid decay? The obvious answer is by eating, drinking, breathing, and (in the case of plants) assimilating.... For a while in the past our curiosity was silenced by being told we feed upon energy... this is absurd.... Surely any calorie is as good as any other calorie. What then is the precious something contained in our food, which keeps us from death? That is easily answered.... What an organism feeds upon is negative entropy [orderliness].[1]

We eat food, change it into the necessary building blocks for the body, and then excrete the waste. Our food gives us energy, but, again, this isn't the essential reason why our food sustains us. The primary reason to eat, said Schrödinger, is to obtain highly orderly energy. We are really consuming the coherence of other natural living systems (plants and animals). All living systems are coherent. All have an internal level of coherence that cannot be duplicated by what is man-made. All have homeostatic coherence-generating mechanisms, and they all perform highly ordered biochemical reactions to obtain energy and sustain life. And even apart from the internal coherence that characterizes the animal and plant kingdom, there is what we could call a perfect match or integration between what the human species needs in order to grow and evolve, and what plants (fruits and vegetables) and certain animals provide. Our bodies require a great variety of vitamins, minerals, carbohydrates, proteins, amino acids, fats and oils, whole grains, phytonutrients (plant nutrients), and other compounds for health in general and to optimally support the complex processes occurring in the body. Too little vitamin A or C or B6 or B12, or insufficient flavonoids, or carotenoids (found in various plant foods), can cause serious health disorders. We need a great variety of biochemical compounds, and nature has given us a huge variety of foods that contain all of what we need. The body needs natural compounds for health, and medicines are not a substitute.

There is another aspect of eating to create coherence in the body. The Ayurvedic principles of eating for coherence generally do not consider it healthy to eat leftovers. And most people recognize that it is good to eat food that is as fresh as possible. The reason for this has to do with the laws of nature that we looked at in Chapter 1, the laws of thermodynamics. Food that is not fresh decays due to the operation of the famous Second Law of Thermodynamics, which, as we recall, says that anything that is dead becomes progressively more disorderly over time. If we leave half of our plate of food on the table after dinner, the next morning it has decayed to a point where it should not be eaten. And the longer it is left on the table, the worse will be its effect on the body. We also know that if we can't eat food that is fresh, we at least refrigerate our foods, but what we may not appreciate is that this is to preserve its coherence.

As mentioned previously, another important law of nature, the Third Law of Thermodynamics, says that *when the temperature of a given system is reduced, the entropy (disorder) is reduced, and when the temperature reaches zero, the entropy will be zero.* In other words, lowering the temperature of a substance reduces disorder and thereby preserves its orderliness. That is why we refrigerate our foods, and since the Third Law says the lower the temperature, the more we can reduce disorder, we can preserve our foods for even longer periods by storing them in the freezer.

Ayurveda gives us other guidelines for eating for coherence, which in the area of consuming food means eating foods that promote balance and are an antidote to any disorders that are present in the body or disorders that are likely to develop based on our body types. Those who are car buffs know that fuel additives work. They boost transmission performance; they clean fuel injectors to increase mileage; they seal head gasket and radiator leaks, and so forth. Similarly, when the body consumes the right foods, herbs, and spices it turns them into specialized "fuels and additives" that promote healthy living, only the effect is even more dramatic because the body is so much more sophisticated in its workings than a car.

What are the Healthiest Foods on the Planet?

Many food experts emphasize an ideal or "best" diet for *everyone*, with possible exceptions for those who are in the throes of some disease where some foods (like acidic foods for those with ulcers) are known to aggravate the condition. The Department of Agriculture and many health organizations and health professionals have dietary recommendations for *all* Americans, which do not distinguish among individuals. They tell us, for example, to eat carbohydrates, fiber foods, proteins, and healthier fats such as lean poultry or meats and oils such as canola and olive oils. But, unfortunately, what is thought to be good advice for eating or losing weight in one year turns out to be false a few years later or is replaced by the next new wonder diet. For many years many medical doctors and the American Heart Association were urging *everyone* to reduce or give up saturated fats in milk, cheese, butter, and meat in favor of polyunsaturated fats. "Polyunsaturated" then became the buzzword that helped sell margarine and certain cooking oils for years. However, more recent research shows some saturated fats are fine for many people but that excess polyunsaturated fats such as margarine are bad for most, as they often cause an increase in "free radical" chemical reactions that may be at the basis of many disorders, including cancer and aging.

As another example of incomplete or incorrect knowledge, a popular magazine recently published an online article called "The Healthiest Foods on the Planet."[2] The article says that one red potato has the same amount of cell-building folate as a cup of spinach or broccoli. The article also says one lemon gives you all the vitamin C for the day, which may help increase good cholesterol. It explains that a small amount of dark chocolate can reduce blood pressure and reduce bad cholesterol, and it says that salmon is a good source of fatty acids, potentially reducing depression, heart disease, and cancer, as well as a source of niacin to reduce Alzheimer's and memory problems. Is this good advice?

The main problem with the list is that it fails to take into account the makeup or body type of the person who will be eating these foods and any disorders he may have. Let's suppose we have a person with a severe case of peptic ulcers or acid reflux. These are what in Ayurveda are typically considered Pitta disorders. When faced with these disorders, the body needs foods that have an anti-inflammatory effect (i.e., a cooling effect) and are not acidic, in order not to aggravate the situation. The principle at work is one of *complementarity*, which means that the antidote to a particular disorder has the opposite effect in the body as the characteristics of the disorder. This is logical and might be expected from a health system aiming to restore coherence. In the case of, for example, acid reflux, Ayurveda would recommend that a person avoid lemons and chocolate, which, however, are on the ten healthiest foods list, and Western medicine would actually agree with avoiding these two items.[3] Ayurveda, however, understands the properties of every food and would also recommend that the person with inflammatory type disorders avoid seafood and most (not all) beans (see next chapter), which while said to be among the ten healthiest foods, are not healthy for those with inflammatory disorders. The same is true for most of the other foods on the magazine's healthiest foods list; they will be good for some, and not good for others, depending on the person's disorders and his or her basic body type, which is referred to sometimes in Ayurveda as the person's body constitution.

Western medicine is starting to recognize that it is important to eat the right foods when a disorder has already grown into a gastrointestinal disease like acid reflux, but Ayurveda understands that it's equally important to eat the right foods to prevent disorders for those body types likely to get the disorder. It is also important to counteract our existing disorders in their earliest stages. If we don't do this, the risk is that our relatively minor disorders will grow into full-blown disease. One way Ayurveda does this is by knowledge of the individual's body type, and knowledge of the foods that should be favored and avoided to aid the healing of particular disorders and to maintain coherence for each Ayurvedic body type.

Ayurveda's History

Before we get into Ayurvedic body types and the right foods for each type, let's step back and get an overall understanding of Ayurveda. It is the part of the Vedic literature dealing with health, and is perhaps the world's oldest and most complete health knowledge, said to be over 5,000 years old. As the oldest system of health, Ayurvedic practices influenced Chinese medicine and all the Eastern as well as Western forms of medicine. But as respected as Ayurveda was in India in the early 1800s, when India came under British colonial rule around 1860, Ayurveda was not encouraged and was even suppressed in an effort to make India a more Western nation. Western medicine was promoted by the government and the knowledge of Ayurveda deteriorated and was in disarray by the time India gained independence in 1947. After its independence, Ayurveda began to regain ground, and in 1971 it became an official part of the government health care system, which during most of British rule had been exclusively Western.[4] Still, at that time Ayurveda for the most part amounted to dispensing herbal medicines,[5] and even in that area shortcuts were taken by many of the Ayurvedic pharmacies, and the greatest experts felt that Ayurveda's potential was not being realized.[6]

In the early 1980s Maharishi turned his attention to Ayurveda as part of his goal of reviving the principal knowledge in the Vedic literature. To restore Ayurveda, Maharishi collaborated with a number of the leading Ayurvedic physicians, including Dr. B.D. Triguna, who was President of the All India Ayurvedic Congress (which is said to be the equivalent of the American Medical Association in this country); Dr. V.M. Dwivedi, a member of the Central Council of Indian Medicine, and an expert in the Ayurvedic herbal preparations; and Dr. Balraj Maharishi, who was considered the leading expert in plants and their medicinal effects.

Today there are hundreds of Ayurvedic schools, colleges and hospitals in India, all with somewhat different approaches and differing degrees of success. The principles and guidelines in this book are those revived by Maharishi and his experts beginning in the 1980s, and are referred to as Maharishi AyurVeda® (MAV) to signify that these approaches are considered authentic by Maharishi and his experts.

One of the most important contributions Maharishi made was to reintroduce consciousness-based approaches to Ayurveda. It was there in all the original texts but had been effectively lost over time. Maharishi revived the use of meditation, specifically Transcendental Meditation, as a primary modality in the prevention and treatment of disease. This is really part of Ayurveda. A second addition was Maharishi's re-enlivenment of pulse diagnosis (discussed in Chapter 16). Most Ayurvedic doctors are trained in the use of pulse to identify imbalances in the physiology, but only at a very superficial level. With the help of Dr. B.D. Triguna, who was regarded as the greatest expert on pulse diagnosis, Maharishi AyurVeda created a unique and complete pulse diagnosis training program, which assesses both the superficial and deep levels of the pulse to detect and prevent disease.

Maharishi and his experts also restored the importance of the traditional means of cultivating and processing the herbal remedies of Ayurveda. MAV herbal supplements contain high-quality herbs that are combined into potent formulas that aim to correct the underlying imbalance (disorder) in the physiology without causing side-effects. Instead of just treating the symptoms, these formulations aim to eliminate the root cause of the disorders.

Finally, Maharishi emphasized a thorough understanding of Ayurveda in the language of modern science, and many hundreds of Western physicians and Ayurveda consultants have now been trained in MAV.

Body Types: The Natural Elements and their Counterparts in the Human Body

In ancient India, as well as in Greece, Egypt, Babylonia, Japan, and Tibet, the five elements of earth, water, air, fire, and space (space is sometimes referred to as ether) were understood to explain the characteristics of all matter in terms of simpler substances.[7] And since man is part of nature, the five elements were also found to have their *counterparts* in the human physiology, and were the basis of highly sophisticated health systems in all these cultures. For example, in the medicine of Hippocrates in ancient Greece, the earth elements in the body were said to be the bones, joints, connective tissues, and all the denser parts of the body; the fire element was represented in the body by the digestive enzymes and digestive fire; and the water element was represented in the body's fluids, including the blood, lymph and mucus fluids, and so on.[8] And just as nature could become imbalanced (which is a form of disorder or incoherence) by too little or too much rain, or unseasonably high or cold temperatures, or excessively windy conditions, many of these ancient systems of medicine considered disease to result from an imbalance in the body's counterparts to nature's five basic elements. This ancient knowledge needs to be better understood by modern medicine.

How a Balanced Body Works

How does a balanced body work? Let's take the fire or heat element in nature. One of its counterparts in the body is inflammation, which isn't necessarily good or bad, but must be in balance for it to have a positive effect on health. When the body is in balance, if we get an infection, our immune system immediately causes inflammation in the area of the injury to protect the body. The temporary result may be warmth and redness, swelling, and even pain in the area, but this normal inflammatory response results in healing and is part of our coherent self-repair mechanisms that keep us alive. On the other hand, too much inflammation is bad. Many diseases are associated with chronic inflammation, including cancer, atherosclerosis, asthma, rheumatoid fever, and inflammatory bowel syndrome.

Similarly, the body obviously has a fluid component to it, which also must be kept in balance, since both dehydration and overhydration can result in mental confusion, seizures, and coma, among other disorders. And the body has earth elements, as the medicine of Hippocrates states, and air or movement elements. All the elements need to be kept in balance.

The Three Doshas

According to Ayurveda, the five elements in nature combine to form three basic tendencies or operating principles of matter. These are known as the three *doshas*, and each person has a different proportion of the doshas at birth (in many respects, this is like saying that we each have a different mixture of genes). Diet, age, weather, and countless other factors influence the proportion of doshas in the physiology at any time, and this has profound implications for health. When the doshas remain in their ideal proportion (which is different for different people), an individual remains healthy according to Ayurveda. When imbalance occurs—for example, if one of the doshas greatly increases or decreases in proportion to the others—the disease process begins. Susceptibility to different diseases, as well as the course of each disease, will vary depending upon which dosha predominates.

The goal of Maharishi AyurVeda (MAV) is to recreate balance in the three doshas, which are called *Vata*, *Pitta*, and *Kapha* (discussed at length below). When the doshas are balanced, the inner intelligence and coherence of the body will be more complete.

How can we know the ideal proportion of doshas in the physiology, and can we diagnose our current state of balance? The traditional texts of Ayurveda describe three means of diagnosis: sight, speech, and touch. The first two involve a physical examination and interview to determine the patient's medical history and current symptoms. However, the subtlest and most effective diagnostic technique is what is known as pulse diagnosis. The pulse contains specific vibrational information about the patient's entire physical and mental condition, and we discuss it more fully in a later chapter. In this chapter we describe another way of determining your body type (a questionnaire, a means of speech). Use of the questionnaire will be helpful if you don't currently have access to someone trained in MAV pulse diagnosis. Based on the body type questionnaire, you will get a better idea of the foods that are best for your physiology, including foods that can be helpful for any disorders that may be present.

Balance Requires Knowledge of your Ayurvedic Body Type

To sum up, Maharishi AyurVeda very clearly states that no one diet is right for all people. What is nourishing for one individual can actually be detrimental for another. For example, some sweets are said to be good for Vata type people and Vata disorders, while for a Kapha type person, they may cause respiratory congestion or excess fat. Hot, spicy foods are very good for Kapha types, yet they aggravate the digestion of a Pitta nature, leading to indigestion and a marked tendency toward anger. Each individual has his own needs.

Everyone has the expression of all the five natural elements in the body, and the extent to which they vary in an individual gives the person his basic Ayurvedic body type (constitution) and personality. The five basic elements are found in three principles or characteristics that regulate the entire body, the three doshas—Vata, Pitta, and Kapha. The doshas are considered by Ayurveda to be a very subtle expression of matter in the physiology, so at this deep level if we can influence the doshas and balance them, we can balance the entire physiology and produce the right coherence effect. In the chart from other chapters, the doshas would be at the level shown below.

MIND-BODY LEVELS

Skin (Outer Organ)

Internal Organs (brain, kidney, liver, etc.)

Tissues (groups of related cells)

Cells

Doshas

In most people, although all doshas are present, one or two will predominate, resulting in our individual characteristics and tendencies, including our tendencies toward developing specific disorders (what are sometimes classified as Vata, Pitta, or Kapha disorders). For example, one might be classified as a Vata-Pitta, Vata-Kapha, or Pitta-Kapha type. Less common is the pure "mono-doshic" person, in which one dosha predominates. In rare instances, all three doshas may be equally in evidence. Please note, however, that these are just tendencies to get certain disorders. An imbalance in any dosha, for example, an imbalance in Vata dosha, can sometimes result in not just a Vata disorder but also a Pitta disorder. That said, here are the tendencies of each individual based on his or her body type. From the description, most people can find their type.

Vata Type Individuals

The Vata characteristics are the body's counterparts of the space and air elements in nature. As such they result in a Vata person's tendency toward dryness (the air element is a Vata element, and blowing air results in dryness), and also toward lightness and movement within the body. Vata in the body controls such functions as breathing, excretion, and neural control of sensory and motor functions. Vata dominant persons (with the space and air elements dominant in the physiology) characteristically are thin and light. They are rarely comfortable in the cold and dislike strong wind. They instinctively prefer warm, balmy weather, warm water, and warm food, which are all good for Vata types. This is the complementarity principle we mentioned earlier.

Vata types tend to be bright, quick to grasp new concepts, quick to learn, but poor on long-term memory. Vata types are also quick to conceive and initiate projects but have difficulty in following through to the end. They are often highly creative, but they can be more emotionally sensitive, and even overemotional, with extreme mood swings. When feeling good, they can be almost euphoric.

Vata Types

Thin or wiry build	Dry (sometimes constipated)
Cold	Light sleepers and nervous tendency
Moody	Fast talkers and learners

Common Vata Disorders

Vata types, when they have not eaten properly and taken care of themselves, tend to get Vata type disorders, which are:

- Dry skin
- Dislike of cold
- Menstrual cramps
- Insomnia
- Anxiety
- Restlessness
- Depression
- Worries
- Degenerative arthritis
- Common fatigue
- Constipation (often from dryness in the body)
- Tension headaches
- High blood pressure
- Nerve pain or other acute pain
- Gas in intestines

There are various steps that can be taken to bring Vata dosha back into balance and thereby restore coherence in the body. One major approach is through diet and providing particular foods that can pacify the imbalanced Vata constitution.

Pitta Type Individuals

The Pitta principle (corresponding to the fire and water elements in nature) is involved with such functions as digestion (the digestive fire) and the regulation of heat in the body. Pitta types will typically have good digestion. They often have red or sandy hair, fair skin, and a medium build as compared to the thin or wiry Vata types. Like Vata types, they tend to have agile minds; however, they have far more energy and staying power than Vata types. They have a fiery or passionate nature with a strong and penetrating intellect. They are well organized and can be good, authoritative decision-makers. Their bodies can take a lot of physical discipline and abuse, and they frequently take over-advantage of this attribute. It is no coincidence that military people and athletes are frequently found to be Pitta types.

Pitta Types

Medium build (may be athletic)	Fair skin and red or sandy hair
Authoritative or impulsive	Tendency to anger (irritability)
Hot and fiery disposition	Sharp mind

Common Pitta Disorders

When Pitta is imbalanced, Pitta types will typically have disorders relating especially to chronic inflammation.

- Inflammatory diseases such as boils and acne
- Excessive hunger
- Excessive thirst
- Bad breath and sour body odors
- Hemorrhoids
- Peptic ulcers and heartburn
- Anger and irritability, self-criticism and resentment
- Intolerance of others and bad temper
- Yellowing of feces and urine
- Premature greying or baldness
- Hot flashes

Kapha Type Individuals

The third major body type is called Kapha and is concerned with the structural basis of the physiology. It is roughly the body's counterpart to the heavier earth and water elements. As a result, Kapha types tend to be more heavily built (more denseness and water in the physiology), with somewhat oily skin, and they often have dark and thick hair. Their digestion tends to be slow, and Kapha people will often tend toward becoming overweight. Unlike Vata types, they are not easily disturbed, and unlike Pitta types, they are slow to anger. Their minds are tranquil and steady, slower to learn but slower to forget. Because they are not easily upset, they often are warm, forgiving, and agreeable. Negative tendencies from excess or imbalanced Kapha can manifest in disorders that typically are characteristic of heaviness and fluid retention.

Kapha Types

Heavy build	Dark and thick hair
Slow moving	Slow digestion
Calm	Warm and likeable

Common Kapha Disorders

Again, any imbalanced dosha can cause any disorder but these are the common disorders for Kapha types.

- Excessive weight
- Diabetes
- Congestion (sinus, chest)
- Frequent colds
- High cholesterol
- Asthma
- Cysts
- Aching joints
- Laziness and lethargy
- Oversleeping
- Depression
- Resistance to change
- Slow digestion
- Oily skin

Note that each body type has its own strengths and weaknesses. In addition, individuals are a combination of different proportions of Vata, Pitta, and Kapha. So, what we consider a Vata type is predominantly a Vata type. However, the key is that each body type needs to be maintained in a balanced and coherent state by, for example, eating correctly for that type and following the right daily routine. According to MAV, disease occurs when Vata, Pitta, or Kapha become aggravated or imbalanced.

Body Type Questionnaire

On the next page is a short questionnaire to better determine your body type. Note that you may currently be mostly one body type (based on the high score), or two or more types may have similarly high scores. Answer the questions based on your current state, not any tendencies you might have had at an earlier age. Your current state will change from time to time as the seasons change and as you age. Vata is cold so in winter everyone exhibits somewhat more Vata characteristics and, similarly, almost everyone experiences more Pitta characteristics in the summer. Youth is more of a Kapha period of life as individuals tend to be more muscular and need more exercise, while our Vata increases as we get in our 50s or higher.

One other word of caution is important. The quiz is a method of determining your body type and will aid in determining the foods you should favor and avoid, especially when the doshas are aggravated and out of balance. However, taking the quiz and reading the information presented in this book is not as good as consulting with a person trained in Maharishi AyurVeda body type diagnosis, which is pulse diagnosis (a list of those trained in diagnosis can be obtaind from the website at the back of the book, in Appendix C). Through this unique method of diagnosis (Chapter 16), the Maharishi AyurVedic practitioner can determine your body type more accurately than by taking a quiz, and they can best determine what disorders are present in the body before they have ripened into a disease. They would then make recommendations to help prevent the disease from developing or to help heal the disease if it has already manifested.

BODY TYPE QUESTIONNAIRE

The short questionnaire may help you determine your body type if you cannot see a Maharishi AyurVedic doctor or well-trained consultant.

VATA TENDENCIES

STRONGLY DISAGREE / STRONGLY AGREE

1. Light sleeper, difficulty falling asleep
   [1]   [2]   [3]   [4]   [5]
2. Has irregular appetite
   [1]   [2]   [3]   [4]   [5]
3. Learns quickly but forgets quickly
   [1]   [2]   [3]   [4]   [5]
4. Easily becomes overstimulated
   [1]   [2]   [3]   [4]   [5]
5. Does not tolerate cold weather very well
   [1]   [2]   [3]   [4]   [5]
6. Feels like you are dashing through life rather than going at a more leisurely pace
   [1]   [2]   [3]   [4]   [5]
7. Speech is energetic, with frequent changes in topic
   [1]   [2]   [3]   [4]   [5]
8. Anxious and worried when under stress
   [1]   [2]   [3]   [4]   [5]

VATA SCORE

(TOTAL YOUR RESPONSES)

PITTA TENDENCIES

STRONGLY DISAGREE / STRONGLY AGREE

1. Easily becomes overheated

   [1]   [2]   [3]   [4]   [5]

2. Strong reaction when challenged

   [1]   [2]   [3]   [4]   [5]

3. Uncomfortable when meals are delayed

   [1]   [2]   [3]   [4]   [5]

4. Good at physical activity

   [1]   [2]   [3]   [4]   [5]

5. Strong appetite

   [1]   [2]   [3]   [4]   [5]

6. Good sleeper but may not need as much sleep as others

   [1]   [2]   [3]   [4]   [5]

7. Clear and precise speech

   [1]   [2]   [3]   [4]   [5]

8. Become irritable and/or angry under stress

   [1]   [2]   [3]   [4]   [5]

PITTA SCORE

(TOTAL YOUR RESPONSES)

KAPHA TENDENCIES

STRONGLY DISAGREE / STRONGLY AGREE

1. Slow eater
   [1]   [2]   [3]   [4]   [5]
2. Fall asleep easily but wake up slowly
   [1]   [2]   [3]   [4]   [5]
3. Steady, stable temperament
   [1]   [2]   [3]   [4]   [5]
4. Doesn't mind waiting to eat
   [1]   [2]   [3]   [4]   [5]
5. Slow to learn but rarely forgets
   [1]   [2]   [3]   [4]   [5]
6. Good physical strength and stamina
   [1]   [2]   [3]   [4]   [5]
7. Speech may be slow and thoughtful
   [1]   [2]   [3]   [4]   [5]
8. Possessive and stubborn under stress
   [1]   [2]   [3]   [4]   [5]

KAPHA SCORE

(TOTAL YOUR RESPONSES)

In general, choose the diet of your dominant type. However, additional instructions are set forth in the next chapter.

Jane's Body Type Knowledge

Jane Roman Pitt is a grandmother, as well as a composer and singer with five albums to her credit. She learned about Maharishi AyurVeda and body types in 1984 and then made changes in her diet according to the Ayurvedic system. She said it greatly helped her health, but one of the biggest things Jane got from Ayurveda was unexpected. She said:

> The health benefits are mostly what are discussed by the Ayurvedic experts, and I've had good health since starting with Ayurveda. But I realized it was also a great tool for my relationships. Knowing people's body types makes it clear that we are not all the same.

> My late husband, for example, was a Kapha type, and I'm Pitta/Vata. So, after learning about Ayurveda we could both understand why I was moving faster, and he was moving slower. If we went for a walk, he would amble along and stop whenever he wanted to make a point, and I wanted to be striding. In addition, I was always working on something, and he was happy to relax more. We also liked different foods, and learning about Ayurveda made for greater understanding and tolerance of our differences—we could compromise more. It also has helped me to understand and appreciate other family members and friends!

Chapter 13

Matching Your Foods and Spices to Your Body Type and Current Disorders

*"Leave your drugs in the pot at the pharmacy
if you can't cure your patient with food."*
—Hippocrates

Coherence requires us to have a balanced diet. That means each day we have a good variety of the essential foods, and that will be discussed later, but we also favor certain foods and reduce others according to the disorders we currently have and those we have a tendency to develop based on our basic body type.

Set forth below are foods to favor and reduce for each body type. Foods are classified in Ayurveda into six tastes: sweet, salty, sour, spicy, bitter, and astringent. This is a good example of the coherence in nature, and how nature gives us a crucial guide for eating. Our foods are composed of many components such as carbohydrates, lipids, and protein, but also water, vitamins, minerals, enzymes, fibers, fatty acids and so on. It is very difficult to take all that into account in establishing a diet. Yet we can generally determine the foods to favor or reduce based on the six tastes. Note also

211

that a recommendation for reducing a taste does not mean to eliminate that taste. This is because Ayurveda says that all six tastes are necessary for maximum coherence, and Ayurveda recommends that foods with all six tastes be eaten every day.

Set forth below are what are considered the ideal foods for different body types so you can see if your diet is right for you. Your diet and digestive strength (discussed in Chapter 15) are not right if you experience, among other things, gas, bloating, loose stool, constipation, abdominal pain, or acidity.

Most Ideal Foods for Vata Types

Vata types again are people with light or airy, dry, and cold characteristics (see the previous chapter for more details). Foods with sweet, salty and sour tastes balance Vata dosha. Vata types should reduce pungent, bitter, and astringent tastes. Qualities of dryness, rawness, and coldness should also be avoided. The foods to favor and reduce in order to balance Vata constitutions are:

Favor	Reduce
Heavy foods	Light foods
Warm (cooked fruit and food, hot cereals)	Cold (frozen desserts, iced beverages)
Oily (nuts, seeds, oil on foods)	Dry (crunchy chips or cereals)
Sweet (wheat, milk, rice)	Spicy or pungent
Salty	Bitter (leafy greens)
Sour (yogurt, citrus)	Astringent (apples, beans)

Special Vata Guidelines. When Vata is out of balance, Vata types tend to be anxious and have weak digestions. They especially need to act in a way that promotes a settled physiology, which includes avoiding caffeine and eating in a calm environment, not while watching TV, driving, or standing up. They tend to have gas develop and gaseous disorders, and therefore need to especially avoid carbonated beverages. Eating heavier foods also means eating enough, especially if they are underweight. Drink Vata Tea, which contains Vata reducing spices, and is available at mapi.com.

Detailed Foods and Spices for Vata Types

1. Best vegetables: asparagus, cucumber, green beans, okra, radishes, sweet potatoes, turnips, carrots, beets, and artichokes. Other vegetables may be eaten in moderation if cooked in ghee or olive oil, including peas, broccoli, cauliflower, zucchini, tomatoes, potatoes, leafy green vegetables, eggplant, orange and yellow peppers, mushrooms, and celery. Vatas should avoid or reduce cabbage, sprouts, and raw vegetables. Ayurveda considers inadequately digested foods to be at least as responsible for disease as eating the wrong foods, and raw vegetables are difficult to digest, especially for Vata types whose digestion can often be weak. In addition, the nutrients of the food are obtained much more readily from cooked rather than raw foods.

2. Best spices: cardamom, cumin, ginger, cinnamon, salt, clove, basil, cilantro, fennel, nutmeg, oregano, sage, tarragon, thyme, and a moderate amount of black pepper (also allspice, anise, asafetida, bay leaf, caraway, juniper berries, licorice root, mace, marjoram, and mustard). Avoid onions and hot spices (cayenne, salsa, and chilies). You can obtain a Vata spice mixture (spices to reduce Vata) from mapi.com. It is called Vata Churna. Sprinkle it over your foods or cook with it in ghee or olive oil.

213

3. Any dairy product is highly recommended. Milk is easier for Vata types to digest when brought to a boil first. The warmth will also help to balance their Vata.

4. Grains: favor rice (best is basmati, Texmati, and jasmine), couscous, bulgur wheat, quinoa, and oats (cooked, not dry), and pasta. And reduce consumption of corn (fresh cooked corn on the cob in season, however, is good), millet, barley, buckwheat and rye.

5. Favor sweet, well-ripened fruits such as sweet grapes, apricots, plums, berries, melons, papaya, peaches, cherries, nectarines, and bananas. Also good are dates, figs, pineapple, mangoes, and avocado. Avoid or better to eliminate bananas and raw apples and pears. If you or a child has digestive problems, fruits are best eaten lightly cooked, stewed, or sautéed or you can soften fruits like raisins, figs, prunes, and dried pineapple by soaking in water for several hours before eating.

6. Generally, all oils are good in moderation.

7. All sweeteners are acceptable but avoid too much sugar. Best to use date sugar, rock sugar, and whole cane sugar in small quantities.

8. Nuts and seeds are fine, especially almonds. Vata types don't have strong digestion and are usually very sensitive to gas-producing foods such as beans. Large beans such as chickpeas, black beans and pinto beans should be avoided. Mung bean soup (split or whole) and red, green, or brown lentils are good and tofu, tempeh, and other soy products in small amounts are fine.

9. For non-vegetarians, favor fresh, organic chicken, turkey, fish, and eggs. Reduce or eliminate the consumption of red meat.

Most Ideal Foods for Pitta Types

Pitta types (the fire and water elements dominating) have strong digestion and are fiery types, and the general guideline is that they should favor foods with a predominantly sweet, bitter and astringent taste. They should avoid or reduce foods with a sour, salty, and pungent taste. The foods to favor and reduce to balance Pitta constitutions are:

Favor	Reduce
Sweet (e.g., wheat, milk, rice)	Spicy
Bitter (leafy greens)	Salty
Astringent (beans)	Sour (cheese, tomatos, yogurt, citrus)

Special Pitta Guidelines. Pitta types need to especially be careful to eat their meals on time, to not skip or unduly delay meals, and to not eat too small a quantity. If they are going to have a difficult meeting or conversation, since their fiery nature creates a tendency to anger, they should eat something before the meeting, especially something sweet. As an experiment, if you or a child is having a bout of anger, eat something sweet and see how quickly it works to reduce the anger or irritability. Because of the fiery nature of Pitta, also drink a good amount of uncarbonated water every day, preferably at room temperature, and especially favor sweet fruits such as melons, pears, grapes, and apples. Avoid stimulants like alcohol and caffeine, which will stimulate the fiery nature. Drink Pitta Tea, containing Pitta reducing spices, which is available at mapi.com.

Detailed Foods and Spices for Pitta Types

1. The vegetables to favor include: all cooked leafy greens except spinach, which should be avoided. Also favor asparagus, potatoes, sweet potatoes, leafy greens, broccoli, cauliflower, celery, okra, lettuce, green beans, peas, and zucchini and other squashes. Also good are brussels sprouts, cabbage, peas, lettuce, cucumber, mushrooms, sprouts, and sweet peppers and sweet corn. Avoid or reduce tomatoes, hot peppers, onions, garlic, and hot radishes.

2. All sweeteners may be taken in moderation, except for molasses and honey, which should be greatly reduced since these are also heating to the physiology. Use date sugar, rock sugar, or whole cane sugar.

3. Dairy is helpful in balancing the heat of Pitta. Favor milk (best if boiled, then allowed to cool down) or lassi (an Indian drink with one part yogurt and three parts water, to which can be added a little sugar and a few drops of rose water), butter, ghee, and ice cream in the warmer months. Since sour tasting foods can increase Pitta, sour or fermented products such as yogurt (except lassi), sour cream, and cheese should be eaten sparingly.

4. Grains such as wheat, rice, barley, and oats are good. Reduce consumption of corn, rye, millet, and brown rice.

5. Sweet and ripe fruits like apples, grapes, melons, cherries, coconuts, avocados, mangoes, pineapples, figs, oranges, and plums are recommended. Pomegranate is also helpful to reduce Pitta dosha. Prunes, raisins, and figs are fine. Reduce or eliminate sour fruits such as grapefruit, cranberries, lemons, and persimmons.

6. Pitta types need seasonings that are soothing and cooling. These include coriander, cilantro, cardamom, saffron, and fennel. Also, turmeric, dill, fennel, and mint are fine. Black pepper

and ginger in moderation, while spicy, do not aggravate Pitta dosha. Spices such as fenugreek, clove, salt, and mustard seed may be used sparingly. Completely avoid pungent hot spices such as chili peppers, and cayenne. You can obtain a Pitta spice mixture (spices to reduce Pitta) from mapi.com. It is called Pitta Churna. Sprinkle it over your foods or cook with it in ghee or olive oil.

7. Most nuts increase Pitta. Pumpkin seeds and sunflower seeds are okay.

8. Favor olive oil, ghee, and sunflower oils. Avoid or reduce almond, corn, safflower, and sesame oils.

9. Favor mung beans and chickpeas. Tofu and other soy products are okay.

10. For non-vegetarians, free range chicken and turkey are preferable. Red meat and seafood increase Pitta and should be avoided.

Most Ideal Foods for Kapha Types

The general guideline is that Kapha types are heavy and tend toward sluggishness and disorders like obesity and congestion, so dry, light and warm foods are best for Kaphas. They should favor foods with bitter, pungent and astringent taste, and reduce sweet, salty, and sour.

Favor	Reduce
Light	Heavy
Dry	Oily
Warm	Cold
Spicy	Sweet (sugar, wheat)
Bitter (leafy greens)	Salty
Astringent (beans)	Sour (cheese, yogurt, sour fruits)

Special Kapha Guidelines. Kaphas tend to put on excess weight and to be sluggish so they, especially, should eat their main meal at midday, and eat lightly in the evening by about 7 PM (see the daily coherence routine in Chapter 17). They need to favor a vegetarian diet with lots of cooked vegetables and lentils, and grains like barley, rye and millet. It is best if they can avoid red meat and refined sweets (candy and cookies) and have fewer dairy products. Sipping hot water from a thermos throughout the day can work wonders and help in reducing weight, along with lots of exercise. If convenient, add a little fresh ginger root and a leaf of basil to the hot water.

Detailed Foods and Spices for Kapha Types

1. In general, all vegetables are recommended, including asparagus, beets, broccoli, brussels sprouts, cabbage, carrots, cauliflower, celery, eggplant, leafy greens, lettuce, mushrooms, okra, onions, peas, peppers, potatoes, spinach, and sprouts, but reduce consumption of sweet potatoes, tomatoes, cucumbers, and zucchini. Best are cooked leafy greens.

2. Dairy. Favor skim milk. In general, reduce dairy intake, which tends to increase Kapha. You can, however, add small amounts of ghee, whole milk, and eggs to the menu.

3. Raw, unheated, organic honey is the only sweetener that helps balance Kapha. Avoid all other sweeteners.

4. Favor grains such as rye, barley, corn, millet, and buckwheat. Reduce intake of oats, rice, and wheat.

5. Beans of all types are good for Kaphas except soybeans, tofu products, and kidney beans.

6. Fruits such as apples, apricots, cranberries, pears, and pomegranates are good. Avoid or reduce fruits like avocados, bananas, pineapples, oranges, peaches, coconuts, melons, dates, figs, grapefruits, grapes, mangoes, papayas, plums, and pineapples.

7. All spices except salt are good for Kapha. Pungent spices like ginger, pepper, and mustard seed are fine, but reduce salt.

8. Except for pumpkin seeds and sunflower seeds, reduce the intake of all nuts and seeds.

9. Use small amounts of extra virgin olive oil, ghee, almond oil, corn oil, sunflower oil, or safflower oil.

10. For non-vegetarians, favor fresh, organic free-range chicken and turkey. Limit or eliminate the consumption of red meat and seafood in general.

Combination Types

If you are a combination of types, chose the diet of your dominant body type, but if you have a disorder that is characteristic of another body type, that will generally indicate that this type is likely out of balance; then try the diet that counteracts what is out of balance. If you aren't sure and must choose, just favor the foods that make you feel better. Ideally, you can obtain a consultation with a trained doctor or consultant in Maharishi AyurVeda, who can best identify which dosha is out of balance and should be addressed to treat your disorder. A website to locate Maharishi AyurVeda doctors and consultants is in Appendix C.

Food Purchasing and Preparation

- Eat fresh food and avoid leftovers, including leftovers from the refrigerator.
- Cook foods more slowly on lower heat.
- Eat a wide variety of foods.
- Avoid processed and frozen foods.
- Eat organic foods when possible.
- Avoid unripe fruits.

A Few Special Rules About Certain Foods

Milk, Cheese, Yogurt, and Ice Cream

According to Ayurveda, milk has valuable properties not found in any other food and, when properly digested, it nourishes all the tissues, and balances Vata, Pitta, and Kapha (less milk for Kapha types). It is considered by Ayurveda to be one of the best foods throughout life for growth, strength, settling the mind, and longevity. However, there are some special rules about milk because when it is taken cold or combined with the wrong foods, it becomes indigestible and can cause the buildup of toxins in the body. Also, in modern times, many people are lactose intolerant, especially at an older age. What this means is that while they can digest the proteins and fats in milk, they may not be able to digest the sugar content. This is because they no longer produce the enzyme lactase, which enables milk sugar to be broken down sufficiently so it can be digested by the small intestines.

Milk's first rule is that it should only be taken either alone or with *sweet foods*. In particular, do not take milk with seafood. Sweet foods that are considered fine with milk in Ayurveda are not just sugary foods but certain other nourishing foods such as all whole grains; many nuts such as unsalted almonds, cashews, macadamia nuts, pecans, and sesame and sunflower seeds; sweet fruits including raisins, dates, and figs; vegetables such as yams and beets; and toast, butter, ghee, cream, jams, sugar, and honey. Wait at least twenty minutes before having milk if you have just eaten foods with the other five tastes (that is, foods that are not considered sweet). Today, well-intentioned mothers make sure their children have milk with most of their meals, and when the child has a school lunch, whatever else is being served, the school will usually provide a small carton of cold milk. It would be better to follow milk's first rule, above.

The second rule is that cold milk is especially hard to digest, and it has a heavy clogging quality. However, most of the difficulties people have with digesting milk can be overcome by first boiling the milk to where the milk starts to foam, and then reducing the heat to a slow boil for five to ten minutes. Then let it cool to a comfortable drinking temperature (warm milk is also most soothing to the mind and body). If boiling the milk does not make it more digestible, you can try adding a pinch or two of turmeric, dry ginger, or cinnamon, and you can add a little sugar to aid digestion and offset the taste of the turmeric or ginger.

A suggestion from Maharishi AyurVeda Products International is that if you have not been a milk drinker for a while, start again gradually to help your body adjust. Start with drinking 1/8 of a cup each day of boiled milk with ginger. Then gradually increase the amount to about a cup a day over a ten-day period.

Whole, organic, cow's milk is considered best, but if there are cholesterol problems and for Kapha types, 2 percent or skim milk can be substituted and raw goat's milk is also okay, but still boil it as indicated above.

Yogurt can also be clogging to the system so should not be eaten in the evening. It is best when eaten within 24 hours of making it fresh. Lassi, a yogurt Indian drink, is an exception, and fresh lassi can be had at lunch or in the evening. Recipes for regular lassi and for those that aid digestion can be found at mapi.com/ayurvedic-recipes/beverages/lassi.html. Store-bought yogurt should be avoided or eaten sparingly.

Ice cream is harmful to the digestive fire so is best not eaten with meals. It is Kapha aggravating so to reduce the Kapha effects, you can sip some hot water after consuming ice cream.

Cheese is also clogging to the system and should only be eaten at lunch and eaten in moderation or avoided by Pitta types, especially in the summer.

Honey

The honey you purchase should be raw, unheated honey. If the processing of the honey has involved heating it, the honey will have changed and, according to Ayurveda, will produce what is known as *ama*, which is the toxic end-product of poorly digested food. For the same reason, don't cook with honey, or put honey directly into hot milk or tea. Instead, wait until the drink is just warm.

Ghee

Ghee, or clarified butter, is good in appropriate and small quantities with meals because it increases the digestive fire without aggravating Pitta. Unlike butter it does not need to be refrigerated if it will be used within about six months and does not burn as quickly as butter. It is considered one of the best foods in Ayurveda to balance the physiology for Pitta and Vata types. Kapha types need to avoid too much oil of any kind, but of all the oils for Kapha types, ghee is best. **Note that ghee and honey should not be taken together if they are in the same proportions (in the same proportions they are toxic).** Ghee in small amounts can be used during cooking by sautéing ghee with your spices at the bottom of a pan, and then adding your vegetables. You can also just put a teaspoon over your food after it is cooked, which will improve your digestion.

Ghee is sold in many health food stores. To make ghee, place a pound of unsalted butter in a pot over low heat. When it has melted, increase the heat to medium, skimming off the foam as it appears. When it starts to boil, then lower the heat again for ten minutes. The ghee is finished when the moisture has cooked away and the solids at the bottom have turned golden brown. There should be no burning, however. Then remove the ghee, filter through unbleached cheesecloth to remove all solids, and store in a glass container, either in the refrigerator or at room temperature. The ghee will be fine for about six months at room temperature and is fine indefinitely in the refrigerator.

Oils

When cooking in oil, cook slowly in low heat since high heat changes the chemistry of the oil and is clogging to the physiology. For cooking or internal use in balancing Vata, favor ghee and olive and sesame oils, then sunflower, canola, and safflower oils; for balancing Pitta favor ghee, sunflower, olive, and canola oils; and for balancing Kapha favor (in small quantities) corn, canola, and sunflower oils.

Vegetables

Vegetables can be sautéed, roasted, steamed, or grilled. Have a priority of eating plenty of cooked, leafy green vegetables. Root vegetables like potatoes, beets, parsnips, turnips, rutabagas, carrots, onions, and garlic are heavier and more difficult to digest and more clogging to the system, so eat less of these.

Sauté your desired spices in olive oil or ghee (olive oil if there are cholesterol issues) and then add the vegetables to the pan. Turmeric is best added toward the end of cooking. All vegetables can be sautéed. You can also sauté for just a minute or two and then add water and boil until the vegetables are cooked.

Roast vegetables by placing sizeable chunks that can cook in their own water in a pan and cover and bake (this is for all squashes, fennel, and root vegetables).

Grill by first stirring vegetables into a mixture of oil and spices and then grill until cooked.

Steamed vegetables are actually less desirable than other methods of cooking as the excess water dilutes the taste and potency of the vegetables. Sautéed spices should be added to the steamed vegetables after cooking or remove the vegetables from the steamer before they are finished and sauté for a few minutes.

Grains

Grains help build bone tissue and muscle and give bodily strength and are particularly important for growing children. Grains are important to vegetarians because they help in creating whole proteins when combined with legumes, beans, or milk products.

Wheat products are the best grains for balancing Vata. If you have a Kapha imbalance you should reduce but not totally avoid wheat. Too much wheat can cause weight gain and increase the amount of mucus in the body if you have a cold or allergies.

Barley products are the best grain for balancing Kapha and are good for Pitta as well. Barley is relatively lighter to digest, and it does not produce excess mucus in the body.

Basmati rice balances all three doshas and is the best grain for balancing Pitta. It is cooling and a little heavy, so it is not recommended to eat every day. Brown rice is more heating and dry, and is better for Kapha and less optimal for Pitta and Vata.

Quinoa is a seed that provides an excellent source of protein. Quinoa is good for all the doshas. If you are trying to balance Vata, you can eat it with a little olive oil or ghee.

Oats are aggravating for Kapha; however, dry baked oats in granola are fine.

Corn is both dry and heating and should be avoided if you are trying to balance Vata or Pitta. It is good for Kapha.

Fruit

Fresh, juicy fruits such as pears, melons, grapes, plums, and cooked apples are excellent. They are especially good for Pitta types. A cooked apple with raisins and spices like cinnamon, nutmeg, and a few cloves is part of an excellent Ayurvedic breakfast. Dried fruits should be soaked, especially by Vata types, except dates, which are fine without soaking. Bananas are hard to digest so limit your intake.

Dahls (sometimes spelled dal)

Dahls provide an astringent taste, which is part of what is necessary for proper nutrition. Eat a variety of dahls, which can be purchased at Indian groceries and health food stores. Mung bean dahl is ideal for overall balance. Split rather than whole mung bean dahl is easier to digest and cooks more quickly, but whole dahl is more nutritious. Cook the dahl by boiling or pressure cooking until lentils are soft. You can add spices to the water as it is cooking or sauté spices in oil and add them to the dahl at the end of the cooking.

Nuts and Seeds

Nuts and seeds are important to help vegetarians get a balanced diet. Soak almonds and cashews in water overnight or at least for a few hours in the morning before eating, which reduces the Pitta aggravating factor and aids in digestion.

Tofu

Tofu is heavy and can be difficult to digest. So, use spices when cooking tofu and cook it for a longer period.

Salad

A small salad on the side can stimulate the digestive process but cooked foods are considered best in Ayurveda. A particularly good salad is grated carrots, beets, and fresh ginger root with, if available, a little basil. Add fresh lemon juice, salt and black pepper. If you have a Vata imbalance or weak digestion have only two tablespoonfuls of salad chewed well.

Spices and Herbs

Spices and herbs can have a particularly powerful effect in creating coherence if you are using the right spices for your body type, but they can lead to disorders if you are using the wrong spices or herbs. In the mid-1980s after the authors and others

225

formed Maharishi AyurVeda Company of America, one of its initial tasks was to work with the expert Indian Ayurvedic physicians (*Vaidyas*) to create Maharishi AyurVeda Vata, Pitta, and Kapha teas as well as spice mixtures called *churnas* that could help balance the different body types. The churnas can be just sprinkled on the foods, or even better, heat a quarter of a teaspoon of the churna in olive oil or ghee and then pour it on the food. The Maharishi AyurVeda spices have a powerful effect so not much should be used. The teas are to be brewed in hot water or hot milk and have the same balancing effect. These spice mixtures and the body type teas can be obtained at mapi.com. Search for Vata Tea or Churna, Pitta Tea or Churna, or Kapha Tea or Churna.

Herbs Recommended for each Type

Vata Balancing Herbs

Valerian   Gotu Kola   Brahmi   Ashwagandha

Maharishi AyurVeda supplements for Vata are *Stress Free Mind*® and *Worry Free*®. There are also *Worry Free* teas that may help those prone to worry. These are combinations of herbs, which Maharishi AyurVeda understands to have a synergistic effect where the herb combinations, when taken together, have an effect that is greater than the sum of the parts. All supplements are available at mapi.com.

Pitta Balancing Herbs

Holy Basil (Tulsi)   Shankapushpi   Arjuna

One Maharishi AyurVeda supplement for reducing Pitta is *Stress Free Emotions*®.

Kapha Balancing Herbs

Ginger   Black pepper   Mustard seed
Coriander   Cumin   Turmeric

The supplement *Blissful Joy*® should be helpful for reducing Kapha.

Chapter 14

Best Foods and Spices for the Immune System

D uring the initial months when the coronavirus first hit the U.S., it devastated Black communities, killing African Americans at a disproportionately high rate. As this book was being finalized in August 2020, Hispanics and Native Americans made up an increasing proportion of Covid-19 deaths.[1] And many experts are pointing to the poor diets among these minority groups that makes them especially susceptible to contagious viruses and other illnesses.[2] In New Mexico, for example, Native Americans make up 9 percent of the population but account for 75% of the Covid-19 deaths,[3] and their diets have for several years now been known to be problematic. An NIH research report from 2016[4] tells us that Native Americans, like other segments of the population, are eating unhealthy foods like canned meats and fast-food meals, but the challenges for Native Americans are especially daunting. The isolated nature of many Native American communities makes access to fresh food difficult because of the long distances to get to modern groceries. As a result, it is not unusual to see rural groceries in Native American communities with large window signs announcing that "fresh food has arrived."[4] The immune system plays an obvious role in who gets sick on a frequent basis, and who quickly recovers and who doesn't, and our eating habits play a big role in the strength of our immune system.

It is well known that we need a steady source of nutrients for our immune system to function properly, and both Western medicine and Ayurveda identify certain foods, spices, and vitamins that are especially important for immunity. Ayurveda also emphasizes the importance of good digestion and periodic detoxification (which are discussed in the next chapter). In addition, both Western medicine and Ayurveda have tests to determine our immunity levels. Tests used in Western medicine can diagnose immune disorders, including blood tests to determine levels of infection-fighting proteins (immunoglobulin) and the level of blood and immune system cells. In Ayurveda, the diagnostic procedure known as pulse diagnosis (Chapter 16) can determine a person's immunity by evaluating the level of what is called *ojas*. Ojas is often equated with immunity, and it is sometimes said that all of Ayurveda is for the purpose of maximizing the amount of ojas in the body, and therefore the strength of the immune system.

Ojas

In Ayurveda, ojas is the most refined byproduct of the physiology resulting from eating the right foods, good digestion, the elimination of toxins in the body, and, in general, the coherent functioning of the mind and body. Ojas is the end-product of perfect digestion and metabolism. It is said to sustain and nourish all the cells and tissues in the body. It is the link between consciousness and matter. It is often said that the main factor in enhancing ojas is raising one's consciousness by becoming more coherent and blissful, more "awake" inside, and the right foods and good digestion are an important part of the formula. Ayurveda says ojas protects cell health, giving each cell the ability to perform its proper functions without being altered by the stresses and strains of daily life. In Ayurveda, the physical body is considered the manifestation of consciousness, and ojas is considered not quite consciousness, but closely connected.

Strong ojas is reflected in a radiance or glow in the person's complexion and eyes (radiant health), as well as physical strength, the absence of significant aches or pains, sharp sense organs, mental clarity, creativity, and a profound sense of well-being. Low ojas is typically evidenced by dry skin, weak sense organs resulting in excessive sensitivity to sound and light, significant muscle or joint pain, frequent infections, illness, drowsiness or fatigue, mental confusion or a poor ability to concentrate, a consistently negative attitude, and anxiety or depression.

Best Foods for Ojas

Fresh organic foods that are easy to digest are good for building ojas, and the fresher the better. Ayurveda lists these foods and especially the first six (shown in bold letters) as best for building ojas:

Ghee	Bananas
Milk	Dates
Almonds	Figs
Rice	Sweet, juicy fruits generally
Raw (unheated) honey	Leafy greens
Oranges	Zucchini
Avocados	Nuts in addition to almonds

Several Maharishi AyurVeda products are powerful antioxidants and up to 1,000 times more powerful than vitamin C in fighting free radicals. They would also be good for building ojas. They are *Amrit Kalash Ambrosia* and *Amrit Nectar and Paste*, and there will be others on the mapi.com website.

Spices to Favor for Immune Strength

The following spices can be used in cooking or sprinkled on your food. Your Ayurvedic doctor can tell you more ways to use these spices:

Turmeric. Turmeric is considered a strong anti-inflammatory and possibly an antioxidant. It supports liver functioning and is said in Ayurveda to help keep the blood less fertile for pathogens.

Ginger. Ginger has a strong anti-inflammatory and antioxidant effect.

Cinnamon. Cinnamon supports sugar metabolism so that sugar does not turn into ama (partially digested food), making the body more acidic. An overly acidic state is a breeding ground for bacterial and viral infections.

Cloves. Clove in a powder form can be purchased in most good groceries or use whole cloves. It is said in Ayurveda to help the body get rid of ama and amavisha, which are toxins in Ayurveda as explained later in this chapter.

Tulsi. Tulsi tea can be taken at any time during the day. It is good in the morning to start the day and some people find it can help you get a good night's sleep if taken before bed. It is said to help in relieving symptoms of asthma, bronchitis, colds, congestion, and coughs, and may help regulate blood sugar and help with flu and stomach disorders.

Western Understandings of What to Favor for Immune Strength

As you can see from the following list, in several important respects Western medicine agrees with Ayurveda on what to eat for immunity.

1. **Vitamin C.** Vitamin C increases antibodies and is believed to increase the production of white blood cells and is considered important for immune strength and fighting free radicals. Foods rich in vitamin C are oranges, grapefruit, strawberries, brussels sprouts, red and green peppers, broccoli, cabbage, and cauliflower.

2. **Vitamin D.** Research has shown that vitamin D may kill viruses and bacteria, may increase white blood cells and help protect against respiratory infections. Foods rich in vitamin D are tofu and mushrooms, and for non-vegetarians, egg yolks, and fatty fish like salmon, sardines, tuna and mackerel. Milk, yogurt, cheese products, and orange juice are often fortified with some vitamin D (check the label).

3. **Beta carotene and Vitamin A.** Vitamin A is important to immune health, helping antibodies fight germs, but too much vitamin A is toxic, and there can be a buildup if you take excessive vitamin A supplements. Beta carotene is an antioxidant that is found in many fresh fruits and vegetables, and while it is not considered an essential nutrient, it is converted into vitamin A. The advantage of dietary beta carotene over lots of vitamin A is that the body only converts as much beta carotene as it needs. Foods rich in beta carotene are dark leafy vegetables such as kale, spinach and chard, carrots, peas, squash, broccoli, sweet potatoes, mangoes, apricots, and cantaloupe.

4. **Zinc.** There are studies showing that the mineral zinc helps keep the immune system strong. Getting enough zinc in a diet is normally not an issue except in developing countries where the soil is poor. Sources for zinc include nuts, seeds, beans, chickpeas, lentils, and wheat germ, and for non-vegetarians, beef, pork chops, dark meat poultry, and dairy foods including milk, cheese and yogurt.

5. **Protein.** Protein is important to maintain the immune system, including helping the body fight viral and bacterial infections. Antibodies and immune system cells rely on protein, but what we want is a "complete protein," which is not always available in single plant-based foods. The body itself makes some of the necessary amino acids in protein, but we need food to give us the remaining amino acids. When food gives us all the remaining amino acids, it is considered a complete protein. Meat, poultry, seafood, eggs, and dairy provide complete proteins. Plant-based sources of complete protein include soybeans (tofu), quinoa, and buckwheat, but not all of these will contain as much protein as the animal-based proteins. You can, however, combine incomplete proteins to have a complete protein in a meal. Good combinations include beans and rice (rice and dahls, for example), beans with nuts or seeds, or whole grains with nuts or seeds (nut butter on whole grain bread). Note that brown bread and multi-grain bread are not necessarily whole grains. Other good sources of whole grains besides whole grain breads are rye, quinoa, faro, brown rice, oatmeal, amaranth, and bulgur, and it's good to vary your grains because they have different amounts of fiber, carbohydrates, and protein.

6. **Prebiotics and Probiotics.** Prebiotics are a type of fiber that is food for probiotics. Probiotics are good, live bacteria and yeasts that aid your digestive system and boost the health of the microbiome (the bacteria, fungi, and viruses) that live inside and on the surface of the body and support our immune system. Sources include yogurt, kefir, whole grains, bananas, asparagus, artichokes, leeks, and beans.

Foods to Reduce or Omit Especially in Times of Greater Vulnerability

The following foods are said to compromise your immune system so you may want to be especially careful with these foods during flu season or other times of heightened vulnerability:

- *Soda* and other foods and drinks high in sugar or high-fructose corn syrup.
- *Processed foods* (much food is processed, but we mean chemically processed foods with additives, preservatives, artificial colors, flavorings and the like). Processed foods and refined carbohydrates (usually found in processed foods) can lead to rapid spikes in blood sugar and insulin levels.
- *Alcoholic beverages* in excess
- *Recreational drugs*
- *Tobacco*
- *Junk food* in general
- *Heavy foods* including red meat

According to Dr. Nader, we should eat lighter in times of vulnerability, and certainly don't eat or snack all the time.

Factors that Diminish Ojas

- Negative emotions
- Stress
- Excessive exercise
- Excessive fasting
- Overexposure to wind or sun
- Staying awake through the night

Bottom Line Advice

Food. As can be seen, it can be complicated to try to boost the immune system through the right foods although it is a proven way to do it. Ayurveda recommends that you have a good variety of foods (all six tastes every day and ideally at most meals), favoring those considered to be especially good for building ojas, and avoid diets that emphasize one or just a few foods or groups of foods at the expense of variety. You can see your doctor for tests to determine if you have any vitamin or mineral deficiencies, and a search of the Internet will yield much advice in this area. But check each food recommended with those recommended in this chapter based on your body type or current disorder. Ayurveda recommends that your vegetables be cooked for easier digestion, so as the authors we don't recommend raw vegetables in an effort to gain more nutrients. Vitamin supplements may help, but it is better to get your vitamins from a variety of foods.

Rest, Exercise and Stay Hydrated. Follow a good daily routine (see Chapter 17 for the daily coherence routine). Go to bed early (before 10 PM is good) and get plenty of rest as well as exercise. Dr. Nader emphasizes not sitting in one place too long. We should get good amounts of exercise and raise the heart rate periodically. Our white blood cells are important tools for the immune system to fight germs. They target bad bacteria and viruses. Good circulation and hydration will allow our white blood cells to be transported around the body as needed. Boosting white blood cells is important, but it takes time to eat right, meditate, and so on, and you need your current level of white blood cells to do the maximum, especially in difficult times. Efficient circulation also helps remove waste from the body. Drinking enough water helps your body naturally eliminate toxins and other bacteria that may cause illness. Six to eight eight-ounce glasses per day is generally recommended, and four to eight ounces every fifteen minutes if you're involved in strenuous exercise.

Chapter 15

The Importance of Good Digestion and Detoxification

According to Ayurveda, an important consideration for our health and for determining our diet is the strength of our digestion. Each body type has a different strength of digestion. In addition, whatever one's type, digestion is influenced by factors such as climate and age, and depends on the level of what is known in Ayurveda as *agni*, the digestive fire. In Western medicine, agni might be considered the combination of the various digestive enzymes that are produced in the stomach, small intestines, and pancreas.

Weak agni leads to improperly digested food, and the by-product of undigested food is a substance which Ayurveda calls *ama*. The accumulation of ama aggravates the doshas and leads to all types of disorders.

New Understandings About Digestion

The concept of disease caused by undigested food products is particularly interesting in light of the recent research on the microbiome,[1] which is defined as all the microorganisms in and on the body. The body is actually host to more bacterial cells than human cells. Most of the microorganisms are the bacteria in our gut, which are strongly influenced by what we eat and how we digest our food. New studies have suggested that the composition of these gut bacteria have a major impact on our physical and mental health. What is particularly interesting is that many of the Ayurveda treatment programs, including diet, and digestive and detox treatments, have a direct impact on the health of these gut bacteria.

Improper digestion and a disruption of the microbiome in Western science would in Ayurveda be the equivalent of the accumulation of ama. The result would be problems throughout the body, such as a disturbance of the proper functioning of our immune system. Ayurveda speaks of *ojas* as the finest product of digestion. If the digestion is not effective it interferes with the production of ojas and disturbs the formation of all the basic tissues in the body, resulting in disease.

More research is necessary to identify the biochemical nature of ama and ojas, but what is remarkable is that these ancient concepts can now begin to be understood in modern scientific terms (for example, the microbiome and our digestive enzymes). Even without modern language and understandings, thousands of years ago Ayurveda understood the intimate connection between the digestive system and other key systems in the body, and precisely how the health of our body depends on the foods we eat and how we digest them.

Digestive Guidelines

Following are Ayurvedic guidelines for improving digestion and reducing ama:

1. Eat at approximately the same time every day so your *digestive power* can be conditioned to "fire up" for the meal.

2. Eat your main meal at noon when digestion is at its peak; eat lighter meals at breakfast and dinner.

3. Eat while sitting down in a settled atmosphere; pay attention to the food when you eat (avoid TV, phone calls, and reading).

4. Ideally engage in pleasant conversation with friends or family; avoid serious business meetings or emotional discussions, and eating in silence is fine.

5. Eat only when the previous meal has been digested. You know this by feeling hunger and sense of lightness in the stomach.

6. Sit quietly for a minute at the beginning of the meal (saying grace before meals is one way to do this) and wait for a few minutes after eating before leaving the table. This gives your digestion a settled start.

7. Eat to only to 3/4 of your capacity. Don't feel stuffed.

An herbal supplement such as *Triphala*, a popular Indian herb, can help digestion and elimination and assists the body in absorbing nutrients. It is useful for supporting the digestion of all other herbal remedies and for the natural relief of occasional constipation. It is usually taken before bed.

Body Detoxification

No matter how vigilant we are in eating the right foods and in trying to follow the guidelines for good digestion, the vagaries of modern life will result in eating foods that are not balancing or that are not fully digested on many occasions. It is just the nature of life in the modern world. And following less than ideal routines will often cause a periodic buildup of toxins in the physiology. As a result, Maharishi AyurVeda recommends a detoxification program for internal cleansing three or four times a year. The purpose is to eliminate toxins that may have built up over the previous three or four-month period. Detoxification is particularly recommended each spring. This is a time of renewal in the environment and our circadian rhythms are also ripe for renewal at this time.

There are basically two main categories of detoxification or internal cleansing, one which can be self-performed at home, and one which is performed by trained technicians in a clinic under the supervision of a doctor or Ayurvedic expert. Supervised detoxification in a clinic is classically known in Ayurveda as *Panchakarma*. It is available in the U.S. at the Panchakarma clinic at Maharishi International University or The Raj Ayurvedic Health Center (the Raj. com), both of which are in Fairfield, Iowa. Panchakarma is also available in other countries at Maharishi AyurVeda facilities. Panchakarma can have remarkable effects even for those with serious disorders; the research and some individual benefits are described in the next chapter.

The Maharishi AyurVedic home self-cleansing routine is for individuals who have only mild to moderate levels of toxins and imbalances in the physiology, which can be determined from the tests below. The self-cleansing routine and the questionnaires were obtained with permission from the website of Maharishi AyurVeda Products International, Inc. (MAPI), found at mapi.com, and the herbs involved can be obtained from that site. The MAPI program has three phases to it: a preparation phase, actual cleansing, and a post-cleansing phase. The more you can follow the guidelines, the better your cleanse will be. However, first take the tests below to see if you qualify for the at home seasonal cleanses or should have the supervised Panchakarma cleanse. The Panchakarma cleanse (Chapter 16) can be done by anyone and is a more thorough cleanse than the home cleanse.

The tests to determine whether you can do an at home cleanse are for the purpose of discovering how much you have of the three different kinds of toxins that can impact the body according to Ayurveda. However, we recommend that you consult your own physician, describe the home detoxification program, and get advice on whether it is right for you. Especially, if you have any serious, acute or chronic health concerns, before beginning any detoxification program, please consult a trained health professional who can fully assess your needs and address them effectively.

The Three Toxins in Ayurveda

Ama

As mentioned, the most common type of toxin is the waste product of undigested foods, known as ama. It is described in the ancient texts as physically sticky, foul smelling, and white. Ama is usually caused by eating before the previous meal is digested; by going to sleep on a full stomach; by eating foods that are wrong for your body type; by eating too much or too little; or by eating foods that are left over, processed, old, or fermented. Ama clogs circulatory channels and organs like the digestive tract, the branches of the trachea leading to the lungs, the arteries, liver, and kidneys. It can be especially dangerous when it clogs the arteries (atherosclerosis). If ama continues to be produced over a long period of time, it can leave the digestive tract and travel to a weak area elsewhere in the body. It will settle there and disrupt the flow of nutrients to that area, as well as the body's natural waste removal systems.

If the undigested food leaks through the gut wall (leaky gut) into the bloodstream, it can result in many disorders. In the field of alternative health this condition is referred to as Leaky Gut Syndrome, and it is associated with celiac disease. When undigested food and bacteria particles leak into the bloodstream, the result can be a severe immune response. A range of disorders have been attributed to undigested food leaking out of the digestive tract, including gas, bloating, cramps, nausea, indigestion, heartburn, food sensitivity, and autoimmune disease.

According to Ayurveda, ama develops when our digestive fire is either weak or irregular. By enhancing the digestive fire through dietary changes or by taking Ayurvedic herbal supplements, the digestive system itself can often digest simple ama and clear it from the body.

Amavisha

A more problematic form of undigested food occurs when ama settles in one part of the body for a long time. This form of ama is known as amavisha (literally poisonous ama). This a more toxic type of ama and must be dealt with differently during detoxification.

Garvisha

Garvisha in Ayurveda is the third type of toxin, and unlike the other two, garvisha comes from outside the body. Included are environmental toxins such as chemicals, preservatives, poisons, air and water pollution, synthetic clothing, chemicals in clothing, synthetic drugs, chemicals in household cleansers, and heavy metals such as lead, arsenic and asbestos. Garvisha also includes toxins from spoiled foods.

How Serious are My Symptoms?

Test for Ama[2]

Circle your response (1 = least; 5 = most)

1. I get colds (or similar conditions) several times each year.

    [1]   [2]   [3]   [4]   [5]

2. My body tends to have a feeling of heaviness.

    [1]   [2]   [3]   [4]   [5]

3. I just tend to feel that "something isn't working right" in the body (digestion, breathing, bowel movements, or something else).

    [1]   [2]   [3]   [4]   [5]

4. I tend to feel lazy. (My capacity to work seems all right, but I have no inclination.)

    [1]   [2]   [3]   [4]   [5]

5. I commonly have indigestion.

    [1]   [2]   [3]   [4]   [5]

6. I tend to feel blocked in my body (constipated, congested in the head, general lack of clarity, or other).

    [1]   [2]   [3]   [4]   [5]

7. In the morning when I wake up, I'm groggy; it takes me quite a while to feel really awake.

    [1]   [2]   [3]   [4]   [5]

8. I tend to feel weak, physically, for no reason that I can see.

    [1]   [2]   [3]   [4]   [5]

9. I often have to spit.

    [1]   [2]   [3]   [4]   [5]

10. Often, I just don't have a taste for food. I have no appetite.

    [1]   [2]   [3]   [4]   [5]

11. I just tend to feel tired, even exhausted in mind or body.

    [1]   [2]   [3]   [4]   [5]

Add up your scores to arrive at a rating of your level of ama.

• 45-55 Severe • 35-44 Moderate • 25-34 Mild • 11-24 Minimal

If this questionnaire indicates that you have minimal, mild, or moderate amounts of ama, then, with your doctor's okay, you can do an at home, self-detoxification program. If you have severe amounts of ama, then it is best to seek the advice of an expert trained in Maharishi AyurVeda (see Appendix C at back of book) before embarking on any detoxification program. The expert may recommend a self-detoxification program or the Panchakarma program for a more effective cleansing.

Test for Amavisha or Garvisha[3]

Circle your response (1 = least; 5 = most)

1. I often feel nauseous for no particular reason.

   [1]   [2]   [3]   [4]   [5]

2. I often have hyperacidity or a burning sensation in my stomach.

   [1]   [2]   [3]   [4]   [5]

3. My skin often suffers from breakouts.

   [1]   [2]   [3]   [4]   [5]

4. I often feel dryness in the mouth.

   [1]   [2]   [3]   [4]   [5]

5. I sometimes feel pain or weakness in my legs or calves.

   [1]   [2]   [3]   [4]   [5]

6. I have acquired sensitivity and intolerance to new foods, new flowers, new pets or other new things in my environment.

   [1]   [2]   [3]   [4]   [5]

7. I often lack mental and emotional energy.

   [1]   [2]   [3]   [4]   [5]

8. I sometimes feel feverish or have whole-body fatigue in the evening.

   [1]   [2]   [3]   [4]   [5]

Add up your scores to arrive at a rating of your level of amavisha or garvisha.
- 32-40 Severe • 23-31 Moderate • 17-22 Mild • 8-16 Minimal

The above test is a guide for how much amavisha or garvisha is present, but if you have these symptoms to any significant degree, it is recommended that you consult with your physician and see an expert trained in Maharishi AyurVeda, who may recommend an individualized detox program.

The Main Methods of Detoxification

Purification therapies of Maharishi AyurVeda use the body's own natural detoxification systems. This includes the bowel, kidneys, urine, skin, sweat glands, and liver. Detoxification methods should never be harsh or forceful, but simply supportive to enhance the body's own ability to release toxins—a body coherence principle. The Maharishi AyurVeda detoxification programs are balanced to create a situation in which the body's natural detoxification systems become stronger. If the person is at the same time following a more intelligent diet and following the Ayurvedic daily routine (Chapter 17), all of these therapies together support the detoxification systems in the body, so they become increasingly powerful. This holistic approach results in the natural balance of the all the body's detoxification systems.

Of course, a person who uses a Maharishi AyurVeda detoxification program will need to detoxify periodically. Everyone today is exposed to influences that create toxins beyond what the body can naturally handle. Seasonal changes also create *ama*. In winter certain of the body's channels for eliminating toxins compress, making it harder for the body to release toxins. And during the transition between seasons, the *agni* (digestive fire) fluctuates, and that can cause some amount of ama to accumulate even if you are careful about your diet and routine. For this reason, Maharishi AyurVeda recommends that you either self-detox or do Maharishi

Panchakarma during each change of seasons, and particularly in the spring. In the spring the body is naturally detoxifying as the impurities flow out of the body, so that is an ideal time to support this detoxification with an herbal program.

Daily Detoxification

If impurities are located in the bowel as can often be the case, you can follow the recommendations below. You can follow these recommendations whenever you feel toxins building up in this area or are having trouble eliminating.

1. **Empty the bowel every morning.** The body's clock always tries to follow the cycles of nature. During nighttime, our body focuses on lubrication and on cooling. In the morning, when the sun rises, our body goes into an absorption phase when agni, the burning and transforming energy dominates. If, during the day, you carry around the waste material you created at night, you may absorb some of that waste material into your system. The toxins your body is trying to get rid of will then be released into the body and weaken your immune system. If you don't support your body's natural ability to evacuate its waste material, you may feel fatigued, drowsy and irritable during the day.

According to Ayurvedic principles, one should evacuate the bowel every morning, and feel that the colon is clean and light. Feeling energetic and relaxed are signs of proper evacuation. Once or twice daily is normal. Don't ignore your urges and don't wait.

If you do not have a bowel movement every day on a regular basis, you are probably constipated. Constipation can be a result of several diet or lifestyle factors such as lack of enzymes and beneficial bacteria in the gastrointestinal system, not eating enough fiber, dehydration, stress, and ignoring one's natural urges.

• To encourage a bowel movement, drink a glass of warm water after cleansing your mouth and teeth in the morning.

• If the stool is very dry or slow, try adding more ghee to the diet and try the following Maharishi AyurVeda herbal water drink for constipation. Boil two quarts of water and then add 1/4 teaspoon whole fennel, 1/4 teaspoon marshmallow root, and two leaves of mint. Add the spices to the boiled water and let steep for 2-5 minutes. Then place in a thermos and sip it when warm throughout the day.

• Eat foods with more soft fibers such as oatmeal, tender leafy greens, summer squashes, and cooked or soaked prunes and figs. Avoid a Vata-aggravating diet or drying diet, and avoid drying foods such as crackers, dried cereal, raw foods and any foods that are drying for the bowel.

• Take *Herbal Cleanse* or *Triphala Plus* (both on the mapi.com website) or psyllium seed husks (take one teaspoon soaked in one cup of warm water before bed) to scrub out the bowel.

2. **Support the digestive system.** We need friendly bacteria in the gastrointestinal tract. Chemicals and pesticides in food, as well as antibiotics, destroy these probiotics. We therefore need to support their existence.

• One good way to do this is to drink lassi (see special foods section in Chapter 12) with lunch.

• To increase natural, water-soluble fiber in your diet, consume whole grains such as quinoa, and different kinds of squash and fruits. Avoid canned, frozen and "fast" food, and leftovers. If your elimination is still not regular, cook some prunes or figs with apples and eat the mixture in the morning. If that does not bring results, take the supplements referred to above (*Triphala Plus* or *Herbal Cleanse*).

• Emotions can directly influence bowel movement. Diarrhea can be induced by fear, while constipation can result from worry. Bowel movement is not just a physical function. If anything disturbs Vata—for example mental or emotional stress—our elimination will suffer too. The main seat of Vata is in the lower abdomen.

• Don't read while evacuating the bowels.

• Take a walk after dinner to enhance circulation through the channels and improve digestion. Regular exercise also helps.

• Practice the TM technique to relax the mind and body, and to reduce the harmful effects of stress.

Seasonal Detoxification

Based on your test scores for ama, amavisha, and garvisha, if you qualify for seasonal self-detoxification and your doctor approves, below are dosha-specific seasonal detoxifications, which are ideally done at the beginning of each of the four seasons. These are recommended by Dr. Clark and were developed by Vaidya Manohar Palakurthi of the Maharishi International University campus Pancharkarma clinic. *Please note that you should not do the seasonal cleanse when you are ill.*

Guidelines During Cleanse and for a Few Days After the Cleanse

• Drink 3–4 glasses of plain warm-hot water daily on an empty stomach or between meals. This is in addition to any teas or drinks during the day. During meals you may sip hot water.

• Avoid caffeine.

• Eat if you are hungry; do not eat if you are not hungry.

• Eat smaller quantities than usual (2/3 of usual amount). Favor lighter foods and semi-solids, e.g. soups, rice, and split mung dahl.

- Maharishi AyurVeda herbs should not be taken during the cleanse. They should be started (or resumed) one day after the cleanse.

- Prescription medications should be continued throughout the cleanse.

- Foods to avoid:
  —cold drinks, carbonated drinks, and alcoholic beverages
  —red meat
  —oily or heavy foods such as fried foods, cream sauces, and heavy dessert
  —raw vegetables or salads, potatoes, tomatoes, eggplant, bell pepper
  —raw fruits (only cooked apples and pears)
  —hot spices such as chili peppers or jalapeno
  —pizza, bread (made with yeast, sourdough, or baking soda/powder), refined sugar, honey, cookies, chocolate, baked goods.

- Stay warm, go to bed before 10 PM, avoid over-exertion.

Cleanse

Do the same cleanse for all body types except as indicated below. All the herbs are available at mapi.com.

- Unless you are principally a Pitta type or have Pitta disorders (like occasional heartburn, stomach acid, or inflammatory disorders) take two tablets of *Elim-Tox* with water at about 8 AM and again at about 5 PM. If you are a Pitta type or have Pitta disorders, substitute *Elim-Tox-O* for *Elim-Tox*.

- For the Vata cleanse, take two tablets of *Herbal Digest* with water after lunch and dinner; for the Pitta cleanse take two tablets of *Aci-Balance* with water after lunch and dinner; for the Kapha cleanse, take one tablet of *MA 154* with water after lunch and dinner.

247

- For the Vata cleanse, take two tablets of *Triphala Plus* about 1/2 hour before bedtime followed by 1/3 cup of aloe vera juice with 1/3 cup of warm water.

- After seven days of the above, on the evening of the eighth day before bed, drink a mixture of 30 ml of ghee with about 2/3 cup of warm milk.

- Next morning at about 4 AM to 6 AM have one cup of senna tea (one to two bags of tea) followed by two tablets of *Triphala Plus*. Stay around the house that day since you will likely have a number of bowel movements.

Summary

The key to detoxification, and to all of Maharishi AyurVeda, is coherence. For that it is helpful to pay attention to the signs of coherence or incoherence in the body. Listen to the signals of your appetite, digestion, need for sleep and proper hydration, proper nutrition, and stress management. Act on those signals rather than ignoring them. Also keep in mind that what creates imbalance in detoxification processes are extremes: too much heat, too much force, or too much attention to one organ (such as the bowel, the colon, or the liver) without coordinating all the body's detoxification organs and systems. Careful attention to preparing the body for detoxification is also necessary. Even Ayurvedic treatments such as Panchakarma [next chapter] can create imbalance if they are not administered properly.

It's important to know that detoxification should always be soothing and nurturing. It should never be drying or aggravating to the doshas. If you are doing any detox program that makes you feel drained or exhausted, or results in symptoms of disease, that is not a safe or balanced detoxification program. The goal is to gain the full value of detoxification without creating any new imbalances.

Chapter 16

The Royal Detoxification Program: Pulse Diagnosis and Panchakarma

Maharishi AyurVeda Pulse Diagnosis

Before undergoing Panchakarma treatment, a patient is first seen by a trained Ayurvedic Vaidya (an Indian doctor) or consultant to determine which specific treatments best suit that individual. In Maharishi AyurVeda (MAV), as we mentioned before, one of the most important diagnostic tools is pulse diagnosis. A history of at least some form of pulse diagnosis shows its use in every culture from ancient to modern times, including its use in ancient India, China, Egypt, Greece, and Western medicine.[1] In Western medicine, one of the first diagnostic steps is to analyze the heart and circulatory system by measuring the pulse and taking the blood pressure. However, in MAV the diagnosis is far subtler and more comprehensive. When the physician puts his or her fingers on the radial pulse just beneath the wrist, he or she is not counting the number of pulses per minute as in Western medicine; the physician is determining the state of balance of the finest levels of the patient's physiology.

The pulse in MAV is taken with three fingers just below the wrist. Each finger is used to feel the state of one of the three doshas and can also detect imbalances or disorders throughout the body.

The finger closest to the wrist determines the state of balance of Vata, the middle finger determines the state of Pitta, and the finger furthest from the wrist determines the state of Kapha. The physician also feels the quality of the pulse—its strength, regularity, and rhythm—with all three fingers and gets information on weaknesses throughout the body and the amount of ojas and ama in the body.

Linda Nocita from Kansas City has gone to The Raj Ayurveda resort in Fairfield, Iowa, eight to ten times since 1996. She said she's always pretty amazed at what the doctors can tell from a pulse diagnosis. In May 2018, she visited the Raj and had her pulse taken by Vaidya Manohar, mentioned in the previous chapter. Dr. Manohar is one of the leading Ayurvedic doctors in the United States and India. For more than thirty years he worked with Maharishi Mahesh Yogi and he is now affiliated with The Raj and the Maharishi International University Integrative Wellness Institute in Iowa. He consults there on patient health matters and recommends treatments and herbs. Dr. Manohar also spends much of his time training Western physicians and medical students in Ayurveda and pulse diagnosis. Linda told us how comprehensive Manohar's analysis and health advice was, just from taking the pulse.

> Dr. Manohar felt my pulse [for just about a minute] and was able to identify from it that I had arthritis in the joints, high cholesterol, and dry eyes. He also told me that I shouldn't hold on to emotions and needed to let things go and not push myself so much. This was all very true. I am a Type A person and need to relax more and be easier on myself. Then he recommended particular treatments I should have at The Raj and gave me a going home two-week program followed by a different two-month program of diet and herbal supplements.

I try to go to The Raj as regularly as I can for the diagnosis and treatments. I always finish the treatments feeling so much better and people tell me how much better I look afterwards.

Dr. Clark was the director of Ayurveda at The Raj in Iowa for fifteen years before relocating to continue his practice in California. For the past fifteen years Mark Toomey, Ph.D., has been the director of Ayurveda at The Raj. Dr. Toomey sees patients daily to take their pulse and prescribe diets, lifestyle changes, and the various purification or detoxification treatments of Maharishi AyurVeda. Toomey says:

> Pulse diagnosis is a bit like harmonics. If you have a string on a guitar or a violin, and you pluck it, there will be a particular wave associated with the key of that string, but then when you want to change the sound or the vibration, you put your finger on part of the guitar's fretboard and then you get a different harmonic. The underlying harmonic is the same, but you get an overtone when you press on the fretboard.

> When you take the pulse, it's similar. In the body, you have the electrical activity in the heart, which stimulates the muscle to contract and that causes a beat. And that beat is a pulse wave. And that pulse wave spreads throughout the arteries. The wave motion is actually propelled through the structure of the artery itself—the walls of the artery, not the blood, because the walls of the artery are a better conductor of the wave. And when the wave goes through the arteries to the organs, we get an overtone and that gives us information about that area of the body.

Toomey explains that according to Ayurveda, there are six stages to disease. Those trained in pulse diagnosis can often determine imbalances in the earliest stages before it becomes a disease. The first three stages are where the doshas are out of balance. After detoxification, they can be brought back into balance through various means to prevent the disease, including diet. In the later stages, however, one or more of the doshas will typically have moved to a location in the body where it should not be, and then instead of the index finger experiencing Vata dosha, which has its characteristic feel, the ring finger could, for example, feel a buildup of Vata in a certain organ. That is a more aggravated situation that requires attention. This is the kind of detail that a quiz can't determine, and that is why a quiz is not a substitute for a pulse evaluation by a doctor or health consultant trained in Maharishi AyurVeda. These health practitioners can make many recommendations, including the proper detox program for each disorder. One example of a recent recommendation was related by Toomey when Jay interviewed him.

> A lady recently came to The Raj with sleep problems. She was a very busy person, had her own business and a lot of stress. She was dependent on Ambien for sleep. A lot of sleep medications like Ambien are addictive and research shows that they block a part of the brain when you sleep. She would wake up with a feeling of emptiness and feeling even more stressed.
>
> I diagnosed her as having both a Vata and a Pitta imbalance. The Vata was expressed in too much thinking, too much worrying, too much pressure and stress, and she was also a very passionate, driven person, like a Type A personality, which are Pitta characteristics. So, we needed to balance both Vata

252

and Pitta, and try to get her off some of her medications so she could be able to go to sleep normally.

She had very poor habits. She was eating too late and, what is especially aggravating to her Vata, she was going to bed late and working too late in the evening. This was unsettling to the mind prior to bedtime.

So, we corrected some of those bad habits, changed how and when she exercised, had her go to bed before 10 PM, gave her some Ayurvedic herbs, and changed her diet to balance both Vata and Pitta. During her stay we also gave her some oil massage and related treatments that reduce Vata and Pitta, and by the end of the seven or eight days that she was at The Raj, we completely changed her physiology to a state of balance. We also got her to learn TM.

Recently she told us she has stayed off her medications, is sleeping well, and she has really noticed a change in how she handles the pressures of the day. In her case it wasn't the diet alone, there needed to be these lifestyle changes as well.

Ayurvedic Treatments

The supervised Ayurvedic treatments, like the self-administered detoxification programs, are designed to cleanse the body of toxins and restore balance. These treatments can be very effective in maintaining general wellness as well as in addressing specific disorders. Again, the difference between the self-administered programs and the treatment programs in a Maharishi AyurVeda clinic is that the supervised treatment programs, called Panchakarma, are deeper, and more thorough.

Panchakarma is an integrated series of treatments and procedures that, taken together, dislodge impurities from the cells and tissues and flush them from the body. These detoxification therapies are generally taken in 3-day, 5-day and 7-day packages, although longer packages are available and recommended for more serious disorders.

Treatment

The treatment programs are tailored to the disorder, but most involve herbalized oil massage (*abhyanga*) by two technicians working simultaneously on the patient in a synchronized manner. The massage promotes the penetration of the oil deep into the tissues to loosen the aggravated doshas and toxins and push them into the body's circulatory system. The massage is then followed by a heat treatment typically designed to move the toxins into the organs of elimination (typically the bowel), followed by elimination therapies to remove the impurities from the bowel (enemas) and other parts of the body.

Personal Experiences with Maharishi Panchakarma

The following accounts should not be considered to be typical experiences. Results will vary greatly depending on many factors, including the nature and severity of the condition and the length of the treatments. The research shows significant decreases in negative moods (anxiety, depression, fatigue) and increased vigor, and a significant decrease in fat soluble toxins in the body from the Maharishi Panchakarma treatments alone. Research also shows significantly reduced inpatient and outpatient care needed by faculty at Maharishi International University who received Panchakarma and also practice TM and generally have Ayurvedic diets, as

254

compared to norms and other Iowa college faculty. The accounts below are also from persons who practice TM and have been educated about their body type and the Ayurvedic diet that is most suitable for them. As a result, they are benefitting from their diet and meditation practice, as well as the treatments.

Thyroid Condition, Menopause Related Fatigue, and Other Symptoms

Olena P. from Des Moines, Iowa was raised in Ukraine about sixty miles from the Chernobyl nuclear plant. That plant exploded in 1986, releasing radioactive material in the area. As a result, Olena had a long-standing thyroid disorder, along with what her doctor told her were menopause-related spikes in her blood pressure, almost constant fatigue and a lack of energy, and more recently excessive hair loss.

Olena's Kundalini Yoga teacher recommended that she go to The Raj in Fairfield for Ayurvedic treatments, and Olena did her research and decided to go. She was interviewed a month after she finished her five days of Panchakarma treatments at The Raj. Olena said in an interview:

> After my yoga teacher recommended the Maharishi AyurVeda treatments, I looked online for information, and the Ayurveda lifestyle and diet advice made sense to me as the right way to live. I didn't want to just take medicines or even supplements all the time. I think I was open to it because so many people in Ukraine use traditional medicine, natural medicine, for healing. As an example, when I was sick as a child my mother would give me special teas for my colds and put ground up mustard seed in my socks and the heat would also help get rid of the cold.

I went to The Raj for a five-day treatment program for elimination of toxins [massage, heat, and elimination therapies]. It was a wonderful experience. I had lost enough weight to go down a full size, and when I came home my son and husband said I looked so much younger and more refreshed. I really felt much better right away.

Before the Raj treatments, my blood pressure would sometimes be normal at 125-130 systolic but often would be up to about 150. After the treatments it is normal again and the fatigue is completely gone. Now I do a vigorous Yoga program three times a day, something I couldn't do before. I also had a blood test as part of a medical exam after I finished treatment. From it my regular doctor saw how much better my thyroid condition was and started a reduction in my medication from 120 mcg to 100 mcg once a day. Also, the excessive hair loss I had been experiencing stopped.

If you go through the treatments your condition definitely changes.

Overcoming Physical Injury

Patricia Glispin, the head women's basketball coach at Clark University in Massachusetts (Chapter 4), decided to visit The Raj for Ayurvedic treatments in 2018, about a year after starting TM. She went for five days of treatments, which included herbalized oil massage each day, and special heat and other treatments. On the last day, her treatments included being massaged by technicians with a cloth ball that had been soaked for many hours in an herbalized Ayurvedic paste. During the treatment the technicians focused their massage on an arm that she had broken five years earlier that had never properly healed. Coach Glispin said in an interview:

I broke my humerus [a long bone in the arm that runs from the shoulder to the elbow] about five years ago. What happened is after I broke it the doctors wanted to put a rod in my arm, but I really didn't want that so I let it heal by itself, and for six months it was immobilized. And there had been so much tissue damage and whatever, and while the arm healed, it healed crooked.

I told the doctor at The Raj about it, and the technicians really worked on my arm during the last day of treatment. That last treatment was amazing, and maybe it was all the treatments combined. But after the last treatment, I could put my arm up over my head for the first time in five years. I had previously had so much physical therapy for the arm, two years straight, plus different massage therapies and acupuncture, but this was far and away the most relief I've gotten. I can't even tell you how struck I was by this.

The whole week of treatments was a huge thing for me on every level. But the fact that my arm is now straight for the first time in five years is a real miracle. After the treatment I noticed right away how different the arm was and the interesting thing is that it has continued to get better this past week or so. When I did physical therapy maybe I would have less pain for a day and then it would be back, but this has had such a lasting effect it must trigger your body's own healing. I'm going back to The Raj in the spring because of this.

Coach Glispin also told us about the other effects from her Ayurvedic treatments. Although she had been practicing Transcendental Meditation for a year, she felt she was doing it too late in the evening and for her it didn't improve her sleep nearly as much as the Ayurvedic treatments and other lifestyle changes she made after her treatments. TM, the Ayurvedic treatments, diet, and lifestyle changes significantly improve the body's coherence. Sometimes the whole package is needed to address a particular disorder, depending on what is going on in the mind and body. Coach Glispin said:

> In the past when I tried to eat a little better it was such a chore. Now I just love it because I feel so much better. But maybe the biggest thing is that since the treatments, I feel that my need to be functioning at some high level all the time has subsided, and I'm much better able to enjoy the day. The week at The Raj has actually shifted my priorities somewhat, so I find that I am prioritizing myself a little more, but there is also so much calmness that I feel I have more to give. I feel I'm moving slower, but accomplishing more and, mainly, just enjoying things more.

Chronic Fatigue and Neurological Symptoms

Carole from Houston (not her real name) saw many physicians and healers before finally being examined by Kulreet Chaudhary, M.D., a prominent integrative neurologist in California (author of *The Prime*, Harmony Books 2016). Chaudhary recommended that Carole go to The Raj for two to three weeks of Panchakarma treatments. Carole suffered from chronic fatigue, insomnia, muscle weakness and pain, exercise intolerance, and had gastrointestinal issues. She said she had been diagnosed with non-specific neurological symptoms. Prior to deciding to do a two-week program in-residence at The Raj, Carole had been suffering with her symptoms for more than four years despite numerous visits to M.D.s, various healers, and numerous diets including a raw foods diet; living foods diet, raw and vegan; Paleo diet; and specific carbohydrates diet (SCD);

acupuncture, which made things worse; intravenous (IV) nutri-
tional therapy; IV detoxification programs; neurofeedback; and an
electrical stimulation program. Carole said nothing really worked,
so following Chaudhary's recommendation, she went to The Raj
in January 2017 for her first series of treatments. Jay interviewed
Carole when she was on a subsequent ten-day treatment program
in August 2017. She said:

> The Ayurvedic treatments were a catalyst, and I've noticed
> the improvements throughout the nervous system. I had
> two marma therapy treatments [marma is a kind of acupres-
> sure on various points of the physiology that are especially
> important in Ayurveda], and I walked out of the treatments
> thinking, "How could I feel this way?" It was amazing.

> After the first trip here [to The Raj], my energy levels changed
> and that was one of the biggest benefits. I would say I have
> 50 percent more energy, about 30 percent reduced pain, my
> exercise tolerance has improved 25 percent, my GI [gastro-
> intestinal] issues have improved, sleep is more reliable, and I
> have much less 'brain fog' as my cognitive abilities had been
> severely impaired.

Carole said that her problems had been caused by exposure to
environmental toxins, so getting rid of the toxins was a high priority. She is also now following much more of an Ayurvedic daily
routine, including an herbal supplement program that was recommended (taking the *ashwaganda* and *brahmi* herbs daily), doing
sun salutes and yoga, and practicing TM.

Weight Loss and Calmness

Kim from Chicago went to The Raj for five days of treatments in March 2017 and then went for another five days in September, the same year. She said the treatments and the knowledge she's gained about diet and health "have been amazing, and I plan to go back to The Raj twice each year." Kim had actually heard about The Raj twenty years ago and had in mind to go at some time but had not had the chance. Prior to her first visit she felt that she had gotten overweight and couldn't find an eating program that worked, and she decided to give The Raj a try. Kim said in an interview:

> It was really great. All the treatments felt manageable and comfortable, and I also started TM during the five days, so it was a very full schedule and a wonderful experience. And the treatments and the routine I was given did result in the weight loss I wanted. I lost 23 pounds from the time I started doing the home prep prior to going to The Raj.
>
> I was given some digestive herbs after the treatments, which I took and one big thing recommended for me was that three nights a week I was told to have soup along with my vegetables, and then not to have breakfast the next day.
>
> I will say that I didn't have such a great understanding about the diet after my first time at The Raj, and after a few months I started to get away from the Ayurvedic routine and gained back much of the weight. But by the second time I went for treatments in September I had a lot more knowledge. I had purchased a few books on Ayurvedic cooking and understood my body type [Kapha/Pitta] and the foods I should be eating much better. Now after the second time at The Raj I have lost back 19 pounds again and feel I am now much bet-

ter equipped to continue with the dietary routine, which for my body type sometimes means just substituting one vegetable for another or when I go to an Indian restaurant I have chapati instead of naan [different Indian breads].

I'm also pretty amazed at how much better I feel generally. Not just getting rid of the weight but both times after the treatments and TM I feel much calmer and am able to accomplish a lot more in my day to day activity. I have a lot more mental clarity and any anxiety due to pressures and work is much more manageable. Previously, I used to get into a cycle of getting tired and stressed and, for me, that would lead to eating and drinking a ton of coffee.

Stomach and Upper Respiratory Ailments

Jane Smith (not her real name) had a history of intestinal problems (ulcerative colitis), as well as sinus colds and upper respiratory infections beginning around 2008. In 2009, she had a major flare up of her colitis, with a severe case of bloody diarrhea. She was hospitalized for five days, during which she said the doctors had a tough time stopping the symptoms.

After her release from the hospital, she was prescribed Prednisone to help control her diarrhea; this medication has many side effects including nausea, vomiting, severe allergic reactions, depression, and thinning skin. Another medication prescribed for her was Apriso, which coats the intestine and helps reduce inflammation, but induces side effects such as headache, nausea, vomiting, and constipation. She said the drugs helped her get out of the acute phase, but she knew she needed to generally get healthier and Ayurveda did it.

After her hospitalization, a health practitioner friend gave Jane Ayurvedic massages and helped her eat a more balanced Ayurvedic diet, and her health started to improve. Then a few years later she started her yearly visits to The Raj for treatments. She went to the in-residence treatment programs at The Raj four times between 2013 and 2018. She says the treatments and better diet have helped her greatly to manage her health.

> I feel like I'm healthier with the PK [Panchakarma] treatments and detoxification, and my immune system is quite a bit better. Before the PK I was sick much more frequently, and I would be throwing up from stomach and respiratory ailments. I was getting sinus colds and infections regularly, and now I almost can't remember the last time I had that problem. Maybe a year and a half ago. And the intestinal problems are much more of a rarity now. I no longer take Prednisone, and whereas I used to take two Apriso pills daily, now I take two pills weekly and plan to talk to my doctor about stopping entirely.

Elimination of Toxins, Eye Pressure, and Knee and Neck Pain and Stiffness

Mary Shatt learned about Ayurveda in the early 1990s and started receiving treatments at Maharishi's residential Panchakarma programs in 1999 or 2000. Since then she and her husband have gone for treatments every other year for many years and have gone every year the last few years. During some of her treatments at Maharishi AyurVeda facilities, she would also get the Vedic Vibration treatments (MVVT) if there was a specific problem that she felt could be addressed. She believes one of the biggest effects of the elimination of toxins (ama) from her Panchakarma treatments had to with the reduction in pressure in her eyes, which is one of the risk factors for glaucoma. Glaucoma is a complex eye disease and higher than normal pressure inside the eye (called intraocular pressure) can often lead to glaucoma, which can result in vision loss or blindness. She consulted an Ayurvedic doctor because she wanted to avoid taking the eye drops that are normally given to reduce the eye pressure. Once started, the drops increase the fluids flowing in the eye and interfere with normal fluid function. The Panchakarma worked, however, and she didn't need to take the drops. Mary tested her eye pressure regularly and it was normal for about ten years. Like most patients who use Maharishi AyurVeda, Mary is not opposed to Western medicine, and a few years ago the pressure in her eyes went up a little and she heard about a laser procedure with little risk that sometimes helped. She tried that and it did work for her.

Mary also credits her Ayurvedic treatments and Vedic Vibration therapy with getting rid of her knee and neck problems. Before these treatments, for years she had pain in her knees, trouble going up and down the stairs, couldn't ride her bike, and had pain and stiffness in her neck. She attributed her neck problems to long work hours seated at a desk and said she was "very stiff despite regularly doing yoga and at times chiropractic." Mary said in an interview:

> The knee and neck issues were medium to low level pain and stiffness, but I had these problems for years and couldn't get rid of them. After the Panchakarma and the MVVT they just went away. There was a 100 percent improvement in my knees and about 90 percent in the neck. About five years after those treatments I tweaked my knee going down the stairs, but it was minor and in later years did another MVVT treatment for my neck. But the treatments, combined with being a little more vigilant getting up from my desk regularly, and

I no longer have either problem [knees or neck] to any real degree.

The Ayurvedic treatments as well as the TM practice and the advanced TM techniques generally were extremely strengthening mentally, emotionally, and physically. I used to be a workaholic but that stopped, and I found I was no longer taking everything at the office home with me.

Vertigo and Changes in Appearance

Murray Shatt, age 73 (Mary's husband), owned several construction and related businesses, which kept him extremely busy until he recently retired. A few years after learning TM he became impressed with the logic of Ayurveda and consulted with Indian Ayurvedic doctors from time to time. He had experienced a few Ayurvedic massages, but he did not have complete Panchakarma treatments and elimination therapy prior to around 2000 when he had a severe vertigo attack. Murray said:

> I'm a practical person. If something makes sense, I will give it a try, otherwise not. I started taking Ayurvedic herbs and consulting at times with the Vaidyas because Ayurveda made so much sense, more so than any other kind of medicine.
>
> We were living in Florida, and there were no Ayurveda treatment centers there, so when a center [MAV] was about to open in North Carolina, my wife and I went there just to check it out. When we got there though something happened to my neck, and I got really bad vertigo. If I stood up it was like being rocked on a boat. I couldn't lie on my back, I could only sit for a short while, and the only way I could sleep was on my stomach with a pillow under my chest and that was mainly falling asleep from exhaustion. I actually had to crawl

around on the floor for a couple of days until the Ayurvedic clinic opened and I could start the treatments. So, it was bad.

Murray went for treatment as soon as he could get into the clinic. He said:

I had Panchakarma for fourteen days and listened twice a day to the Vedic sounds, which had a nice effect. I gradually got better, and by the last day the vertigo was gone. And it lasted. About ten years later I had a mild case of vertigo for a short time, but nothing like the first one.

My wife and I generally do a week of Panchakarma at a time. Over the years, the treatments and TM really helped us be stable and healthy, especially as my businesses have gone up and down with the economic changes in the construction industry.

In general, I would say Panchakarma is very cleansing to the system. Besides addressing various ailments, it makes you feel lighter, gives you more energy, and you look healthier. You can look in the mirror and see how much better you look when the body has gotten rid of its toxins. You also see it in the others who are there for treatment. After a few days of treatment, they look a lot better, and you can tell they're happier.

Research

Drs. Orme-Johnson and Herron compared the Blue Cross/Blue Shield data on the use of inpatient and outpatient medical services and health-care costs from 1985 to 1995. They looked at three groups, an Ayurveda group consisting of from 417 to 701 people who were faculty and staff at Maharishi International University, a group of non-meditating Iowans, and a control group of 3,285 to 5,000 people consisting of faculty members and their covered dependents from other private colleges in Iowa. The faculty and staff at Maharishi University were selected because they participate in many of the Maharishi AyurVeda modalities for coherence: all practice Transcendental Meditation (TM is the primary mental technique of Maharishi AyurVeda), most perform Pranayama breathing exercises and yoga daily, they eat a largely vegetarian diet according to Ayurvedic principles, and many will follow the daily and seasonal routines including periodic Panchakarma treatments at the campus clinic for students, faculty and staff. The results were quite staggering. Among those 45 or older, hospital patient days for the Maharishi AyurVeda group were 91 percent lower than the norms and 88 percent lower than the control group from other colleges in Iowa. Outpatient visits were 53 percent and 61 percent lower in the Ayurveda groups as compared to the norms and the controls. Expenditures followed a similar trend.[2]

Decreased Inpatient and Outpatient Medical Care Utilization By Age Category
Through Maharishi AyurVeda

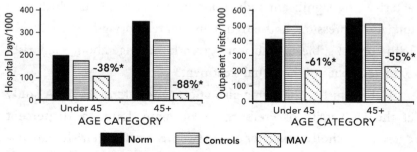

* Percent reduction compared to controls

Reference: *The American Journal of Managed Care,* 1997, 3(1): p. 135-144.

Decreased Hospitalization By Disease Category
Through Maharishi AyurVeda

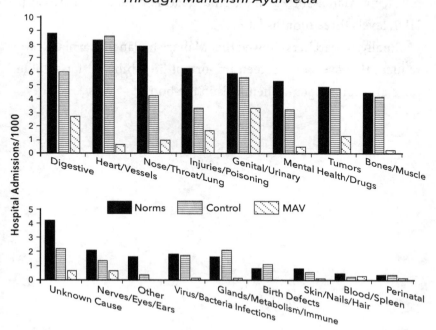

Reference: *The American Journal of Managed Care,* 1997. 3(1): p. 135-144

267

Maharishi Panchakarma, studied alone, has been shown to improve mental and physical health. In one study researchers found that with Panchakarma, patients demonstrated improved mental health characterized by significant reductions in negative moods (including anxiety, depression, and fatigue) and increased vigor as compared with control subjects who were given knowledge about Maharishi AyurVeda but not the actual treatment.[3]

Maharishi Panchakarma also affects cholesterol levels. A study at the University of Freiburg in Germany found a 10 percent decrease in cholesterol after one to two weeks of Maharishi Panchakarma treatment, compared with no change in a control group. There was also a decrease of 8.7 percent in LDL. These results have been replicated and extended by a recent study in the United States, which found an acute decrease in cholesterol immediately following Maharishi Panchakarma treatment and an increase in HDL levels three months later.[4]

Finally, researchers showed that Maharishi Panchakarma greatly reduces the levels of fourteen important lipophilic, or fat-soluble, toxic and carcinogenic chemicals in the body.[5]

Chapter 17

The Coherence Healing Lifestyle

A new medical field called lifestyle medicine holds that by simply changing our lifestyle, we can significantly improve our health. In a 2018 interview on CNN, Dan Buettner, author of *The Blue Zones*, suggested that small lifestyle changes can add up to ten years to most people's lives, and that aging is 10 percent genetic and 90 percent lifestyle. So, what lifestyle is "right"?

The American Academy of Family Physicians advocates four lifestyle strategies: first, that the physicians promoting lifestyle changes adopt healthy practices to set an example for their patients. They then initiate open-ended discussions with their patients to help them understand what are said to be the *three* critical components of a better lifestyle: the value of healthy eating, the value of 30–60 minutes of exercise a day, and the value of strategies for coping, such as learning to express feelings in appropriate ways, using relaxation methods, and taking time for self-care. The Academy advises that everyone is different and warns that what is right for a patient who is young, or obese, may be wrong for a person who has heart disease or diabetes. While these general strategies may help the patient move in the right direction, the problem is that they lack crucial details. In contrast, Ayurveda describes in detail the behaviors for generating coherence and longevity.

269

Yoga and Ayurveda

In the mid-1980s Maharishi adapted the strategies of Ayurveda and yoga for use in the modern world. These are adaptations of the routines that have been used by yogis from ancient times. When most people think of yoga, they think of a series of exercises or poses (sometimes called *asanas*), but this is just a small part of yoga. Yoga means "union" and can also mean "silence," and it is really a manifold group of practices (including meditation, breathing exercises, behaviors, and daily routines), the purpose of which is to elevate the individual to the highest state of consciousness. As a part of that process, the different yoga practices, to a varying degree, rid the mind and body of disease and disorder and generate higher brain functioning.

As part of his revival of the Vedic knowledge, Maharishi corrected not only the misunderstandings about meditation (that it involved concentration, and was difficult, and only for those with a reclusive lifestyle), but also other misconceptions about yoga's approach to health and human development. Those who have done some reading about yoga, for example, may be familiar with what has been characterized as yoga's eight-step process to human development, with eight consecutive steps proceeding from interaction with others (non-violence, truthful behavior and other moral conduct), to activities to cleanse the outer body and care in eating, to activities to develop the inner body such as performing yoga postures, and then subtler practices such as breathing techniques and meditation. Some proficiency in the initial practices was seen as a prerequisite for the more subtle inner practices.

Maharishi, however, corrected this misunderstanding. Instead of being eight steps toward full development, Maharishi described them as eight limbs, which can be likened to eight legs of a table, all of which support the table. Using this metaphor, you can pull on any of the legs and the whole table will move. As a result, Maharishi said all of the approaches can begin at once and are part of the ideal health lifestyle.[1]

The Daily Coherence Generating Routine of Ayurveda

Biological Rhythms

One interesting area of Ayurveda that Western medicine is starting to appreciate is the field of *chronopharmacology*, which is taking medicines at the right time of day to have an optimum effect. The body has various internal clocks and a master clock in the brain called the suprachiasmatic nucleus (SCN) that keeps the other clocks working in a synchronous fashion. These clocks and triggers from the environment result in changes in the body's temperature, hormones, and chemicals, which greatly influence bodily functions. Due to these biological changes, at night, the body secretes melatonin to help us sleep. Then for several hours beginning around 4 AM, the body secretes cortisol, epinephrine, and norepinephrine to give us the energy to get up and start a productive day. The digestive system is strongest at mid-day and weakest when we sleep. The body requires a regular supply of energy for nerve impulses, muscle contraction, and other bodily functions, but the need for energy diminishes greatly when we sleep, so the digestive system slows markedly at that time.

As a result of these biological rhythms, modern medicine has learned that the positive effects of medicine can be enhanced and negative effects reduced, depending on the time of day medicines are taken. We have learned that cholesterol synthesis is maximum at night so certain drugs are best as a single dose at night. On the other hand, natural steroids in the blood are much higher in the early morning than the later part of the afternoon, which is why split doses of steroids are often given two-thirds in the morning and one-third in the evening.

Maharishi AyurVeda accounts for the varying biological rhythms in all phases of prevention and treatment. The principal goal of Maharishi AyurVeda is to establish balance or coherence. Thus, it places a special significance on establishing harmony between our individual rhythms and the rhythms of nature through various daily and seasonal routines. According to Maharishi AyurVeda, seasonal changes in nature can increase susceptibility to a number of disorders. The type of disorder can depend on the season and our body type, and the seasons themselves are related to the different doshas.

For example, at the beginning of Kapha season (early spring), the weather is often cold and damp and therefore more likely to cause an increase in Kapha. Especially in Kapha type people, this can create an imbalance resulting in colds, bronchitis, etc. On the other hand, at the beginning of Pitta season (early summer), Pittas, who are generally "hot" to begin with, may become imbalanced, leading to increased digestive problems and bouts of anger. Vatas are most susceptible to disease in Vata season, which are the cold and windy winter months. To protect the individual during these times of greater susceptibility, Maharishi AyurVeda makes many dietary and behavioral recommendations for each body type.

The Vedic seers knew that the rhythms of the human body were tied to the rhythms of nature. They knew that for each person there was an ideal daily and seasonal routine to ensure that his or her rhythms were continually reset and resynchronized with those of the earth, moon, and sun. Further, they knew that the timing of a medical treatment was critical to its success. Therefore, all Maharishi AyurVeda treatments are individualized not only for the body type, but for the time of day, the season, and the age of the patient. This is living in accordance with the laws of nature.

Times of Day for Different Activities

The ideal daily Ayurvedic coherence routine prescribes the most advantageous times for specific behaviors in accordance with the cycles occurring in nature. There are actually Vata, Pitta, and Kapha cycles of each day, which dictate the times for certain behaviors. According to Ayurveda there are two rhythmic periods of twelve hours each during a 24-hour daily cycle, with each period having in it a Vata, Pitta, and Kapha sub-cycle of four hours each. Vata, Pitta and Kapha cycles rotate consecutively through each 24-hour period at the following approximate times:

First Period
Vata cycle 2 AM to 6 AM
Kapha cycle 6 AM to 10 AM
Pitta cycle 10 AM to 2 PM

Second Period
Vata cycle 2 PM to 6 PM
Kapha cycle 6 PM to 10 PM
Pitta cycle 10 PM to 2 AM

Because there are these periodic cycles in nature, it makes sense that there are optimal times to perform certain activities. For example, many cultures have long recommended eating your main meal at lunch. This is a Pitta time of day when the sun is at its peak and internally the digestive fire is strongest. And the old adage "early to bed, early to rise," is actually a prescription of Ayurveda, but Ayurveda is more precise. In Ayurveda, the Kapha time of night (6 PM to 10 PM) is generally a settled time in the environment and getting to bed in the Kapha time of night has a calming effect and is conducive to sleep.

Modern science is beginning to understand these principles even without knowledge of Ayurveda. A 2012 article on circadian rhythms in *The Wall Street Journal* ("The Peak Time for Everything")[2] tells us that body temperature starts to rise in the morning and continues through midday; Ayurveda would say this is a natural consequence of early morning being the colder Vata period, then a cool Kapha period before the hotter midday Pitta period. The article also states that cognitive work is best performed in the morning and through midday, which, as indicated above, Maharishi AyurVeda describes as Vata and Pitta periods, when memory, alertness and other cognitive functions associated with both Vata and Pitta are highest. The same article states that posts to Facebook at about 8 PM tend to get the most "likes," which the article states is a time when people are feeling less stressed, and this is also consistent with Ayurveda's analysis. According to Ayurveda, 8 PM is the middle of a Kapha period, when the environment's nature is Kapha like, meaning easy going and settled (you might notice that the wind dies down and calmness in the environment generally prevails more in the Kapha periods than other times of day). Therefore, the *Journal* article concludes that you might impress your girlfriend, boss, or a client more during a dinner date or a breakfast date (that is, a date at the relaxed Kapha periods) than during a lunch date. Finally, the *Journal* article states that if you want late-night excitement, follow Twitter between 10 PM and 11 PM (the beginning of the more intense and potentially irritable Pitta period), when people tend to send more emotion-laden tweets.

In addition to these daily cycles, there are life cycles. Ayurveda teaches what we all experience—that our bodies and body types change as we age. Youth is more of a Kapha period in life, when, for example, the body is strong, growing, and vigorous. At this time of life more strenuous exercise is beneficial according to Ayurveda. In middle age Pitta is more predominant when ambition, achievement and drive are at a peak. But as we age and get into our 60s we enter a more Vata period, when most people experience that the body becomes dry and we are more susceptible to anxiety, worry, and sleep difficulties, which are tendencies when Vata is out of balance.

As a result of these various considerations, the ideal, coherence-generating daily routine is listed and then explained more fully below the list.

Ideal Morning Routine:

1. Get up early, preferably prior to 6 AM or soon thereafter. Wake naturally without an alarm.

2. Urinate and have bowel movement (don't strain, and it can be done later if there is no urge right away).

3. Swish cured (explained below) sesame oil or sunflower oil in the front of the mouth (it is not a gargle in the back of the mouth), rinse the mouth with warm salt water, then brush teeth, and then scrape the tongue with a tongue scraper.

275

4. Drink a glass of warm water to which a few squeezes of fresh lime can be added.

5. Perform an oil self-massage with warm oil (you can use a baby bottle warmer or just place the oil in a covered glass and let it sit in hot water until warm).

6. Take a warm bath or shower.

7. Walk for half an hour at sunrise if possible or walk later.

8. Yoga postures (15-20 minutes).

9. Practice the Pranayama breathing exercise (5 minutes).

10. Practice TM (usually 20 minutes for adults).

11. Eat a light breakfast. Sit quietly after eating for a few minutes to aid digestion.

Ideal Lunch and Afternoon Routine

12. Eat lunch between noon and 1 PM.

13. Sit quietly for few minutes to aid digestion.

14. Walk or do other exercise in the afternoon.

15. Practice TM late in the afternoon (usually 20 minutes for adults).

Ideal Dinner and Evening Routine

16. Eat moderately between 6 PM and 7 PM.

17. Sit quietly for a few minutes.

18. Walk to aid digestion.

Bedtime

19. Go to bed before 10 PM. You can have a small glass of warm milk a half hour before bed as an exception to not eating late in the evening. The milk is soothing and encourages sleep.

Conduct Throughout the Day

In a Facebook lecture on dealing with the Covid-19 pandemic in March 2020, Dr. Tony Nader, mentioned earlier, discussed specific hygienic, dietary, exercise, and rest strategies, but also mentioned the importance of positive emotions and feelings and our state of happiness. Dr. Nader was addressing these emotions during the coronavirus pandemic, but the principles can be applied throughout our lives. A priority of course is our own health, but we should also consider the health and happiness of others in our vicinity. Acts of kindness and consideration help those around us, but also will help our own emotions and our own health. Dr. Nader reminded us of this principle with an example.

There is a disorder now known as *dissociative identity* disorder, previously called multiple personality disorder. People with this disorder have what are sometimes called split personalities, where in one personality the individual may be kind and considerate, whereas their other personality is the opposite. Interestingly, in the first personality, not only is the mental state different but the physical state as well. Dr. Nader's example was that during the kind and compassionate personality, one of the individual's favorite foods may be strawberries, whereas when the mind takes on the different personality, the person may actually be physically allergic to strawberries. The mental state greatly influences the physical. So, don't dwell on negativity. Dr. Nader said, think how we can be happy and helpful to others; think how to make our enemies our friends. This advice is similar to something the Dalai Lama once said, which was, "If you want others to be happy, practice compassion. If you want to be happy, practice compassion."

During the coronavirus pandemic, Dr. Nader organized an online twice-daily group meditation program. All meditators, regardless of type of practice, were invited to meditate at the same time of day, which has been shown to have a positive effect on individuals as well as the society.

Priorities, if Time is a Factor

Please note that an ideal daily routine may add an hour or so to your present routine so on some days there may not be time for everything. As a result, there should be priorities. The first priority is Transcendental Meditation. TM is actually considered the highest form of yoga, what is known as *Raj Yoga*, because of how it can produce higher brain functioning, resulting in higher states of consciousness. Our mental state has the most influence on our success and happiness, and, as coherence grows through Transcendental Meditation, the subtler benefits of other lifestyle strategies will be recognized and more willingly incorporated into your routine.

A second priority to keep in mind is the predominance of the Vata, Pitta, and Kapha elements in your body type, and whether any symptoms you are experiencing are Vata, Pitta, or Kapha symptoms. Rest (adequate sleep and TM) is the most fundamental tool for balancing Vata dosha and Vata symptoms, as well as for preventing Vata disorders (such as anxiety, insomnia, and nerve disorders). A Pitta reducing diet, not skipping meals, and regular practice of TM are the most important tools for balancing Pitta and preventing Pitta disorders. Exercise, light diet, and TM are the most important tools for balancing Kapha and preventing Kapha disorders (such as obesity, heaviness, and dullness).

Morning Routine Details

- *Waking*. Awaken naturally from sleep without an alarm clock. Try to go to bed early enough so that you can comfortably get out of bed to begin the day as close to 6 AM as possible or earlier. This is because the Kapha period begins about 6 AM and if you get up too far into the Kapha period, you will wake feeling duller and more sluggish; if you continually get up late in the day, the negative Kapha qualities of dullness and chronically feeling sleepy can become habitual. For this reason (and others discussed below), it is better to arise in the Vata period of the morning (prior to 6 AM) or as close to it as possible, which will tend to infuse the Vata qualities of exhilaration and mental clarity.

- *Urinate and move bowels*. To aid elimination, an hour before bed you can take a tablet or two of the Maharishi Ayurveda product *Triphala Plus* (mapi.com), which, for those familiar with Ayurveda products, is an excellent natural source of *triphala*, a fruit and herb mixture that aids in digestion and elimination. Also, drinking a glass of warm water (below) can help encourage elimination. Elimination may follow placing oil in the mouth depending on the need.

- *Oil Swishing, Brushing Teeth, and Scraping Tongue*. First swish the oil in the front of the mouth (teeth and gums), not in the throat, for a few minutes with just a tablespoon or so of preferably organic sunflower oil or organic refined (sometimes referred to as cured) sesame oil. Refined sesame oil is available from mapi.com or you can save money by refining your own unrefined sesame oil (*the instructions for refining or curing the sesame oil are immediately below*). Then spit out the oil and rinse the mouth with warm salt water. Along with brushing the teeth and scraping the tongue, swishing oil in the mouth is ideal for oral hygiene to prevent not just tooth problems but even more serious disorders (*see below*). After swishing with oil, brush the teeth, and then scrape the tongue. Ayurveda says to gently scrape the white coating from the tongue. Ayurveda considers the white coating to be the residue from poor digestion in the past. A tongue scraper can be purchased online (mapi.com or elsewhere), and you simply scrape the tongue with just two or three passes of the scraper over it. This is good for the taste buds and has deeper significance.

Several research studies show that poor oral health is connected to many diseases including heart disease, diabetes, and mouth and throat cancer. For example, the bacteria from inflammation of the gums and periodontal disease or gingivitis can enter the bloodstream and travel to the arteries and the heart possibly causing atherosclerosis and increased risk of heart attack. Inflammation of the gums also makes it harder to control blood sugar and can cause increased problems for diabetics. Improper daily cleansing of the mouth can be life threatening. See the following studies.

- Saravanan, D., Shubaashni, R., Vineeta, K, "Effect of Oil Pulling [swishing] with Sesame Oil on Plaque-induced Gingivitis: A Microbial Study," *J. of Orofacial Research*, 3(3):175-180, July–September, 2013

- Naseem, S., et al., "Oral Hygiene Practices and Teeth Cleaning Techniques Among Medical Students," *Cureus*, 2017 Jul., 9(7).

- Smith, D. E., Stevens, M. M., "Pilot Project: The Effects of a Sesame Oil Mouth Rinse on the Number of Oral Bacteria Colony Types," Paper presented at the Third Annual Scientific Meeting of the College of Health Professions, Wichita State University, 1988

- Salerno, J.M., Smith, D., "The Use of Sesame Oil and Other Vegetable Oils in the Inhibition of Human Colon Cancer Cells in Vitro," 1991, *Anticancer Research*, 11: 209–216.

- Smith, D., Salerno, J.M., "Selective Growth Inhibition of Human Malignant Melanoma Cell Line by Sesame Oil in Vitro," 1992, *Prostaglandins, Leukotrienes, and Essential Fatty Acids*, 46: 145–150.

How to refine sesame oil for oil swishing or oil massage:

To "cure" or refine the sesame oil, heat the oil to 212 degrees Fahrenheit (you can place just a few drops of water in the oil and remove from the heat when the water bubbles pop). Then allow to cool and use as needed. Be careful when refining the oil as all oil is flammable. Stand away from the stove until removing the oil from the heat, and don't leave the oil unattended. You can refine up to a quart of oil at a time.

- *Massage the head and body with oil for 5–10 minutes.* The daily massage is described at the website of Maharishi AyurVeda Products International. Use just five or six tablespoons of oil. The massage has many benefits, including increased circulation, especially to nerve endings, lubrication of the joints, a calming effect on the nerves, increased stamina, improved sleep, and help in eliminating toxins from the body. The oil massage is especially good for Vata types to prevent dryness in the physiology and many neurological disorders that Ayurveda associates with aggravated Vata. A gentle oil massage can also be performed by mothers for their young children and can have a settling effect throughout the day, especially for hyperactive children. According to Ayurveda, the oil massage balances all the doshas by loosening the excess doshas in the body and pushing them into the circulatory system. Then a warm bath (ideally), or a shower, can help move the aggravated doshas through the circulatory system into the organs of elimination, generally the intestines, where they are naturally removed from the body. Refined sesame oil is best for the massage, but olive oil (which does not need to be refined but should be cold pressed, virgin olive oil) and coconut oil (which does not need to be refined) especially for Pitta types and in the summer can be substituted (coconut oil has a cooling effect). The sesame or olive oil is best used by warming it first, which can be done by placing it in a glass jar under hot water or in a bottle warmer. In Ayurveda, the massage is called *abhyanga*, for those who want to research it online. One good strategy to allow for more penetration of the oil into the body is to wait five or more minutes after the massage before bathing. Men may want to shave after the massage for example.

When you are ready for your bath, first wipe off the excess oil with a paper towel and avoid oil on the feet to avoid slipping.

- *Bathing*. Use warm water, not hot or cold. A tub bath is best after an oil massage (*as described above*), but a shower is also fine.

- *Early Morning Walk*. Walking at various times during the day is important in Ayurveda. One of the classical Ayurveda texts, the *Charaka Samhita*, states that walking for half an hour at sunrise is one of the best activities for balancing the body. The fresh rays of the sun have some special significance for renewing the body each day. As noted in Chapter 12, we should get good exercise and raise the heart rate periodically during the day. With good circulation our white blood cells for fighting germs are transported around the body as needed. Efficient circulation also helps remove waste from the body.

- *Yoga postures or asanas*. Yoga postures are the most reliable way to tone or "exercise" and increase blood flow directly to the various organs. Some postures, for example, tone the abdomen, the liver, the kidneys, or the spleen, or strengthen the back, and so on, which are areas that typically don't get much of a workout through more conventional exercise strategies. Yoga balances all three doshas, and different poses have different effects. Backward bends are heating, and thus balancing to Vata types. Forward bending postures are cooling for Pitta types. Twists are good for Kapha and stimulate digestion. So, depending on your body type, you can spend a little more time on those postures that are good for your type. Yoga postures tone every area of the body and help cleanse the internal organs of toxins. In addition, as discussed in the chapters on Transcendental Meditation, the unique mental state that results in coherence in the entire physiology is the restfully alert mental state, where the mind is relaxed and calm at the same time as it is fully alert. This combination of rest and dynamism is also promoted by the yoga postures.

Yoga should not be done in a hurried fashion and each posture, when done correctly, is held in an easy pose, without straining. Just as the restfully alert mind in TM produces increased EEG coherence and order in the physiology, the restfully dynamic yoga postures can produce somewhat similar changes. The Vedic knowledge holds that meditation is the supreme technique of yoga, because the mind, being subtler than the body (a more inner level), is capable of producing more positive changes than a purely physical approach to coherence. Ideally, however, both TM and yoga postures would be part of daily coherence routine. Many different types of yoga are now offered around the world. The course we are familiar with and that we recommend is the 16-lesson Maharishi Yoga course available at miu.edu/yoga. In addition, the tm.org website sometimes offers free Maharishi Yoga instruction. Another resource for online yoga is YogaUOnline.com, which offers many different courses.

- *Breathing for Coherence.* Practice the breathing exercise (known as Pranayama) below for two or three minutes or so before Transcendental Meditation. The yoga asanas, followed by the quieter breathing technique, provides a head start for the mind and body to reach very settled levels during the meditation practice. Because the breathing alternates between the right and left nostrils, it helps integrate the two hemispheres of the brain.

Breathing Exercise:

Sit comfortably in a chair with the eyes closed. Place your right thumb next to your right nostril and your middle and ring fingers of the right hand next to your left nostril. Then close the right nostril with your thumb and breathe out through your left nostril. Then breathe in through the left nostril while your right thumb keeps the right nostril closed. Then close the left nostril with your two fingers as your right thumb comes off its nostril and breathe out through the right nostril. Repeat for several minutes. Just breathe naturally, not trying to hold the breath for any particular length of time. Both the practice of yoga asanas (poses) and pranayama are quiet practices while the mind remains alert, just as in the TM technique. Yoga asanas, followed by Pranayama, followed by TM are also successively subtler practices. Yoga done without strain quiets and orders the body; Pranayama quiets and orders the breath; and TM quiets and orders the mind. If yoga is followed by Pranayama, then by TM, it is like a head start on settling down during your TM practice.

Note that there are some Pranayama techniques that advocate very rapid breathing while alternating nostrils. That is not recommended without getting approval from a Maharishi AyurVeda doctor. For example, it is not recommended for those with a tendency toward high blood pressure.

- *Practice Transcendental Meditation* for the time instructed.

- *Breakfast.* Eat a light breakfast according to the Ayurvedic dietary considerations. Note again that milk is only taken as part of a meal with sweet tasting foods. So, don't have eggs and a glass of milk. If you want eggs and milk, have your milk at least twenty minutes later. Sweet tastes for breakfast that are okay with milk are cereal, toast, butter, cream, jams, sweet fruits, sugar, and honey. Raisins, dates, figs and unsalted nuts like walnuts can also be added to the cereal. Milk is best had after boiling it and then let it cool to room temperature. You can add a Vata or Pitta tea bag, which are available from mapi.com (Kapha tea bags with Kapha spices may be too pungent to combine with milk) and a small amount of ghee (ghee especially for Vata types). A small amount of sugar also helps with digestion and taste. A favorite breakfast recommended by Ayurvedic doctors is cooked apples and/or pears and raisins. You can add cinnamon, turmeric, and a few cloves before cooking.

- *Give digestion a chance to get started.* Sit quietly for a few minutes after eating to allow the digestive process to start without competition from other active parts of the body.

- *Work or exercise.*

Lunch and Afternoon Routine

- *Lunch.* Eat your main meal at lunch at around noon to 1 PM (when Pitta and digestion are at their peak) and ideally at about the same time each day.

- *Give digestion a chance.* Sit quietly for a few minutes after eating.

- *Walk or other exercise.* A half hour walk after eating is good for digestion followed by work or afternoon exercise. You want to get at least a half hour of exercise each day.

- *Breathing and yoga postures* just before meditation.

- *Late afternoon practice of Transcendental Meditation.*

Dinner Routine

- *Dinner.* Dinner should not be too late since you want to eat early enough so that there are at least three hours before an early bedtime. Dinner between 6 PM and 7 PM would be ideal. Have a light or moderate dinner ideally at about the same time each day.

- *Give digestion a chance.* Sit quietly for a few minutes.

- *Walk* to aid digestion (even five or ten minutes is good).

Improving Sleep

- *Early bedtime.* Bedtime before 10 PM. Going to bed during the settled Kapha time of day promotes sleep. Bedtime should ideally be no sooner than two and a half hours after eating.

- *To enhance elimination,* one or two tablets of Triphala Plus from mapi.com can be taken an hour before bed.

- *Avoid TV right before bed.* Don't watch TV for about half an hour before retiring. The flickering screen images aggravate Vata and can interfere with sleep.

- *Warm milk.* A glass of warm milk before bed is an exception to not eating within three hours of bed. Bring the milk to a boil (see Chapter 13 instructions), and let the milk sit just a little to cool a bit. You can then add a small amount of sugar for taste and digestion and half or quarter teaspoon of ghee. A Vata tea bag (Vata reducing tea), or a Pitta tea bag for Pitta types (available from mapi. com) can be added to the milk before boiling.

Ayurvedic Exercise Principles

(The exercise principles are largely taken with permission from a handout to guests from The Raj.)

Exercise plays a key role in developing and maintaining both mental and physical health and cognitive functioning. Among other things, exercise increases blood circulation, helps remove toxins and impurities in the physiology, increases muscle tone, increases coordination between the mind and body, increases dopamine levels helping your mood, and increases your heart rate to promote blood flow to the brain. Research shows the benefits of walking, running, bicycling, swimming, balance and coordination exercises, Pilates, playing musical instruments, and even brain exercises like playing with a Rubik's cube. Using the opposite hand for tasks like brushing your teeth or writing are beneficial (opposite hand activities stimulates the other side of the brain). There are also Eastern exercise routines, which many people practice, including Tai Chi, Aikido, Qi Gong, and numerous types of yoga. For coherence, however, exercise should also be based on one's body type (see below), should be performed daily or at least regularly most days of the week, and should not be overdone as we get older, as described below.

Exercise by Body Type

Vata types as they get older generally need lighter exercise (yoga, dance aerobics, walking, bicycling shorter distances). They are generally slender and have less strength in the joints and cannot take the pounding of certain exercises. Half an hour of mild exercise is generally fine. Student age people and young adults can exercise more, but Vata types still have to be more careful.

Pitta types should have more moderate exercise (brisk walking or jogging, hiking, swimming, tennis, skiing, and climbing). Pitta types have more stamina and can exercise more, and students and young Pitta types may be quite strong and athletic. Exercising outside when it is very hot is not good for Pitta types. In the summer, swimming would be best.

Kapha types should have moderate to heavy exercise (running or jogging, aerobics, dance classes, skiing and swimming). Because they have strong frames and joints, they can handle vigorous exercise and it will greatly help them with their efforts to balance their weight.

For all body types, the TM organization recommends yoga, Pranayama breathing exercises (above in this chapter), and what are known as sun salutations. The latter can be done in only about five minutes and are a good workout for the physiology as a whole, resulting in both stretching the body and toning the muscles. As its name suggests, these exercises are generally performed when the sun is out early in the morning and/or at sunset. Search online for sun salutations and you will find instructional videos and apply the principles in this chapter—don't overdo it, don't strain, breathe through the nose, and exercise according to your age and body type.

Professor Sarath's Ayurvedic Routine

Ed Sarath is a jazz composer, and for the past thirty years he has been a professor of music at the University of Michigan School of Music. He was at a course in India that Maharishi gave in the 1980s and got interested in Ayurveda at that time. Ed said:

My whole Ayurveda involvement got me established in a solid routine with my diet and exercise for more than the last 30 years, and even if I am not strictly adhering to it, the principles are always in my awareness, and I do what I can, which is very valuable.

Ed said when he first learned about Ayurveda, he was doing a lot of long distance running and the idea that you could over-exercise was very foreign to him. He said in an interview:

> I remember the first time I took the Ayurvedic treatments [Chapter 16] I had run fifteen miles that morning in Iowa City and I arrived at the Ayurvedic clinic and they were talking about the different Ayurvedic body types. They said that for Vata/Pitta types you had to be moderate in your exercise, and that it could vary according to the season, and that just did not compute. But I discovered it was true—that my problem with exercise was doing too much.
>
> Now, I appreciate how useful that information is. I cut back especially in the winter Vata months, and it's been good. If I do too much exercise, it's interesting. I still feel great when I do the exercise, but I get fatigued later in the day or even for several days. I don't think this is just getting older because if it was a function of age, I think I wouldn't be able to tolerate the exercise at all, but that's not the case. Two years ago, my wife and I were hiking in Yosemite with her brother and we did eight miles and it was a real trek, and I finished a half hour before them. I felt great, but the next three or four days I paid for it.

Avoid Exhaustion—Allow the Breath to Dictate Your Capacity

Another important Ayurvedic principle for all body types is not to exercise to the point of exhaustion. Exercise is one activity that people can tend to exhaust themselves at. Because of the potential strain to the body, seeing a medical doctor to make sure the exercise can be tolerated is always a good idea. Maharishi AyurVeda recommends exercising to 50 percent of capacity. Gradually, over a period of time, your capacity will increase. Fifty percent capacity is usually when strain begins to appear and it is no longer easy to breathe through the nose and becomes difficult to maintain your focus during the exercise. In Ayurveda, it is not considered healthy to go beyond 50 percent capacity as it strains the body and the body's energy is diverted to repairing the damage from straining. Exercise should invigorate the physiology leaving it ready for work, instead of exhausting the body and requiring a period of extra rest. Exercise is considered exhausting in Ayurveda if you are sweating heavily or panting or feel weak.

During exercise it is best to breathe through the nose and if you can no longer breathe comfortably through the nose, slow down your pace. Breathing through the nose helps balance the brain and body.

Part V

SPIRITUALITY
AND
MORALITY

Chapter 18

The Spiritual and Moral Effects of Coherence

Pranav Chhalilyil, age fourteen at the time of his interview a few years ago, was then a tenth grader at Maharishi School in Fairfield, Iowa. At age five, he started practicing a modified version of TM for those under age ten. Pranav knows his Ayurvedic body type (Vata/Pitta), and follows a coherence generating lifestyle and daily routine. Jay interviewed him about his experience with TM after learning that Pranav won the top science award in Iowa for his oral hygiene research. Pranav became interested in oral and dental hygiene and developed a technique of rubbing the gums and teeth, cleaning the tongue, and swishing water in the mouth, which costs nothing and is very efficient for eliminating harmful bacteria in the mouth. Jay wanted Pranav to talk about his experiences with TM, but Pranav seemed almost not to hear those questions and just talked about the programs he was involved in teaching disadvantaged youth in India. Even though they live in the United States, Pranav and his mother run five or six schools in India for very poor Indian youth. Pranav said:

Many parents in India don't encourage the children to go to school because the parents typically are not educated and even with public schools, the parents find the schools expensive due to the cost of books and everything.

Pranav and his family raised the money to rent space for the schools, recruited teachers, bought a few computers, and put the young children into a Montessori education. Pranav's mother taught English to the students, and at age fourteen, Pranav taught science. Pranav said:

The students are really passionate about school and I really enjoy it [the teaching]. I believe the more you give the happier you are, so one thing I do is every morning from 7:00 to 7:30 last year and this year from 7:20 to 7:50 is teach them what they find hard. Science was very hard for them, and it might sound very funny here, but they didn't even know what the senses were, so I started very basic. But now they are so interested…they've gone all the way to learning chemical change, physical change, chemical properties.

Pranav's schools have about 200 students in total, including infants who are given Montessori movement activities. He also goes to India in the summers, where he brings his $300 annual birthday present and buys books and other necessaries for the children, teaches dental hygiene, and even holds competitions with awards for the students who remove the most bacteria that builds up in the mouth during sleep. He said:

Poor dental hygiene leads to cancer, diabetes and heart disease, and these people can't afford insurance or anything so I felt they should have an awareness. In my research I found that just finger rubbing and water swishing and toothpaste

293

brushing and tongue cleaning removes most of the bacteria and prevents these diseases.

After winning the top science award in Iowa, Pranav won the US 2017 Genius Challenge in San Diego for his oral hygiene research. The event gave the entrants just a minute or two to explain who they are, the problem their research solves, and why the rest of the world should care, with a follow up question and answer session.

There is a common thread between Pranav's experience and that of Arizonan Kyle Amsberry. Kyle joined the U.S. Army at age eighteen and served for five years, with tours in Iraq and Afghanistan. Like many of his fellow combat veterans, he came back with PTSD, and after military service he spent several years going from job to job without much purpose in his life and without effectively dealing with his PTSD. Then, with a veterans' scholarship from the David Lynch Foundation, he started TM in 2015. Kyle said he found "calmness and silence" in his life. He said "the chatter wasn't there anymore. I wasn't on edge that much." Kyle was so surprised by the transformation in his own life, he decided he wanted to be involved with helping veterans learn TM. When he learned about Maharishi International University in Iowa, he applied, was accepted, and joined the organic agriculture program where he wrote a business plan for the idea of an organic farm and TM retreat for veterans. He wants now to promote TM for veterans so they can better integrate into society.

Pranav's and Kyle's stories are typical of what happens to many who learn TM. For example, students see changes in themselves, feel they are on a positive track, and they start engaging in what is known in the moral development literature as "pro-social" behavior. This is behavior focused on helping others and following societal rules, as opposed to self-centered behavior that takes advantage of others and breaks the rules when it is advantageous to do so.

Research on Moral Judgment

A number of studies on students at Maharishi International University (MIU) show the relationship of their TM meditation practice to increased moral development and pro-social behavior. All the students at the university at both the undergraduate and graduate levels practice the Transcendental Meditation technique.

Early research of Dr. Wallace and his colleagues attempted to determine whether EEG brain wave coherence was associated with pro-social behavior. Their initial study[1] evaluated thirty graduate students in the Masters-in-Education program at MIU, thirteen of whom were rated as *highly* pro-social individuals. This is a distinction made in the field of social psychology based primarily on finding that these individuals were on the "leading edge" of the group, and that their behavior enhanced the overall well-being and interaction of the members of the class. They made constructive and uplifting comments to the professor and class members, showed an absence of negativity in their speech and behavior, inspired others to follow the group norms, and showed a sincere desire to improve the present state of society. The comparison group of students was friendly and interacted well with others, but they did not exhibit highly pro-social behavior. The results of the research showed that the EEG coherence in the frontal area of the brain was importantly related to pro-social behavior, irrespective of the student's grade point average or age.

Another study of seventy-six undergraduate students compared four groups: students at MIU who practiced TM, students at MIU who practiced the TM-Sidhi® program, which is an advanced program taught to those already practicing TM and which generates even more coherence than TM, students from another university who did not meditate, and students from that same university who were planning to start TM. It was found that the students who practiced the advanced TM-Sidhi program (information about this program is near the end of Appendix B) had the highest levels of principled moral thinking, and next were those practicing the Transcendental Meditation program alone. The students at the other university had lower levels of moral development, which were the same whether they were planning to start TM or not, indicating (at least in this study) that those interested in TM don't have a higher level of moral development than other students.[2]

Finally, in a study conducted at the University of Cincinnati on the TM program and moral values,[3] a psychologist administered Kohlberg's Moral Judgment interview (a highly respected tool for measuring moral maturity) to ninety-six student meditators at MIU and to thirty non-meditator students at the University of Cincinnati. The study used Kohlberg's hierarchy of moral levels of development, which places a person at a particular level of moral development based on the reasons they give for engaging in a certain activity. For example, if you believe that it is right to keep a promise, your reasons indicate your level of moral maturity. At one level, you may keep a promise because of the possibly unpleasant physical consequences for not doing so. At a slightly higher level, you may keep a promise for reasons of mutual benefit, meaning "You scratch my back and I'll scratch yours." At another level, you may value the maintenance of the social order for its own sake. At a still higher level, you define right action by a decision of conscience in accordance with principles of justice, equality, and respect for

296

individual dignity. Partly because the classifications are so sophisticated, the interviews in this study were all sent to the Harvard
University Moral Development Center to be scored by experts.

Statistical analysis of the study confirmed that the moral maturity of meditating students was more highly developed than that of
the non-meditators. The meditators exhibited significantly higher
levels of moral development in their thinking. Their attitude was
not merely "conformity to social order, but loyalty to it, of actively
maintaining, supporting, and justifying the order, and of identify-
ing with the person or group involved in it." The non-meditators
exhibited significantly more "pre-conventional thinking," a lesser
state of development in which behavior depends merely on the
physical consequences of action (reward, punishment, exchange of
favors) or on the physical power of those who issue the rules.

The Vedic Perspective on Moral Development

We all know the unfortunate stories of educated people, including
religious leaders, businessmen and women, athletic coaches, teachers, and politicians who still do terrible and immoral things. And
most polls show that despite a relatively educated society, there is a
moral decline that is widespread. A recent Gallup poll indicated 76
percent of Americans believe morals in this country are declining.

Isn't there something wrong in our education when so many
students value what is right and moral based on a lesser state of
development where moral choices depend on the possibility of
punishment and the adverse physical consequences of not following the rules?

Moral education was vastly different in the ancient Vedic civi-
lization. From the Vedic perspective, moral education is not primarily a matter of teaching the rules of proper moral conduct (for

instance, teaching the values of charity and sharing, or that killing is immoral) although that is not ignored. And moral values don't come from simply establishing politically free and democratic regimes. Instead, the Vedic perspective and Maharishi's teachings hold that a more coherent brain (that is, higher brain functioning) and higher levels of consciousness are caused by the regular experience of the silent, transcendental state (experienced at the deepest state during the TM practice), and the support of a balanced physiology. Such development necessarily leads to greater moral behavior. In other words, EEG coherence, a quiet or settled state of mind, higher consciousness, and moral values go hand in hand.

Moral behavior according to the Vedic perspective is automatic and spontaneous with the development of brain coherence and higher consciousness. What do we mean by saying it is automatic? One example is this: two people walk past a jewelry store in the evening, which has been left unlocked and is open. One person looks around to see if anyone is watching and weighs the risk of being caught with the rewards of his theft. But the person with a higher consciousness has totally different thoughts that automatically come into the mind. He or she thinks only of how best to contact the police or the owner to help prevent a theft. Higher consciousness automatically results in morally appropriate decisions.

Higher Consciousness

In every age, the world's great thinkers have noted that honorable and noble values were the natural qualities of men and women with a well-developed consciousness. Confucius said, "The superior man thinks always of virtue; the common man thinks of comfort." Artistotle said, "Honor and dishonor are the matters with which the high-minded man is especially concerned." Sir Francis Bacon said, "There is a great difference between a cunning man and a wise man, not only in point of honesty but in point of ability... and nothing doth more hurt in a State than that cunning men pass for wise." There is nothing new about the principle that a more developed consciousness is accompanied by higher values and more moral behavior. What is new is the understanding that a more developed consciousness depends on more coherence in brain functioning and the quiet or silent mind that accompanies it. What is new is that higher brain functioning is "higher" in every sense.

How Silence has been Valued Through the Ages

Veteran Kyle Amsberry, above, said that for the first time after starting TM, he found "calmness and silence" in his awareness. This is one thing we subjectively experience when the brain is more coherent (along with more clarity of thinking). It is something of real value that great men and women have recognized throughout the ages. In ancient Egypt, many centuries before the birth of Christ, masses of people would travel to the caves in the desert seeking solitude. They were on a quest to find Ammon, the principal deity of the Egyptian empire, who is said to have liked "silence." The custom is derived from a long tradition of "silent prayer,"[4] which is described in this way in an ancient Egyptian mandate:

> Do not multiply words,
> Keep silent if you want to be happy,
> When you pray with a loving heart,
> A prayer whose words are hidden,
> He gives you what you need,
> He hears what you say,
> He accepts your offer.

And throughout history great thinkers, both secular and religious, have counseled us to seek the silence within.

> Within man is the soul of the whole; the wise silence; the universal beauty, to which every part and particle is equally related.... [5]
> —*Ralph Waldo Emerson*

> In the attitude of silence, the soul finds the path in a clearer light, and what is elusive and deceptive resolves itself into a crystal clearness.[6]
> —*Mahatma Ghandi*

> Not merely an absence of noise, Real Silence begins when a reasonable being withdraws from the noise in order to find peace and order in his inner sanctuary.[7]
> —*Peter Minard, French Benedictine monk*

The fact that silence is valued so highly by at least some religious leaders does not make TM a religion or a religious practice. Father Len Dubi, a Roman Catholic priest in Chicago for 45 years, has been a TM meditator for most of that time. He says, "I'm a better Christian, a better priest, because of this technique." Rabbi Abe Shainberg of New York City says, "TM leads me to better prayer, better service, and I feel I'm more on a path to God than ever" (videos of the full statements by Father Dubi and Rabbi Shainberg are at tm.org/blog/maharishi/maharishi-tm-religion). And Buddhist nun Dr. Maeche Aunampai Passakchai, who was named the 2017 outstanding woman in Buddhism by a major Buddhist organization, said in an interview:

> With technology today people are farther away from inner values and then will be in suffering and sad. Because most people are looking for something outside, rather than inner

values. TM and the TM-Sidhis [an advanced program for TM meditators] is the technique for us to dive within and bring us to the good.

After I finished my TM teacher training course, I never doubted that there was no contradiction between Buddhist teachings and TM knowledge.

Dr. Passakchai is the founder and director of the Dhammjarenee Witthaya School in Thailand, a free Buddhist school for disadvantaged girls. Passakchai liked TM so much she had it taught to all the students (775 girls) at her school and saw dramatic changes. Many of these girls had been abused and were unhappy before coming to the school. She said she told the girls that "if you just dive deep within according to what Maharishi has taught, you will be happy and help create peace for yourselves and the world." Passakchai learned TM in 2008. She was already a Buddhist monk but saw something special that the simple TM mental technique could do for others and she became a TM teacher in 2010.

How Meditation is Viewed in the East

In the East, meditation of any kind has long been appreciated as a procedure for gaining higher consciousness and enlightenment, but gaining enlightenment is often understood to be an exclusively spiritual pursuit. In fact, in the East worldly pursuits of a practical nature (for example, business dealings, family matters) are usually considered an obstacle to enlightenment. Moreover, most believe that very few can succeed. This Eastern misunderstanding of enlightenment emphasizes avoiding worldly responsibilities in the name of spirituality.

On the other hand, for the most part in the West, there has only recently been an appreciation of the development of higher values through meditation. Here, the TM technique is still understood primarily as a technique for relaxation, its health benefits, greater efficiency, and material success and enjoyment. It is not widely appreciated (other than by those who learn the technique) as promoting higher values or any spiritual development because, after all, how could more orderly brain wave activity result in greater morality or spirituality? In the United States particularly, the word "spirituality" itself tends to be confused with religion, but spiritual development is just one aspect of the natural development of consciousness and brain functioning.

How did these misunderstandings develop? Maharishi explains that there were originally two separate types of meditation. One, he says, was for the recluse, or monk, and the other was for the active person with family responsibilities. The meditation for monks was preserved in monasteries, while the TM technique as taught to the public was evidently lost over time, accounting for the popular impression in the East that meditation leads to a life of withdrawal.

Maharishi's understanding of human evolution and the mechanics of the TM technique allowed him to interpret the most important texts of the Vedic literature in a way that had not been understood by scholars anywhere. For example, his commentary on the *Bhagavad-Gita*,[8] a key text in the Vedic literature, demonstrates that the Gita's repeated references to the need for withdrawal to gain higher values and enlightenment refers not to a reclusive way of life but to the withdrawal from all activity and all thoughts, which occurs in the silent state of consciousness that occurs at the deepest point in meditation. In reviving the TM technique, Maharishi thereby restored the understanding that an active person can effectively develop an integrated life of both higher values and material fulfillment. Maharishi has also corrected the mistaken belief that renunciation and withdrawal from the world are the primary means of developing higher values. Seen in this light, "spiritual growth" through the TM program means the growth of consciousness, supported by coherent brain development and a balanced physiology. It is more than just learning the rules of right behavior. It is developing the brain and nervous system so that what is good and positive automatically comes to mind and is all that the mind entertains.

A Moral Atmosphere in a Coherence Creating Community

A study on high school students at Maharishi School in Fairfield, Iowa, showed an unusually high *moral atmosphere* in the school, something its administrators had known for years in its interactions with the students.[9] The special moral atmosphere was noted in an unusual incident that occurred in the school, but also was confirmed by research results. The incident was that one day an administrator at the school noted that a $5 bill had been tacked to one of the bulletin boards in the school with a note as to where it was found on the school grounds. But this was not just a good deed by one individual. What made this incident so unusual was that the $5 stayed tacked to the bulletin board for several weeks without anyone pocketing it until it was finally taken down by the administrator with a note as to where it could be claimed.

The research study at Maharishi School used what are known as "dilemma interviews" developed at Harvard's Center for Moral Education. Questions posing significant moral dilemmas have been developed by leading researchers to determine the moral atmosphere in schools or other institutions. The subjects reported taking the community needs into account in making decisions in 73 percent of the cases, whereas students at their previous schools would, on average, take community needs into account in approximately 20 percent of the situations. The study found that the TM program was the major contributing factor in the extremely high level of moral atmosphere at the school. The number of years practicing the TM program was also relevant. In general, the longer the individuals had been meditating, the greater the pro-social behavior, a further indication that it was the TM program that was responsible for the change.[10]

Changing Society by Spreading Coherence through our Interconnectedness

When we think of being connected, we think of conscious connections through the Internet, social media, smart phones, and other technologies, as well as our obvious physical interactions with others during the course of a day. But we're more connected than we think. We've learned that we're connected subconsciously in various ways. In *The Tipping Point*, author Malcolm Gladwell describes a famous research project conducted in the 1960s where the researcher, William Condon, spent hours studying a four to five second segment of a film of a family having dinner. Condon discovered that the family was not just talking and listening to one another, but rhythmically generating micro movements that were in perfect synchrony.[11] Each person would move a hand or a shoulder or tilt the head or blink the eyes within the space of a fraction of a second as they talked, while the others at the dinner table were making their own movements to coincide with the speaker's in a rhythmic dance. Gladwell also points out that subsequent research has shown that when two people talk, the pitch and volume and number of sounds they make per second also become synchronized, so there's a rhythmic song going along with the dance movements that we're all engaged in. This is all taking place without being consciously aware of the process, indicating that below the conscious thinking mind, people are mentally connected more than they think.

Moreover, the phenomenon appears to be universal. Even babies, in their first days before they have much conscious awareness, synchronize the movements of their heads, elbows, feet, and shoulders with the sounds of the adults in their vicinity. Gladwell calls this synchronous song and dance an "interactional synchronicity," and, according to Gladwell, the movements, sounds, and even the emotions of everyone involved tend to become the same as the dominant or charismatic personality, those whom Gladwell calls *senders*.

The concept of an interactional synchronicity as one kind of subconscious interconnection is interesting, but the Vedic literature describes an even more intriguing influence people have on one another. It derives from their connectedness at the deepest level of consciousness and the power of coherence.

Due to this connection, an unseen but powerful influence of coherence can be transmitted from coherent groups of *senders* to those in the vicinity. That interconnectedness and its practical effects underlies how groups of TM meditators have been able to spread coherence to everyone in the vicinity and how groups of Vedic pandits can create peace in their vicinity. The research and theoretical basis is explored fully in an earlier book by Wallace and

Marcus, *Victory Before War*, published by Maharishi International University Press (2007). One interview from that book gives some idea of the societal atmosphere that is possible.

Hassan Sbaba, a former student at Maharishi International University (MIU) talked to Jay for an earlier book about the unusual atmosphere that had been created by the meditators at the university. Then age 32, Hassan had a traditional Muslim upbringing in Morocco. He was raised in a religious home, and he continued his religious observances as he got older, including prayers to Mecca five times per day. After receiving a degree in physics at Mohammed V University in Rabat, Morocco, Hassan came to Iowa to study computer science at MIU. He became interested in the university because he wanted to continue his education and combine it with learning the Transcendental Meditation technique. After experiencing the collective consciousness in the university atmosphere, following his receipt of a master's degree in computer science Hassan decided to remain at the university as a network engineer. Hassan said:

The people in my country and those in America are not so very different, but there are big misunderstandings about Muslims. I was shocked when I came here to find that many Americans think that Muslims hate the American people. It's not true. Even if America is aggressive against some Muslim countries, the people distinguish between the positions the American government may take and the American people, who are generally well liked.

Most Americans also think that in Muslim countries religion dominates more than in America, but even that is not true. We don't have [a Muslim equivalent to] Christian radio and talk shows or anywhere near as much open religious activity in my country as in America. Americans and Moroccans have much more in common than they do differences, but most Americans would think Moroccans are like aliens, and it is difficult for the American and Islamic world to become integrated in a way that eliminates any tension.

That is one reason why I think Maharishi's programs are so important. They are programs that anyone can enjoy, and they don't conflict with any religion. Here at the university we can also see what happens as the group meditation programs continue and more people learn to meditate. This campus is very different from other campuses. Here there are students from all different cultures and civilizations, which may also be true at other universities, but there is a special bond here. We all have Transcendental Meditation in common and the atmosphere is changed as a result of all the students meditating peacefully. There is an immediate respect for others in this environment. We are all on the same path. Even you [Jay] and I, due to our different backgrounds, would probably not be having this same kind of conversation in another environment, or if we were not both meditators.

Throughout the world there is a growing awakening to the benefits of inner quiet or silence and spiritual values, which is uplifting the lives of people of all religions, all cultures, and all ages. For example, since the mid-2000s, TM has been taught in over a hundred schools to several hundred thousand students in India, and to many more students throughout South and Central America. In Mexico, there are 11 large schools with over 9,000 students who have learned TM and the advanced TM-Sidhi program (see Appendix B); in Peru,

307

45,000 children were taught TM in the schools; and in Colombia, over 60,000 young children have learned in centers run by Father Gabriel Mejia, a Catholic priest.

Colombia has a serious problem of children living on the streets whose parents have been killed or otherwise cannot take care of them. These street children try to survive any way they can, typically working as prostitutes, or in bars, or selling drugs. Father Mejia began taking these children off the streets and housing and feeding them and showing them kindness. When he personally learned Transcendental Meditation, having it taught to the children became a central part of his program because of the traumatic stress these children have experienced. Father Mejia operates fifty centers in Latin America and funds for his children to learn TM were provided by the non-profit David Lynch Foundation. The filmmaker's foundation has provided the funds to teach Transcendental Meditation to over half a million school children in Brazil, Colombia, Peru, Bolivia, Vietnam, Nepal, Northern Ireland, Ghana, Kenya, Uganda, South Africa, and Israel.

In an online video (davidlynchfoundation.org), Father Mejia described his TM experience and the experience of the thousands of traumatized young people who have come to his centers. He said:

> When I learned the Transcendental Meditation technique, I was very impressed. I would define it in one phrase, one word—happiness. You experience happiness and bliss when you practice the technique. For me as a Catholic priest saying my prayers, celebrating communion, reading the Psalms, is all part of a religious life and religious commitment. Transcendental Meditation does not take the place of the com-

munion. It's a space for personal development. It prepares me to experience the liturgy in its fullness.

And when the child closes his eyes to meditate, the world opens up for him, and then the children discover their essential nature, which is love. I have seen thousands of children pass through the foundation [Father Mejia's centers], and every case is fascinating—to see what state a child arrived in and how he has been transformed.

Appendix A

Selected Research on Higher Brain Functioning

1. **Improved Cognitive Function Throughout the Lifespan.** The Transcendental Meditation technique increases general intelligence and positive self-concept and holistic cognitive abilities in children, adolescents, and college students and adults. In octogenarians it improves cognitive flexibility and memory and makes them feel "less old." Two six-month studies and a year-long study found that TM practice increased creativity, practical intelligence, field independence, mental efficiency, and fluid intelligence, as well as reducing anxiety. **Reference**: *Intelligence* 29, no. 5 (2001): 419–440.

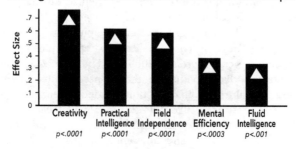

Increased General Cognitive Ability
through the *Transcendental Meditation®* technique

Three randomized controlled studies among secondary school and vocational school students found that, in contrast to controls, those who learned the Transcendental Meditation technique showed significant improvement in five measures of intellectual functioning; they also showed deceased anxiety.

Intelligence is considered the top ranking journal in its field.

Reference: *Intelligence* 29 (2001): 419-440

2. The Transcendental Meditation technique increases EEG alpha coherence both during and outside of the period of meditation.

References: Travis, F., Tecce, J., Arenander, A., Wallace, R.K., "Patterns of EEG coherence, power and contingent negative variation characterize the integration of transcendental and waking states," *Biological Psychology* 2002 61(3): 293–319; Travis, F., "Brain functioning as the ground for spiritual experiences and ethical behavior," *FBI Law Enforcement Bulletin* 2009 78(5): 26–32; Travis F.T., "Autonomic and EEG patterns distinguish transcending from other experiences during Transcendental Meditation practice," *International Journal of Psychophysiology* 2001 42(1): 1–9: Travis, F., Arenander, A., "Cross-sectional and longitudinal study of effects of Transcendental Meditation practice on interhemispheric frontal asymmetry and frontal coherence," *International Journal of Neuroscience* 2006 116(12): 1519–38; Travis, F., Arenander, A., DuBois, D., "Psychological and physiological characteristics of a proposed object-referral/self-referral continuum of self-awareness," *Consciousness and Cognition* 2004 13(2): 401–420; Travis, F., Brown, S. "My brain made me do it: brain maturation and levels of self-development," in Pfaffenberger, P.W., et al. (eds), *The Postconventional Personality: Perspectives on Higher Development* (pp. 23–38), New York: SUNY Press, 2011; Travis, F., Grosswald, S., Stixrud, W., "ADHD, brain functioning, and Transcendental Meditation practice," *Mind & Brain, The Journal of Psychiatry* 2011 2(1):73–81; Travis, F., Haaga, D., Hagelin, J.S., et al., "A self-referential default brain state: patterns of coherence, power, and eLORETA sources during eyes-closed rest and the Transcendental Meditation practice," *Cognitive Processing*, 2010 11(1): 21–30; Travis, F., Tecce, J.J., Guttman, J., "Cortical plasticity, contingent negative variation, and transcendent experiences during practice of the Transcendental Meditation technique," *Biological Psychology*, 2000 55(1): 41–55; Hebert, J.R., et al., "Enhanced EEG alpha time-domain phase synchrony during Transcendental Meditation: implications for cortical integration theory," *Signal Processing* 2005 85(11): 2213–2232; Dillbeck, M.C., Araas-Vesely, S. Participation in the Transcendental Meditation program and frontal EEG coherence during concept learning. *International Journal of Neuroscience* 1986 29(1/2): 45–55; Dillbeck, M.C., Bronson, E.C., "Short-term longitudinal effects of the Transcendental Meditation technique on EEG power and coherence," *International Journal of Neuroscience*, 1981, 14(3/4): 147–151; Dillbeck, M.C., Orme-Johnson, D.W., Wallace, R.K., "Frontal EEG coherence, H-reflex recovery, concept learning, and the TM-Sidhi program," *International Journal of Neuroscience* 1981 15(3): 151–15; Orme-Johnson, D.W., Dillbeck, M.C., Wallace, R.K., Landrith III, G.S., "Intersubject EEG coherence: is consciousness a field?" *International Journal of Neuroscience*, 1982, 16(3/4): 203–209

312

3. **Increased Brain Integration.**

The Transcendental Meditation technique increases brain integration, which is characteristic of:
- world-class athletes
- high-level managers
- musicians
- successful police officers who possess a spiritual orientation that buffers them against the toxic effects of the stresses encountered in police work
- flexible and original creative thinkers

References: *International Journal of Psychophysiology* 71, no. 2 (2009), 170–176; *Biological Psychology* 38, 37–51 (2002); *Management, Spirituality & Religion* 214, 230–244 (2014); *Creativity Research Journal* 26 (2), 239–243 (2014); Harung, H.S., Travis, F., Blank, W., Heaton, D., "Higher development, brain integration, and excellence in leadership," *Management Decision* 2009 47(6): 872–894; Heaton, D., Harung, H.S., "Awakening creative intelligence and peak performance: reviving an Asian tradition," chapter in J. Kidd, et al. (eds), "Human Intelligence Deployment in Asian Business," London: Macmillan, and New York: *St. Martin's Press*, 2001; So, K.T., Orme-Johnson, D.W., "Three randomized experiments on the holistic longitudinal effects of the Transcendental Meditation technique on cognition," *Intelligence* 2001 29(5): 419–440; Sridevi, K., Krishna, R., "Temporal effects of meditation on cognitive style," *Journal of Indian Psychology* 2003 21: 38–51.

4. **Enhanced cognition from TM in older adults.**

References: Nidich, S.I., Schneider, R.H., Nidich, R.J., Foster, G., Sharma, H., Salerno, J., Goodman, R., Alexander, C.N., "Effect of the Transcendental Meditation program on intellectual development in community-dwelling older adults," *Journal of Social Behavior and Personality* 2005 17(1): 217–226; a study of 80-year-olds conducted at Harvard found that practice of the Transcendental Meditation technique increases cognitive flexibility and the ability to memorize new material, *Journal of Personality and Social Psychology* 57, no. 6 (1989): 950–64.

5. **Higher Brain Integration in Long-Term Meditators.** Long-term practitioners of the Transcendental Meditation technique have a higher level of brain integration than any other group studied— top athletes, top managers, professional musicians, or successful

police. **References**: *International Journal of Psychophysiology* 71, no. 2 (2009): 170-176; *Biological Psychology* 38, 37-51 (2002); *Management, Spirituality & Religion* 214, 230–244 (2014); *Creativity Research Journal* 26 (2), 239–243 (2014).

6. **Improved Basic Math and English Skills in Middle School Children.** Middle school students who learned the Transcendental Meditation technique and practiced it twice daily as part of the school day were found to increase significantly after three months in achievement scores on mathematics and language (English) in comparison to control students matched on previous mathematics and English performance level scores. **Reference**: *Education* 131, no. 3 (2011): 556–564.

7. **Improvements in Students "Below Basic."** Students who were "below basic" or "far below basic" and who practiced the Transcendental Meditation technique improved ten times as much on a composite of Math and English as those who received only the usual school curriculum. **Reference**: *Education* 131, no. 3 (2011): 556–564.

Improved Academic Achievement in Students Below Basic

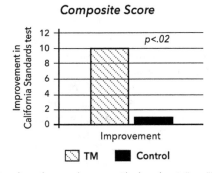

Composite Score

Urban middle-school students who were "below basic" or "far below basic" who practiced the Transcendental Meditation technique improved 10 times as much on a composite of Math and English as those who received only the usual school curriculum.

Reference: *Education* 131, no. 3 (2011): 556-64

8. **Increased rates of graduation and college acceptance and decreased dropout rates for students.** **Reference:** Colbert, R.D., Nidich, S., "Effect of the Transcendental Meditation program on graduation, college acceptance and dropout rates for students attending an urban public high school," *Education*. 2013 Jun;133(4):495–501.

9. **Increased cognitive development in preschool and elementary school children.** **References:** Dixon, C., Dillbeck, M.C., Travis, F., Msemaje, H., et al., "Accelerating cognitive and self-development: longitudinal studies with preschool and elementary school children," *Journal of Social Behavior and Personality* 2005 17(1):65–91; Warner, T.Q., "Awareness and cognition: the role of awareness training in child development," *Journal of Social Behavior and Personality*, 2005 17(1): 47–64.

10. **Increased Creativity.** Three studies found that the largest effect of the TM technique on cognitive processes was on "whole-brain creativity," a blend of intelligent thinking and balanced feeling. The studies show increases in such traits as comprehension, analysis, curiosity, unconventionality, synthesis, and willingness to take risks. **Reference:** *Intelligence* 29, no. 5 (2001): 419–440.

11. **Increased Practical Intelligence.** Three studies of high school students found that the TM technique increases practical intelligence, which means nonintellectual abilities and attitudes that predict success in work, love, and social relationships. **Reference:** *Intelligence* 29, no. 5 (2001): 419–440.

12. **Increased Field Independence.** Multiple studies have found that the Transcendental Meditation technique increases field independence, which reflects the growth of broad comprehension together with the ability to focus, indicating a greater ability to see other people's points of view, greater ability to organize thoughts, and greater resistance to social pressure. **Reference:** *Perceptual and Motor Skills* 39 (1974): 1031–34.

13. **Increased Fluid Intelligence.** Multiple studies indicate that the Transcendental Meditation technique develops fluid intelligence in adolescents, college students, and adults. Fluid intelligence is

"street smarts" as opposed to "book smarts" and reflects executive control functions of the frontal lobes, which are involved in keeping attention on the goal and finding patterns and relationships that lead to effective solutions. **Reference**: *Personality and Individual Differences* 12 (1991): 1105–1116.

Increased Fluid Intelligence
through the *Transcendental Meditation* technique

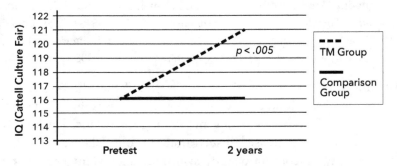

A controlled study found that two years of practice of the Transcendental Meditation technique increased fluid intelligence by 5 IQ points in college students. Control subjects who received only the usual college curriculum and not TM training did not change, as expected.

Reference: *Personality and Individual Differences* 12 (1991): 1105-16

14. **Improved Attention.** A study published in *Personality and Individual Differences* also found that TM practice improves attention. When a person is able to stay on target, their reaction time is very similar from one trial to the next. However, if they get distracted or their mind wanders, then their reaction time will be slower on some trials and faster on others. This increases the variability. Thus, the degree of trial to trial variability (standard deviation) of choice reaction time is a measure of sustained attention; the less the variability, the more stable the attention is. This study found that the TM group had more stable attention at pretest (less variability) than the comparison group and improved even more over the two years of the experiment, whereas the comparison group

tended to get worse. This reduction in variability in choice reaction time has also been interpreted to indicate reduced noise in the nervous system. **Reference**: *Personality and Individual Differences* 12 (1991).

Reduced Wavering of Attention:
Reduced Noise in the Nervous System

through the *Transcendental Meditation* technique

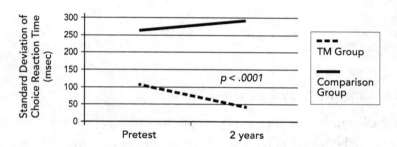

Wavering of attention, measured by variability of choice reaction time, was less in the TM group and improved even further after two more years of TM practice. The comparison group tended to get worse.

Reference: *Personality and Individual Differences* 12 (1991): 1105–16

Learning to Meditate Correctly:
What it Costs and Advanced Programs

TM is Taught by Certified Teachers

Transcendental Meditation is taught individually by trained teachers. Teachers have taken an intensive training course, with a number of months of it in residence. The report of Jane Smith (not her real name due to certain health concerns) in Chapter 4 indicates the value of taking the official course from a trained teacher. Like the TM technique itself, the teaching has its subtleties. The technique is not simply repeating a mantra. That would be a focusing technique.

Meditation Instruction/Fee/Satisfaction Guarantee

The TM teaching is interactive. In the first day of instruction, the TM instructor asks you questions from time to time and gives further instructions based on your experiences. The TM technique is always taught orally and individually on the first day of instruction.

Because TM is taught over a four-day period of instruction (about an hour and a half or two hours a day), it generally costs more than techniques that do not require the same level of instruction. The course fee includes a lifetime of free check-ups of your meditation to make sure you are practicing the technique effort-lessly for maximum benefits, as well as a wide range of free online and in-center offerings. The cost of the instruction and check-up sessions as of the date of publication is set forth below and is based on the household income of the person being instructed. The cur-rent fee as of the date of printing includes:

- **4 session TM course**
  Day 1:   personalized one-on-one instruction
  Days 2–4:   small group training sessions
- **Lifetime follow-up and support (checking sessions at TM centers)**
- **Satisfaction guarantee (check with the TM center on current details)**

Payment for the course can be over four months or in a single pay-ment.

Annual Household Income (AHI)	TM Course Fee with Free Lifetime Support
Receiving federal assistance	Ask us about partial grant support.
Less than $50,000	$125 x 4 months = $500
$50,000 – $99,000	$185 x 4 months = $740
$100,000 – $199,000	$215 x 4 months = $860
$200,000 or more	$240 x 4 months = $960
Full-time students	$95 x 4 months = $360

TM is taught by non-profit organizations in each country. The details above are for the United States; other countries may have different fees that in many instances are also based on the income levels of the person learning TM as well as income levels in the country. The technique itself is taught in the same systematic way worldwide.

As of the publication date, the TM organizations in the United States offer a satisfaction guarantee, which may also be available in other countries. If you meditate regularly for at least 30 days and are not satisfied after attending the four-day course and several free follow-up sessions during that period, you can receive a full refund of the course fee (refund requests must be made within 60 days of the date of personal instruction). Check at your TM center to see if any conditions for the refund have changed.

Practicing Transcendental Meditation/Advanced Programs

The TM technique is practiced for two 20-minute sessions each day: in the morning as a preparation for the day's activity, and again in the late afternoon or early evening to relieve the stress of the day. Practicing TM itself does not require any change in lifestyle or diet, although people often do change their diets and other practices after beginning TM as they become more health conscious. One reason for practicing the technique twice a day is to train the physiology to be relaxed and coherent all the time. This is the principle of habituation. Whatever we do repeatedly becomes ingrained and, as stated earlier, the objective is not just to be relaxed and more coherent during the TM practice, but to maintain that state even in the midst of dynamic activity.

There are times when TM can be practiced more than twice per day, for example when a person is attending a TM retreat. From time to time the local TM centers or the TM national center will organize two-day to even week-long or longer TM retreats. These are valuable because the increased number of meditations done on those retreats can often get rid of more deeply rooted stresses and accelerate the benefits from the TM practice. Coach Patricia Glispin (Chapter 4) decided to go on one such retreat in the Boston area in 2018 over the July 4th weekend. She said:

> The weekend retreat created a significant change in my own TM routine, and, while I had very good benefits from TM before the retreat, the retreat gave me a new heightened respect for TM and its power on so many levels. I had a big release of stress during the retreat, and feel that it changed me physically, mentally, emotionally, and spiritually... feeling better in all areas of life. My mind is sharper and for the first time in 38 years I am sleeping through the night.

> The respect I have for TM's power as a result of the retreat also created a significant change in my daily TM practice. I used to scramble to find 20 minutes to squeeze in TM... sometimes even forgetting until late in the day. I now reserve an hour for each session... leaving time for yoga and pranayama and lying down to rest after TM. The time taken from my busy schedule is well-spent and easily "recovered." My focus is laser sharp and I accomplish far more every day.

> In my opinion, TM is by far the most powerful tool to change our lives and manage the stress of daily living. I am grateful to all the folks that helped me find it and trained me. I hope my experience might help others try TM... it is a true "game changer."

The TM-Sidhi Program (a "mental yoga" for maximum coherence)

In the 1970s Maharishi began teaching what are known as Patanjali's Yoga Sutras, giving the program the name the TM-Sidhi program. *Sutras* are formulas or techniques and the Yoga Sutras are the mental formulas of a great sage named Patanjali, who is generally credited with being Yoga's founder. Patanjali's Yoga Sutras are considered by many to be the pinnacle of Yoga, but over the centuries there have been relatively few people who could successfully perform the sutras or find practical benefits from Patanjali's knowledge. However, Maharishi showed that the sutras will work in the presence of a catalyst, that being a coherent state of consciousness. In other words, these mental formulas will work for those who have already learned to experience a coherent state of consciousness through their TM training and have been practicing TM for some time.

Professor Ed Sarath of the University of Michigan, who we quoted in the chapter on Panchakarma, learned the TM-Sidhi program in 1979, five years after he learned TM. In response to our question of how the TM-Sidhi program compared to TM, Professor Sarath said:

> Getting the sidhis opened up a channel in my psychophysiology that wasn't there before. It was like turning on a light in terms of the depth of the meditative experience. In fact, while taking the Sidhi preparatory course something happened that was permanent. When I would sit down to meditate, the depth of the experience was instantaneous and sustaining, that is the depth of the transcending. And over the years, that became richer and fuller. So in one word, I would say that going from TM to the sidhis is "dramatic."

Rabbi Alan Green, formerly the senior rabbi of congregation Shaarey Zedek in Winnipeg, Canada and the 2017 recipient of the prestigious annual humanitarian award of Canada's Jewish National Fund, learned the TM-Sidhi program in 1977. He emphasized how the program enhanced the "heart value" of life. He said:

322

When we learned the TM-Sidhi program back in 1977, virtually everyone on the course experienced the same thing: tremendous expansion of the heart value of our lives. Deep feeling and expanded intuition carried over from the course into our daily lives, as we continued our practice. Certainly, in my role as a rabbi, the TM-Sidhi program has been tremendously helpful, enabling me to tune into others and respond to them in highly sensitive circumstances involving death, grief, and illness, as well as in peak experiences like weddings and other celebrations.

I credit the program with the ability to interact with people, and to radiate a calming, positive influence in these kinds of difficult life situations.

I also love interfaith work, and that brings me into contact with all different faiths and ideologies. And I meet people who are not particularly enamored with the State of Israel—some Christian groups, and Muslims especially. While I can have all kinds of differences and strong disagreements with them, in the actual presence of the person, I can only feel warmth and kindness, harmony and love. I see them as people rather than ideologies, and there is reciprocity in those feelings. And while we may feel this way or that, and perceive things quite differently, we find we can still be loving human beings to each other.

This is what the TM-Sidhi program brings about on an individual basis. But Maharishi has done more. He figured out a way to cause those warm feelings to spread collectively—in society as a whole—with his group program to overcome and transform the negativity that seems to come at us from every direction these days.

Over the years, researchers have shown how much the TM-Sidhi program adds to practicing Transcendental Meditation.[1] Peer-reviewed research by Dr. Wallace and others showed that the TM-Sidhi program, as compared to TM alone, further enhanced creativity and intelligence,[2] concept learning, and moral reasoning[3], the growth of a positive outlook on life[4], psychological health[5], nervous system functioning (as measured by what is known as Paired H-Reflex time)[6], and more acute hearing after the practice of the TM-Sidhi program.[7] The physiological basis of these results is the finding of significantly increased frontal brain coherence in those having learned the TM-Sidhi program compared to a group of meditating controls who had not learned the TM-Sidhi program[8].

Notes to Appendix B

1. Pearson, C., *Yogic Flying*, Maharishi University of Management Press (2008), pp. 118–119.

2. Orme-Johnson, D.W. and Haynes, C.T., "EEG Phase Coherence, Pure Consciousness, Creativity, and TM-Sidhi Experiences," *International Journal of Neurosciences*, (1981), pp. 211–217.

3. Nidich, S.I., Ryncarz, R.A., Abrams, A.I., Orme-Johnson, D.W., and Wallace, R.K., "Kohlbergian Cosmic Perspective Response, EEG Coherence, and the Transcendental Meditation and TM-Sidhi Program," *Journal of Moral Education*, Vol. 12(3)(1983), pp. 166–173.

4. Gelderloos, P., Goddard, P.H., Ahlstorm, H.H.B., and Jacoby, R., "Cognitive Orientation toward Positive Values in Advanced Participants of the TM and TM-Sidhi Program," *Perceptual and Motor Skills* 64 (1987), pp. 177–197.

5. Gelderloos, P., "Psychological Health and Development of Students at Maharishi International University: A Controlled Longitudinal Study," *Modern Science and Vedic Science* 1(4) (1987), pp. 471–487.

6. Wallace, R.K., Mills, P.J., Orme-Johnson, D.W., Dillbeck, M.C., and Jacobe, E., "Modification of the Paired H-Reflex through the Transcendental Meditation and TM-Sidhi Program," *Experimental Neurology* 79 (1983), pp. 77–86.

7. Clements, G. and Milstein, S.L., "Auditory Thresholds in Advanced Participants in the Transcendental Meditation program," *Scientific Research on the Transcendental Meditation Program Collected Papers* Vol.1, Maharishi European Research University Press, Seelisberg, Switzerland (1977), pp. 719–722.

8. Orme-Johnson, D.W., Wallace, R.K., and Dillbeck, M.C., "Longitudinal Effects of the TM-Sidhi Program on EEG Phase Coherence," *Scientific Research on the Transcendental Meditation Program Collected Papers* Vol. 3, MIU Press, Vlodrop, The Netherlands (1990), pp. 1678–1686; Travis, F.T., and Orme-Johnson, D.W., "EEG Coherence and Power During Yogic Flying," *International Journal of Neuroscience*, Vol. 54, 1990, p. 1; Orme-Johnson, D.W., Clements, G., Haynes, C.T., Bodaori, K., "Higher States of Consciousness: EEG Coherence, Creativity, and Experience of the Sidhis," *Scientific Research on the Transcendental Meditation Program Collected Papers*, Maharishi University of Management Press, Vol. 1, 1976, p. 707.

Appendix C

References for More Information

For More Information on Transcendental Meditation or to find a TM teacher:

Go to TM.org and davidlynchfoundation.org.
Also go to drtonynader.com. Dr. Nader is the worldwide leader of the TM organizations and has many online videos, including on how TM compares to other meditation techniques.

For More Information on Maharishi AyurVeda and for individual consultations:

Go to the website of the Maharishi Integrative Ayurveda Institute at maharishi-ayurveda.us/. Trained consultants who may be close to your area or available by phone for consultations can be located by going to the directory tab on this site, then click for the listing of doctors, trained consultants, and Maharishi Panchakarma Centers, updated regularly.

You may also contact your local TM Center (TM.org) to find out if experts trained in pulse diagnosis are or will be available in your area.

For Maharishi Panchakarma, either of the Centers below:

The Raj in Fairfield, Iowa
Phone: 800-864-8714
Email: info@theraj.com
Website: theraj.com

Maharishi Ayurveda Integrative
Health Center
Phone: 641-472-7000, ext. 3406
Website: miu-clinic.org

For Ayurvedic Supplements
(healing herbs, teas and spices)

Website: mapi.com.

For Maharishi Yoga Training:

The 16-lesson course on Maharishi Yoga Asanas is available online from Maharishi International University. Go to miu.edu/yoga

For Maharishi International University, go to miu.edu

Endnotes

Chapter 1

1. Pinker, Steven, "The Second Law of Thermodynamics," at www.edge. org/response-detail/27023, January 12, 2017.

2. Lawrence Domash, Ph.D., a renowned physicist, was the first to describe how the laws of thermodynamics relate to human development in a series of lectures at Maharishi International University in the 1970s.

3. Schrödinger, E., *What is Life?*, Cambridge University Press (1944).

4. Meymandi, A., M.D., "Music, Medicine, Healing, and the Genome Project," *Psychiatry* (Edgmont), Vol. 6 (9) (September, 2009), p. 43–45.

5. Ibid.

6. Fitzgerald, M., "Vibrating Cells Disclose Their Ailments," *MIT Technology Review*, Sept. 9, 2008.

7. Von Bubnov, Andreas, "Getting the Vibe," at http://sciencenotes.ucsc. edu/0501/sound/index.html; Niemetz, A. and Pelling, A., "The Dark Side of the Cell, at www.darksideofcell.info/about.html; Thompson, C., "Listening for Cancer," *The New York Times Magazine*, December 12, 2004.

8. Binns, C., "Do Cells Make Noise? Listening to Cells Might Help Scientists Catch Cancers Without Painful Biopsies," *Popular Science blog*, http://www.popsci.com/scitech/article/2008-01/do-cells-make-noise.

9. Gonzalez-Jimenez, M., Ramakrishnan, G., Harwood, T., Lapthorn, A.J., Kelly, S.M., Ellis, E.M., and Wynne, K., "Observation of coherent delocalized phonon-like modes in DNA under physiological conditions, Nature Communications," June 1, 2016; Chou, K.C., "Low-frequency vibrations of DNA molecules," *Biochem. J.* 221 (1984), pp. 27–31.

10. Rimer, S. and Drexler, M. "The biology of emotion—and what it may teach us about helping people live longer," *Happiness & Health* (Winter 2011), at www.hsph.harvard.edu/news/magazine/happiness-stress-heart-disease.

11. Ibid.

12. www.independent.co.uk/life-style/health-and-families/health-news/high-life-expectancy-in-japan-partly-down-to-diet-carbohydrates-vegetables-fruit-fish-meat-a6956011.html.

13. www.nhlbi.nih.gov/health-topics/sleep-deprivation-and-deficiency.

14. Munro, D., "U.S. Healthcare Ranked Dead Last Compared to 10 Other Countries," *Forbes*, June 16, 2014.

15. drhyman.com/blog/2010/07/18/why-treating-your-symptoms-is-a-recipe-for-disaster/.

16. Ibid.

Chapter 2

1. See, e.g., Field, T., "Massage Therapy for Infants and Children," *J. Dev. Behav. Pediatry*, Vol. 16, pp. 105–111 (1994); Post-White, J., et al; "Therapeutic Massage and Healing Touch Improve Symptoms in Cancer," *Integrative Cancer Therapy*, Vol. 2, (2003) pp. 332–344.

2. Marshall, L., "Just the Two of Us: Holding hands can ease pain, synch brainwaves," *CU Boulder Today*, Feb. 28, 2018 at www.colorado.edu/today/2018/02/28/just-two-us-holding-hands-can-ease-pain-sync-brainwaves; Goldstein, P., Weissman-Fogel, I., Dumas, G., and Shamay-Tsory, S., "Brain to brain coupling during handholding is associated with pain reduction," *Proceedings of the National Academy of Sciences*, Feb. 26, 2018, at https://doi.org/10/pnas.

3. Uhihass, P. and Singer, W., "Neural Synchrony in Brain Disorders: Relevance for Cognitive Dysfunctions and Pathophysiology," *Neuron*, Vol. 52 (2006), pp. 155–168

4. Hebb, D.O., "The Organization of Behavior: A Neuropsychological Theory," *Psychology Press Edition* (2002).

5. Hummel, F., Gerloff, C., "Larger Interregional Synchrony is Associated with Greater Behavioral Success in a Complex Sensory Integration Task in Humans," *Cerebral Cortex*, Vol. 15(5) (2004), pp. 670–678.

6. Ibid.

7. Bergland, C., "Alpha Brain Waves Boost Creativity and Reduce Depression," *Psychology Today*, April 17, 2015 at https://www.psychologytoday.com/blog/the-athletes-way/201504/alpha-brain-waves-boost-creativity-and-reduce-depression.

8. Hummel, F., Gerloff, C., "Larger Interregional Synchrony is Associated with Greater Behavioral Success in a Complex Sensory Integra-

tion Task in Humans," *Cerebral Cortex*, Vol. 15(5) (2004), pp. 670–678. The studies in this area sometimes refer to brain wave "coherence" and sometimes to brain wave "synchrony." Both terms in general mean a high degree of orderliness or balance, but the terms also have their own technical meaning in measuring brain waves. First, in addition to their frequency (i.e., the number of brain waves in a given period of time), brain waves are analyzed in terms of their amplitude, that is, the peak height of the wave, and their phase, whether two waves are in step with one another. So, if you analyze the wave activity in two different areas of the brain, the two waves may have an ongoing relationship with each other such that they are perfectly in step (in phase) over time, which means that the crest or height of each wave lines up with or matches the height of the other wave at a particular point in time. When the phase is perfectly in step like this it is technically called "synchrony." On the other hand, if the phase of the two waves maintain a precise relationship over time, but the crest of one wave is perhaps always just a little lower or higher than the other, there is still that orderly relationship, but that is technically referred to as "coherence."

9. Moran, B., "People learn faster with synced brain waves," October 11, 2017 at www.futurity.org/electrical-stimulation-brain-1570953-2/.

10. Hamid, A., Gall, C., Speck, O., Antal, A., and Sabel, B.A., "Effects of alternating current stimulation on the healthy and diseased brain," *Frontiers in Neuroscience*, Vol. 9 (2015), p. 390 available at www.ncbi. nlm.nih.gov/pmc/articles/PMC4621306/.

11. Basar, E., and Guntekin, B., "A review of brain oscillations in cognitive disorders and the role of neurotransmitters," *Brain Research*, 1235 (2008), pp. 172–193; Zhen-yang, J., "Abnormal cortical functional connections in Alzheimer's disease: analysis of inter- and intra-hemispheric EEG coherence," *Journal of Zhejiang University Science B*, Vol. 6, Issue 4 (April 2005), pp 259–264.

12. Murias, M., Webb, S.J., Greenson, J., and Dawson, G., "Resting state cortical connectivity reflected in EEG coherence in individuals with autism," *Biological Psychiatry*, Vol. 62, No. E (2007), pp. 270–273.

13. Ibid., p. 160.

14. Warren, C.P., Hu, S., Stead, M., Brinkmann, B.H., Bower, M.R., and Worell, G.A., "Synchrony in Normal and Focal Epileptic Brain: The Seizure Onset Zone is Functionally Disconnected," *J. Neurophysiol.*, Vol. 104(6) (2010), pp. 3530–3539.

15. Theoden, I., Netoff, G., and Schiff, J., "Decreased Neuronal Synchronization during Experimental Seizures," *Journal of Neuroscience*, 15 August 2002, Vol. 22 (16), pp. 7297-7307 at doi.org/10.1523/JNEUROSCI.22-16-07297.2002.

16. Harung, H.S., and Travis, F., *World-Class Brain*, Harvest AS, Oslo, Norway (2019).

17. Ibid., p. 28

Chapter 3

1. Banquet, J., "Spectral Analysis of the EEG in Meditation," *Electroencephalography and Clinical Neurophysiology*, Vol. 35 (1973) pp. 143–151.

2. Levine, P.H., Hebert, J.R., Haynes, C.T., and Strobel, U., "EEG Coherence During the Transcendental Meditation Technique," *Scientific Research on the Transcendental Meditation Program Collected Papers*, Maharishi International University Press, Vol. 1 (1976), p. 187.

3. See research studies at the Center for Brain, Consciousness and Cognition at Maharishi International University. Go to www.research.miu.edu/center-for-brain-consciousness-and-cognition.

4. Dillbeck, M.C., and Bronson, E.C., "Short-term Longitudinal Effects of the Transcendental Meditation Technique on EEG Power and Coherence," *International J. of Neuroscience*, Vol. 14, 1981, Issue 3–4, published online July 7, 2009.

5. Travis, F.T., and Arenander, A., "Cross-Sectional and Longitudinal Study of Effects of Transcendental Meditation Practice on Interhemispheric Frontal Asymmetry and Frontal Coherence," *Intern. J. Neuroscience*, Vol. 116 (2006), pp. 1519–1538.

6. See Note 3, above.

7. Travis, F.T., and Shear, J., "Focused attention, open monitoring and automatic self-transcending: Categories to organize meditations from Vedic, Buddhist and Chinese traditions," *Consciousness and Cognition*, Vol. 19 (2010), pp. 1110–1118.

8. Travis, F.T., "Temporal and Spatial Characteristics of Meditation EEG," *Psychological Trauma: Theory, Research, Practice, and Policy* (2019), available at https://doi.apa.org/doiLanding?doi=10.1037%2Ftra0000488.

9. See Note 7.

Chapter 4

1. theweek.com/speedreads/679874/there-are-more-than-1300-apps-dedicated-mindfulness-meditation; blog.hubspot.com/news-trends/million-dollar-mindfulness-meditation-apps.

2. Kabat-Zinn, J., "Mindfulness-based interventions in context: Past, present, and future," *Clinical Psychology: Science and Practice* 10, (2003), pp. 144–156; Cahn, B.R., and Polich, J., "Meditation states and traits: EEG, ERP, and neuroimaging studies," *Psychol. Bull.* (2006) pp. 132 and 180–211.

3. Maharishi Mahesh Yogi, the founder of the TM program who introduced TM to the Western world, first used the analogy of thinking of the mind as an ocean in his book *The Science of Being and Art of Living*, Age of Enlightenment Press, Tenth printing (1984), pp. 53–55.

4. Maharishi Mahesh Yogi, *Maharishi Mahesh Yogi on the Bhagavad-Gita: A New Translation and Commentary, Chapters 1–6*, Age of Enlightenment Press, Fifth Printing (1984), pp. 103–104, 335–336.

5. Maharishi Mahesh Yogi, *The Science of Being and Art of Living*, Age of Enlightenment Press, Tenth printing (1984), p. 56.

6. Maslow, A.H., *The Farther Reaches of Human Nature*, The Viking Press, New York (1971), p. 76.

Chapter 5

1. Wallace, R.K., Benson, H., and Wilson, A.F., "A Wakeful Hypometabolic Physiologic State," *American Journal of Physiology*, Vol. 221 (1971), pp. 795–799; Wallace, R.K., "Physiological Effects of Transcendental Meditation," *Science*, Vol. 167 (1970), pp. 751–754; Wallace, R.K., and Benson, H., "The Physiology of Meditation," *Scientific American* (February, 1972), pp. 84–90.

2. Ibid.

3. Orme-Johnson, D., Kielbauch, J., Moore, R., and Bristol, J., "Personality and Autonomic Changes in Prisoners Practicing the Transcendental Meditation technique," *Collected Papers: Scientific Research on the Transcendental Meditation Program* (hereafter in these footnotes referred to as "*Collected Papers*"), Vol. 1, MIU Press, New York (1976), p. 556.

4. Jevning, R., Wilson, A.F., and Davidson, J.M., "Adrenocortical Activity during Meditation," *Hormones and Behavior*, Vol. 10, No. 1 (1978), pp. 54–60; Jevning, R., Wallace, R.K., and Beiderbach, M.,

"A Wakeful Hypometabolic Integrated Response," *Neuroscience and Bio-Behavioral Review*, Vol. 16 (1992), pp. 415–424; MacLean, C.R.K., Walton, K.G., Wenneberg, S.R., Levitsky, D.K., Mandarino, J.B., Wazari, R., and Schneider, R.H., "Altered Cortisol Response to Stress After Four Months' Practice of the Transcendental Meditation Program," presented at the 18th Annual Meeting of the Society for Neuroscience, Anaheim, California (October, 1992).

5. Hebert, J. Russell, Jr., "Periodic Suspension of Respiration During the Transcendental Meditation Technique," in *Collected Papers*, p. 134 (see Note 3 for this Chapter).

6. Jevning, R.J., Wilson, A.F., and Davidson, J.M., "Adrenocortical Activity During Meditation,"*Hormones and Behavior* 10 (1978); pp. 54–60; Bevan, A.J.W., Symons, R.C., Bong, C.C., and Willby, M.X., "Short-term Endocrine Changes in Transcendental Meditation," *Proceedings of the Endocrine Society of Australia* 2, Abstract 56 (1979); Walton, K.G., Fields, J.Z., Levitsky, D.K., Harris, D.A., Pugh, N.D., and Schneider, R.H., "Lowering cortisol and CVD risk in postmenopausal women: a pilot study using the Transcendental Meditation program," *N.Y. Acad. Sci.*, (2004), 1032: pp. 211–215.

7. Steptoe, A., Wardle, J., and Marmot, M., "Positive affect and health-related neuroendocrine, cardiovascular, and inflammatory processes," *PNAS*, Vol. 102, No. 18 (2005).

8. Bujatti, M., and Riederer, P., "Serotonin, Noradrenaline, Dopamine Metabolites in Transcendental Meditation," *Journal of Neural Transmission*, Vol. 39 (1976), p. 257; Walton, K.G., Lerom, M., Salerno, J., and Wallace, R.K., "Practice of the TM and TM-Sidhi Program May Affect the Circadian Rhythm of Five-Hydroxyindole Excretion," *Society for Neuroscience Abstracts*, Vol. 7 (1981), p. 48.

Chapter 6

1. Munro, D., "U.S. Healthcare Ranked Dead Last Compared to 10 Other Countries," *Forbes*, June 16, 2014.

2. www.cbsnews.com/news/us-life-expectancy-expected-to-fall-further-behind-other-countries/.

3. https://www.stress.org/workplace-stress/; www.stress.org/stress-is-killing-you

4. Ibid.

5. Krebs, H., "On the Overuse and Misuse of Medication," *Executive Health*, Vol. 11, No. 2 (1974).

6. www.dummies.com/religion/spirituality/how-to-use-mindfulness-to-cope-with-anger/.

7. Infante, J.R., Fernando, P., et al., "Levels of Immune cells in transcendental meditation practitioners," *Int. J. Yoga*, Vol. 7 (2) (2014), pp. 147–151.

8. Orme-Johnson, D.W., "Medical Care Utilization and the Transcendental Meditation Program," *Psychosomatic Medicine* 49 (1987), 493–507.

9. Herron, R.E., "Changes in physician costs among high-cost transcendental meditation practitioners compared with high-cost nonpractitioners over 5 years," *Am J. Health Promot.*, Vol. 26 (1) (2011), pp. 56–60.

Chapter 7

1. Avennuti, G., et al., "Reductions in perceived stress following Transcendental Meditation practice are associated with increased brain regional activity at rest," *Brain and Cognition*, 139 (2020), p. 105517.

2. Eppley, K., Abrams, A., and Shear, J., "The Effects of Meditation and Relaxation Techniques on Trait Anxiety, a Meta-Analysis," presented at the Convention of the American Psychological Association (Toronto, Canada), (August 1984); Dillbeck, M.C., The Effect of the Transcendental Meditation Technique on Anxiety Level," *Journal of Clinical Psychology* 33 (1977), pp. 1076–1078.

3. Orme-Johnson, D.W. and Barnes, V.A., "Effects of the Transcendental Meditation Technique on Trait Anxiety: A Meta-Analysis of Randomized Controlled Trials," *The Journal of Alternative and Complementary Medicine*, Vol. 20, No. 5 (2014), pp. 330–341.

4. Ibid, p. 337.

5. Claes, J., *The Field Paradigm: 20 Experiments That Can Change the World* (2017), p. 134.

6. Lewis, R., study conducted at the Lawrence County Mental Health Clinic, Newcastle, Pennsylvania, under the sponsorship of the Pennsylvania Governor's Justice Committee (1976).

7. Tolliver, D., "Personality as a Factor Determining Response to Two Different Meditation Techniques," *Senior Thesis*, Princeton University (1976).

8. Boyd, J., Lanius, R.A., McKinnon, M.C., "Mindfulness-based treatments for post-traumatic stress disorder: a review of the treatment literature and neurobiological evidence," *J. Psychiatry Neruoscience*, Vol. 43(1) (2018), pp. 7–25.

9. www.psychologicalscience.org/publications/observer/obsonline/the-facts-about-prolonged-exposure-therapy-for-ptsd.html

10. www.psychologytoday.com/us/therapy-types/prolonged-exposure-therapy.

11. Ibid.

12. Nidich, S., Mills, P., Rainforth, M., Schneider, R.H., Rosenthal, N.E., Salerno, J., Gaylord-King, C., and Rutlidge, T., "Non-trauma-focused meditation versus exposure therapy in veterans with post-traumatic stress disorder: a randomized controlled trial," *Lancet Psychiatry*, Vol. 5, December (2018) pp. 975–986.

13. Bandy, C.L., Dillbeck, M.C., Sezibera, V., Taljaard, L., Wilks, M., Shapiro, D., de Reuck, J., and Peycke, R., "Reduction of PTSD in South African University Students Using Transcendental Meditation Practice," *Psychological Reports* (Feb., 2019); Rosenthal, J.Z. et al., "Effects of Transcendental Meditation in Veterans of Operation Enduring Freedom and Operation Iraqi Freedom with Posttraumatic Stress Disorder: A Pilot Study," *Military Medicine*, Vol. 176 (6): 626, 630 (2011); Lim, K.O., et al., "Transcendental Meditation for Veterans with Post-Traumatic Stress Disorder," *Psychological Trauma: Theory, Research, Practice and Policy, a publication of the American Psychological Association*, July 19, 2018 at www.ncbi.nlm.nih.gov/pubmed/30024219.; Rees, B., Travis, F., Shapiro, D., Chant, R., "Significant reductions in posttraumatic stress symptoms in Congolese refugees within 10 days of Transcendental Meditation practice," *Journal of Traumatic Stress* 27(1) (2014), pp. 112–115; Herron, R. and Rees, B., "The Transcendental Meditation Program's Impact on the Symptoms of Post-traumatic Stress Disorder of Veterans: An Uncontrolled Pilot Study," *Military Medicine*, Vol. 183, Issue 1–2 (2018), pp., e144–e150 at academic.oup.com/milmed/article-abstract/183/1-2/e144/4781643?redirectedFrom=fulltext.

14. www.researchgate.net/publication/232512773, comparing mindfulness and psychoeducation treatments for combat-related PTSD using a telehealth approach.

15. Polusny, M.A., Erbes, C.R. et al., "Mindfulness-Based Stress Reduction for Posttraumatic Stress Disorder Among Veterans," *JAMA*, 314(5) (2012), pp. 456–465.

16. Sloan, D.M., Bovin, M.J., and Schnurr, P.P., "Review of Group Treatment for PTSD," *Journal of Rehabilitation Research and Development*, Vol. 49, No. 5 (2012), pp. 689–702.

17. See note 5.

18. Nidich, S., Rainforth, M., Haaga, D., Hagelin, J., Salerno, J., Travis, F., Tanner, M., Gaylord-King, C., Grosswald, S., Schneider, R., "A Randomized Controlled Trial on Effects of the Transcendental Meditation Program on Blood Pressure, Psychological Distress, and Coping in Young Adults," *American Journal of Hypertension*, Vol. 22, Issue 12 (2009), pp,1326–1331.

19. See footnote 5.

20. "Brain Architecture Alters to Compensate for Depression," March 7, 2017, at www.chla.org/press-release/brain-architecture-alters-compensate-depression.

21. Fingelkurts, A.A., Rysala, H., Suominen, K., Isometsa, E., and Kahkonen, S., "Impaired Functional Connectivity at EEG Alpha and Theta Frequency Bands in Major Depression," *Human Brain Mapping*, 28 (2007), pp. 247–261.

22. Ibid.

23. "Brain 'rewires' itself to enhance other senses in blind people," Massachusetts Eye and Ear Infirmary, Boston University Medical School, March 22, 2017 at sciencedaily.com/releases/2017/03/111170322143236.htm.

Chapter 8

1. www.cdc.gov/heartdisease/facts.htm.

2. www.nhlbi.nih.gov/health/educational/hearttruth/lower-risk/risk-factors.htm.

3. O'Connor, M., Schneider, R.H., "Meditation increases blood flow to the heart, PET scans show," *Cardiovascular Imaging*, Dec. 6, 2019 at https://www.healthimaging.com/topics/cardiovascular-imaging/meditation-increases-blood-flow-heart-pet.

4. Castillo-Richmond, A., Schneider, R.H., Alexander, C.N., Cook, R., Meyers, H., Nidich, S., Haney, C., Rainforth, M., and Salerno, J., "Effects of Stress Reduction on Carotid Atherosclerosis in Hyperactive African Americans," *Stroke*, Vol. 31 (2000), pp. 568–572.

5. Schneider, R.H., Staggers, F., Alexander, C.N., Chandler, H.M., Davies J.L., "A randomized controlled trial of stress reduction in older African-Americans," *Hypertension*, Vol. 26 (1995), pp. 820–827.

6. Rainforth, M.V., Schneider, R.H., Nidich, S.I., Gaylord-King, C., Salerno, J.W., Anderson, J.W., "Stress reduction programs in patients with elevated blood pressure: a systematic review and meta-analysis," *Current Hypertension Reports*, 9 (6) (2007), pp. 520–528.

7. Schneider, R.H., Alexander, C.N., Staggers, F., Rainforth, M., Salerno, J.W., Hartz, A., Arndt, S., Barnes, V.A., and Nidich, S.I., "Long Term Effects of Stress Reduction on Mortality in Persons 55 Years of Age with Symptoms of Hypertension," *American Journal of Cardiology* 95 (2005), pp. 1060–1064.

8. Anderson, J.W., Liu, C., Kryscio, R.J., "Blood Pressure Response to Transcendental Meditation: A Meta-analysis," *American Journal of Hypertension*, Vol. 21, No. 3 (2008), pp. 310–316.

9. Interview with the David Lynch Foundation, posted at davidlynch-foundation.org.

10. Cooper, M.J., and Aygen, M.M.,"Effect of Transcendental Meditation on Serum Cholesterol and Blood Pressure," *Harefuah* (the Journal of the Israel Medical Association), 95 (1978), pp. 1–2.

11. Interview with the David Lynch Foundation, posted at davidlynch-foundation.org.

12. Silgy, C., Lancaster, T., Stead, L., Mant, D., and Fowler, G., "Nicotine replacement therapy for smoking cessation (Review)," *The Cochrane Library*, Issue 3 (2007), pp. 4–5.

13. www.lung.org/stop-smoking/smoking-facts/e-cigarettes-and-lung-health.html?referrer=www.google.com/.

14. Alexander, C.N., Robinson, P., Rainforth, M., "Treating and Pre-venting Alcohol, Nicotine, and Drug Abuse Through Transcendental Meditation: A Review and Statistical Meta-Analysis," *Alcoholism Treatment Quarterly*, Vol. 11., Nos. 1/2 (1994), p. 13.

15. www.livestrong.com/article/278074negative-effects-of-video-game-addiction.

16. Alexander, C., Swanson, G., Rainforth, M., Carlisle, T., Todd, C., and Oates, R., "Effects of the transcendental meditation program on stress reduction, health, and employee development: a prospective study in two occupational settings," *Anxiety, Stress & Coping*, Vol. 6, Issue 3 (1993).

17. tmforveterans.org/research-on-tm-and-insomnia.

18. Miskiman, D.E., "The Treatment of Insomnia by the Transcendental Meditation Program," and "Long Term Effects of the Transcendental Meditation Program on Insomnia," University of Alberta, Edmonton, Canada, in *Collected Papers* (see Chapter 7, note 3), Vol. 1, New York, MIU Press (1976).

19. Alexander, C.N., Robinson, P., Rainforth, M., "Treating and Preventing Alcohol, Nicotine, and Drug Abuse Through Transcendental Meditation: A Review and Statistical Meta-Analysis," *Alcoholism Treatment Quarterly*, Vol.11., Nos. 3/4 (1993), pp. 40–42.

20. Alexander, C.N., Langer, E.J., Newman, R.I., Chandler, H.M., and Davies, J.L, "Transcendental Meditation, mindfulness, and longevity: An experimental study with the elderly," *Journal of Personality and Social Psychology*, 57(6) (1989), 950–964.

Chapter 9

1. www/cymascope.com/cymresearch/sound/healing.html.

2. www.thefamouspeople.com/profiles/pythagoras-504.php; https://voices.no/community/?q=country-of-the-month/2005-music-therapy-egypt.

3. McKelvie, P., and Low, J., "Listening to Mozart does not improve children's spatial ability: Final curtains for the Mozart effect," *British J. of Dev. Psychology*, December, 2010, available at https://onlinelibrary.wiley.com/doi/abs/10.1348/026151002166433.

4. "Complementary Therapies in Cancer Care Music Therapy" at news.cancerconnect.com/complementary-therapies-in-cancer-care-music-therapy.

5. "The Effectiveness of Vibroacoustic Sound Therapy in Medicine," at sites.duke.edu/soundscapes/2015/12/04/the-effectiveness-of-vibroacoustic-sound-therapy-in-medicine/; Boyd-Brewer, C., McCaffrey, R. "Vibroacoustic Sound Therapy Improves Pain Management and More," *Holistic Nurs. Pract.*, Vol 18(3) (2004), pp. 111–118.

6. Ibid.

7. Ibid.

8. Saarman, E., "Feeling the beat: Symposium explores the therapeutic effects of rhythmic music," *Stanford Report*, May 31, 2006.

9. www.zoominfo.com/p/Harold-Russell/569773192.

10. Fitzgerald, M., "Vibrating Cells Disclose Their Ailments," *MIT Technology Review*, Sept. 9, 2008.

11. Ibid.

12. Sharma, H.M., Kauffman, E.M., and Stephens, R.E., "Effect of different sounds on growth of human cancer cell lines in vitro," *Alternative Therapies in Clinical Practice* 3, 4 (1996), pp. 25–32.

13. Nader, T.A., Smith, D.E., Dillbeck, M.C., Schanabacher, V., Dillbeck, S.L, Galois, P., et al., "A double blind randomized controlled trial of Maharishi Vedic Vibration Technology in Subjects with Arthritis," *Frontiers in Bioscience*, Vol. 6 (April, 2001), at pp. H7–17.

14. Ibid.

15. Nidich, S.I., Schneider, R.H., Nidich, R.J., Rainworth, M., Salerno, J., Scharf, D., Smith, D.E., Dillbeck, M.C., and Nader, T.A., "Effects of Maharishi Vedic Vibration Technology on Chronic Disorders and Associated Quality of Life," *Frontiers in Bioscience*, Vol. 6 (April, 2001), at pp. H1–10.

Chapter 10

1. Travis, F., Parim, N., Shrivastava, A., "Higher Theta and alpha1 coherence when listening to Vedic recitation compared to coherence during Transcendental Meditation," *Consciousness and Cognitition* 49 (2017), pp. 157–162.

Chapter 11

1. Boyd-Brewer, C., McCaffrey, R., "Vibroacoustic Sound Therapy Improves Pain Management and More," *Holistic Nurs. Pract.*, Vol 18(3) (2004), pp. 111–118.

2. Saarman, E., "Feeling the beat: Symposium explores the therapeutic effects of rhythmic music," *Stanford Report*, May 31, 2006.

3. Yoshisha, K., Iwamoto, S., Kimata, Y., Nohno, T., et al., "Low-Frequency Vibratory Sound Induces Neurite Outgrowth in PC12M3 Cells in which Nerve Growth Factor-Induced Neurite Outgrowth is Impaired," *Tis. Cult. Res. Common*, 23 (2004), pp. 81–90.

4. musicforhealthservices.com/Music_as_therapy/Pages/Module%2004_Music_and_the_Brain.

5. Nader, T.A., Smith, D.E., Dillbeck, M.C., Schanbacher, V., Dillbeck, S.L, Galois, P., et al., "A double blind randomized controlled trial of Maharishi Vedic Vibration Technology in Subjects with Arthritis," *Frontiers in Bioscience*, Vol. 6 (April, 2001), pp. H7–17.

6. Solon, O., "Transfer a secret audio message by poking someone with your finger," *Wired*, Sept. 2013; www.wired.co.uk/article/Disney-touch-audio.

7. www.physlink.com/education/askexperts/ae479.cfm.

8. www.livescience.com/34608-break-stride-frequency-of-vibration.html

9. Wilson, E., "Socionomics and Fibonacci: The Golden Ratio Governs Life, Beauty and the Universe," *Socionomist*, March, 2010; http://www.socionomics.net/2010/03/socionomics-and-fibonacci-golden-ratio-governs-life-beauty-and-the-universe-2/

10. www.theguardian.com/artanddesign/2009/dec/28/golden-ratio-us-academic.

11. Ibid.

12. www.goldennumber.net/dna.

13. Persaud, D., O'Leary, J.P., "Fibonacci Series, Golden Proportions and the Human Body," *Austin Journal of Surgery*, July 2, 2015; http://digitalcommons.fiu.edu/cgi/viewcontent.cgi?article=1026&context=com_facpub: http://goldenratio.wikidot.com/human-body.

14. Holmes, E., *The Life of Mozart*, Dutton and Company, New York (1912); Marcus, J.B., *TM and Business*, McGraw-Hill (1977), pp. 58–59

15. Nader, T., *Human Physiology: Expression of Veda and the Vedic Literature*, Maharishi Vedic University Press, Vlodrop, Holland, 2nd edition (1995).

16. Ibid., pp. 144–162.

17. Ibid., pp. 85–90.

18. Ibid., pp. 138–140.

19. Ibid., p. 201; Sands, W., "Maharishi's Program of Reading the Vedic Literature: Unfolding the Total Potential of Natural Law," *Modern Science and Vedic Science*, Vol. 7, No. 1 (1997).

20. Wallace, R.K. and Marcus, J.B., *Victory Before War*, MIU Press (2005).

21. See note 15, p. 1.

Chapter 12

1. Schrödinger, E., *What is Life?*, from *The Great Ideas Today 1967*, Encyclopedia Britannica, London (1967), p. 415.

2. www.fitnessmagazine.com/recipes/healthy-eating/superfoods/the-10-healthiest-foods-on-the-planet.

3. www.healthline.com/health/gerd/diet-nutrition#helpful-foods2; www.gicare.com/diets/no-gastric-irritants-ulcers-dyspepsia/.

4. Sharma, H. and Clark, C., *Ayurvedic Healing*, Singing Dragon, London and Philadelphia, 2nd Ed. (2012), p. 10.

5. Ibid.

6. Ibid.

7. www.greekmedicine.net/b_p/Four_elements.html.

Chapter 14

1. www.washingtonpost.com/health/2020/07/31/covid-us-death-toll-150k/?arc404=true.

2. www.ncbi.nlm.nih.gov/pmc/articles/PMC2716544/; https://www.nhlbi.nih.gov/news/2016/native-american-foods-dietary-habits-take-center-stage.

3. See note 1.

4. www.nhlbi.nih.gov/news/2016/native-american-foods-dietary-habits-take-center-stage.

Chapter 15

1. Wallace, R.K., *The Rest and Repair Diet*, Dharma Press (2019), p. 154.

2. The Test for Ama is from the book *The Answer to Cancer* by Hari Sharma, M.D. with James Meade, Ph.D., and with the assistance of Vaidya Mishra, Select Books (2002). Reprinted with permission.

3. The Test for Amavisha and Garvisha is on the MAPI (Maharishi AyurVeda Products International) website at mapi.com. Reprinted with permission.

Chapter 16

1. Ghasemzadeh, N. and Zafari, A.M., "A Brief History of the Arterial Pulse," *Cardiology Research and Practice* Volume 2001, Article ID 164832, at dx.doi.org/10.4061/2011/164832.

2. Orme-Johnson, D.O. and Herron, R., "An Innovative Approach to Reducing Medical Care Utilization and Expenditures," *The American Journal of Managed Care*, Vol. 3, No. 1 (1997).

3. Schneider, R.H., et al., "Health Promotion with a Traditional System of Natural Health Care: Maharishi Ayurveda," *Journal of Social Behavior and Personality*, 5(3) (1990), pp. 1–27.

4. Waldschutz, R., "Physiological and Psychological Changes Associated with Ayurvedic Purification Treatment," *Erfahrungsheilkunde—Acta Medico Empirica—Zeitschrift fur die drztliche Praxis*, 2 (1988), pp. 720–729.

5. Herron, R. and Fagan, J., "Lipophil-mediated reduction of toxicants in humans: An evaluation of an ayurvedic detoxification procedure," *Alternative therapies in health and medicine*, 8(5) (2002), pp. 40–51.

Chapter 17

Many of the guidelines have been reproduced with the permission of The Raj Ayuvedic Health Center in Fairfield, Iowa (theraj.com) and are taken from its publication "*Introduction to the Knowledge and Practice of Healthy Daily Routine*," (June 2007).

1. Sands, W.F., *Maharishi's Yoga—The Royal Path to Enlightenment*, MUM Press (USA) 2013; Sands, W.F., *Maharishi Mahesh Yogi and His Gift to the World*, MUM Press (USA) (2012).

2. Shallenbarger, S., "The Peak Time for Everything," *The Wall Street Journal*, September 26, 2012.

Chapter 18

1. Nidich, S.I., Nidich, R., Abrams, A., Orme-Johnson, D.W., and Wallace, R.K., "Frontal Lobe Functioning: EGG Coherence as a Predictor of Highly Pro-Social Behavior with Subjects Practicing the Transcendental Meditation and TM-Sidhi Program," *Collected Papers*, Vol. 4, (1982), pp. 2277–2282.

2. Nidich, S.I., and Nidich, R., "The Transcendental Meditation and TM-Sidhi Program and Moral Development," *Collected Papers*, Vol. 3 (1983), pp. 2034–2037.

3. Nidich, S.I., "A Study of the Relationship of the Transcendental Meditation Program to Kohlberg's Stages of Moral Reasoning," *Collected Papers*, Vol. 1 (1975), pp. 585–593.

4. Dreuille, M., *The Rule of Saint Benedict*, Paulist Press (2002), p. 137.

5. shereenielsen.wordpress.com/2010/11/22/a-quote-from-ralph-waldo-emersons-essay-ix-the-over-soul/.

6. theplanetwhisperer.blogspot.com/2011/03/in-attitude-of-silence-soul-finds-path.html.

7. www.thechristianmeditator.com/christian-meditation-silence-solitude-and-the-christian.

8. Maharishi Mahesh Yogi, *Maharishi Mahesh Yogi on the Bhagavad-Gita: A New Translation and Commentary*, Penguin Press, Middlesex, England (1967), pp. 155–161.

9. Nidich, R., and Nidich, S.I., "An Empirical Study of the Moral Atmosphere at Maharishi International University/University High School," *Collected Papers*, Vol. 4 (1983), pp. 2407–2413.

10. Ibid.

11. Gladwell, M., *The Tipping Point: How Little Things Can Make a Big Difference*, Little Brown and Company (2000), pp. 80–83.

Acknowledgments

Many thanks to all those who helped with the book, including in editing, providing access to their research, recommending people to be interviewed, and taking time to be interviewed.

Thanks especially to Susan Marcus, Jay's wife, and Fran Clark for editing, and to Tony Nader, M.D., Ph.D., M.A.R.R., for his Foreword, his research, and encouragement with the book.

Thanks to our agent Ben Camardi of the Harold Matson-Ben Camardi agency for working on the book's placement and for his enthusiasm for the book for many years.

A special thanks to Drs. Fred Travis and Alarik Arenander for their research on brain coherence and discussions with us about sections of the book; to Harris Kaplan for his insights on the Vedic recitations; to Nancy Londsorf, M.D., for her accounts of patient experiences with Maharishi Vedic Vibration Therapy; to Dr. David Orme-Johnson for his research and for helping us with the charts for the book; to Drs. John Hagelin, David Scharf, Michael Dillbeck, Sandy Nidich, Robert Schneider, Robert Herron, Ken Walton, and Ron Jevning for research in their areas; to Dr. Mark Toomey for his accounts of patient experiences, knowledge of pulse diagnosis, and his work at The Raj (Ayurveda resort); to Jim and Nina Meade and Joseph and Denise Gerace for information on their activities teaching TM and introductions to meditators for interviews; to Sara Sica for her stories of TM teaching activities and information about teaching meditation to young children.

Thanks to Dr. Lawrence Domash for his lectures at Maharishi International University on the laws of thermodynamics and their relationship to Transcendental Meditation, and thanks to the following for help on various other matters: Vaidya Manohar Palakurthi, Eva Norlyk Smith, Dr. Melanie Brown, Anna Walsh, Dean Draznin, Emily Kelly, Bill Goldstein, David Hooper, Michael Cuddehe, Fred Swartz, Adrienne Shoenfeld, Elaine Pomfrey, Howard Chancellor, and Samantha Wallace.

Thanks to Dr. Nader, the David Lynch Foundation, Maharishi Foundation, and The Raj Resorts for their helpful websites and/ or brochures, and thanks to Robert M. Johnson for the layout and design of the book and the chart graphics, and to George Foster for his cover.

Finally, special thanks to Maharishi International University for its knowledge of human development and Maharishi AyurVeda, and to its Presidents who have guided the growth of the university over the years: Drs. Robert Keith Wallace, Lawrence Domash, Bevan Morris, and John Hagelin.

About the Authors

Robert Keith Wallace, Ph.D.

Dr. Wallace received his B.S. in Physics and his Ph.D in Physiology from UCLA, and he conducted postgraduate research at Harvard. He is a pioneering researcher on the physiological effects of meditation and one of the world's leading authorities on Vedic health practices (meditation and Ayurveda). He is Professor and Chairman of the Department of Physiology and Health at Maharishi International University (MIU) in Fairfield, Iowa and was MIU's first President. Dr. Wallace was the initial researcher leading scientists to the study of the mind/body connection and the importance of meditation in behavioral medicine. His research has been published in the most prestigious scientific journals, including *Science*, the *American Journal of Physiology*, and *Scientific American*. He has lectured on meditation at major universities and institutes in all European countries, as well as Russia, China, Australia, New Zealand, Canada, Brazil, Argentina, Colombia and Mexico.

Dr. Wallace has helped establish graduate programs to train physicians, health professionals, and wellness consultants in Maharishi AyurVeda and Integrative Medicine. He is the author of a number of books including *Dharma Parenting* (Tarcher/Penguin), *Gut Crisis*, and *The Rest And Repair Diet*. He and his wife reside in Fairfield, Iowa.

Jay B. Marcus

Mr. Marcus is a graduate of Rutgers University and the University of Virginia Law School. He began his career practicing law in New York City and is now a practicing attorney in Iowa. For three years he was chairman of the Iowa Bar Association permanent ethics committee for business lawyers, and he has taught legal education seminars on ethics, securities, and constitutional law. Mr. Marcus was a co-founder and Associate Editor of *Contemporary Drug Problems*, a respected drug abuse journal, and he has lectured extensively on drug abuse, prison reform, and meditation. He is the author of four prior books, including *TM and Business* (McGraw-Hill Book Company) and *The Crime Vaccine* (Claitor's Books of Baton Rouge, LA). *The Crime Vaccine* was designated by Bookviews as one of the five best non-fiction books of 1996. Mr. Marcus is an avid basketball fan and golfer. He was a Captain in the U.S. Army Infantry, and co-captain of the Rutgers University basketball team. Mr. Marcus and his wife reside in Fairfield, Iowa.

Christopher S. Clark, M.D.

Dr. Clark is a graduate of Yale Medical School and did his residency at Yale in the Department of Psychiatry. Dr. Clark has pioneered the integration of Ayurvedic medicine into the practice of medicine and psychiatry since 1985. He studied one-on-one with leading experts of Ayurvedic medicine in consultation with patients for fifteen years. While absorbing the knowledge of Ayurveda, especially pulse diagnosis and herbal pharmacopeia, he wrote two books on Ayurveda, most recently *Ayurvedic Healing—Contemporary Maharishi AyurVeda Medicine and Science* (Singing Dragon Press, 2012). He was the founding medical director of The Raj Ayurvedic health treatment facility for the purification treatments of panchakarma, stress management, yoga, and marma therapy. Currently he is the director for well-being initiatives and digital development for Garten, a leading Silicon Valley innovator for nutrition, technology and wellness in the workplace. Dr. Clark and his wife reside in Santa Rosa, California.

CPSIA information can be obtained
at www.ICGtesting.com
Printed in the USA
LVHW020326161120
671611LV00002B/31